ENGINEERING MECHANICS

Volume II
DYNAMICS

Paul H. Wirsching

Assistant Professor of Mechanical Engineering,
Loyola University of Los Angeles

John W. Murdock

Assistant Professor of Theoretical and
Applied Mechanics, University of Illinois

Allyn and Bacon, Inc.
Boston 1965

Printed in the United States of America

Library of Congress Catalog Card Number:
65-13904

Engineering Mechanics

VOL. II — DYNAMICS

This book is a part of the
Allyn and Bacon Series in Mechanical Engineering and Applied Mechanics

Consulting Editor,
Frank Kreith
University of Colorado

Preface

Because of the recent explosion in technical knowledge, it has become necessary to upgrade all areas of undergraduate instruction to keep pace with the state of the art. In the undergraduate courses in analytical mechanics, relatively sophisticated problems in particle and rigid-body mechanics are now considered. Problems such as gyroscopic motion and motion of a point mass referred to a moving coordinate system, which were formerly considered only in advanced studies in mechanics, are now being examined by undergraduates. This new approach to mechanics is made possible by the use of such mathematical techniques as vector and matrix algebra.

It has become increasingly popular to use vector algebra and vector equations in analytical mechanics on the undergraduate level. The vector approach is employed for the purpose of simplifying and generalizing the derivations. The vector equation permits us to express three scalar equations as one. The mathematical expression for Newton's second law for a single particle written in scalar form consists of three equations:

$$F_x = ma_x$$
$$F_y = ma_y$$
$$F_z = ma_z$$

The three equations may be written in vector form as $\boldsymbol{F} = m\boldsymbol{a}$. Basic operations with vectors eliminate much of the algebra and geometry involved in derivations; this allows the instructor to consider a wider range of problems.

For the most part, dynamical problems are made no simpler by using vector notation. There are, of course, some notable exceptions. Some problems in three-dimensional rigid-body motion are made simpler by writing the equation of motion in vector form and using vector operations to obtain a solution. Also, the problem of determining the motion of particles moving relative to other moving bodies may often be more easily solved by using vector operations than by any other approach. In this text, vectors are used in all problems except those in which the problem is complicated by their introduction.

It is assumed in this text that the student has a rudimentary knowledge of vector algebra. It is necessary that the student be familiar with the method of expressing physical quantities in vector form. The student should also be familiar not only with the method of performing a dot and cross-product, but also the geometrical significance of these operations. The text also assumes a basic knowledge of differential equations, although it is not necessary for the student to have completed a formal course in this topic. Knowledge of differential and integral calculus is sufficient.

In this text, dynamics of a single particle is discussed first, followed by dynamics of systems of particles and rigid-body dynamics. Following is a chapter-by-chapter résumé of the text. Kinematics, as discussed in Chapter 2, is the study of the geometry of motion. Here we are interested in methods of describing motion, with no concern for the causes of the motion. More complicated problems in kinematics are discussed in Chapter 3. In Chapter 4, the relationship between the motion of "point masses," or particles, and the forces causing the motion is examined. Through Newton's second law, one is able to predict motion of a particle under the action of a given force, and inversely, the force causing a given motion.

Special integrations of the equation of motion are discussed in Chapter 5. In Chapter 6 (on the dynamics of systems of particles), motion and the methods of predicting motions of several interacting particles are examined. Treated in Chapter 7 are such special topics in particle dynamics as orbital mechanics, vibrations, and motion of systems of variable mass. The last two chapters are concerned with rigid-body dynamics. Chapter 8 deals with rigid-body motion in two dimensions, and Chapter 9 deals with motion of a rigid body in three dimensions. Rigid-body motion is discussed as a separate topic because methods of treating two-dimensional rigid-body motion is somewhat different from those of three-dimensional motion.

In conclusion, I should like to express my gratitude to my wife Jeanne, who generously donated her time to type the manuscript.

Paul H. Wirsching

Los Angeles, Calif.

Contents

Engineering Mechanics

VOL. II — DYNAMICS

1

Introduction

1-1. INTRODUCTION TO DYNAMICS

Dynamics is the study of motion. It is a study, not only of the geometry of motion, but also of the effect of external forces on existence of particles, systems of particles, and rigid bodies. In the study of dynamics, the two basic problems are (1) given the external forces that are acting on a body, to determine the response or motion of that body; and the inverse problem (2) given the motion of the body, to identify forces on the body that are causing the motion.

The study of dynamics is divided into two general areas of investigation. The first area is kinematics, a study of the description of the motion of bodies without regard for the forces that act on the body to cause the motion. In kinematics, one is concerned not only with the description of the position of the body, but also with the rate at which the body is moving at different instances of time.

The second area of investigation is the study of kinetics. In kinetics, one examines the forces acting on a body and tries to determine how the body will react. Problems of forces and motion confront the mechanical engineer as he designs the engine for an automobile, the physicist as he examines the motion of charged particles in electromagnetic fields, and the astrodynamicist as he calculates the orbits of space vehicles.

Dynamics appears in most contemporary engineering curricula as one of the engineering sciences and as the second of two courses in engineering mechanics. It is a required course for all engineering undergraduates. It is important for the prospective engineer, no matter what his professional emphasis, to become familiar with the principles of mechanics.

1–2. HISTORICAL NOTE

Scientists, from Aristotle to Einstein, have made important contributions to the set of principles of mechanics that today's student reinvestigates in his studies. For the most part, the principles of classical mechanics were formulated by seventeenth and eighteenth century scholars. The study of the history of mechanics is fascinating in itself, but will be left here to the natural curiosity of the student. Three references of interest are the following:

1. H. F. Girvin, *A Historical Appraisal of Mechanics,* International Textbook Company, 1948.
2. Ernest Mach, *The Science of Mechanics,* Open Court.
3. Heinrick Hertz, *Principles of Mechanics,* Dover Publications (paperbound) (of particular interest here are Hertz's introductory statements).

Rather than present a history of mechanics here, historical notes will be made in the discussions.

1–3. UNITS AND DIMENSIONS

In order to measure a quantity, a standard measure must be first established; then the quantity to be measured is referred to this standard. The magnitude of the measured quantity may be specified by giving (1) the standard measure, and (2) the comparison of the measured quantity to the standard. Suppose that a certain distance is to be measured. First a standard measure of length (say, a meter) is established; then, upon comparing the meter to the distance to be measured, it is found that the distance is $2\frac{1}{2}$ times as long as the meter. The distance is said to be 2.5 meters.

In the study of dynamics, it is found that only three types of dimensions are required. These three fundamental and independent dimensions are force, length, and time. The motion of bodies may be described as combinations of these dimensions. Velocity, for instance, is distance per time (L/T). The dimensions of force, length, and time are called *fundamental dimensions,* and the dimensions that are combinations of the fundamental units are called *derived dimensions.* Velocity, acceleration, mass, and momentum are all derived dimensions. It is also possible to express the fundamental dimensions as mass, length, and time (instead of force, length, and time). In this case, force becomes a derived dimension.

Table 1–1 lists the dimensions associated with each of the physical quantities commonly used in dynamics. The dimensions are expressed in both the FLT (force, length, time) and the MLT (mass, length, time) systems.

TABLE 1-1. DIMENSIONS OF PHYSICAL QUANTITIES

Quantity	*FLT*	*MLT*
Force	F	MLT^{-2}
Mass	FT^2L^{-1}	M
Length	L	L
Time	T	T
Velocity	LT^{-1}	LT^{-1}
Acceleration	LT^{-2}	LT^{-2}
Angular velocity	T^{-1}	T^{-1}
Angular acceleration	T^{-2}	T^{-2}
Moment of inertia	FT^2L	ML^2
Product of inertia	FT^2L	ML^2
Radians	Unitless	Unitless
Work	FL	ML^2T^{-2}
Energy	FL	ML^2T^{-2}
Power	FLT^{-1}	ML^2T^{-3}
Moment	FL	ML^2T^{-2}
Momentum	FT	MLT^{-1}
Moment of momentum	FTL	ML^2T^{-1}

Any equation of state that is written must be dimensionally homogeneous. That is, the dimensions on the left-hand side of the equation must be the same as the dimensions on the right-hand side. It would be most incorrect to say that force (F) is equal to acceleration (L/T^2), since force and acceleration do not have the same dimensions. It is permissible to say that force is equal to mass times acceleration as long as mass has dimensions of FT^2/L. Then, when mass and acceleration are multiplied, the resulting dimension is a dimension of force, and the equation is said to be dimensionally homogeneous. In writing an equation, it is necessary not only to make sure that the equation is dimensionally homogeneous, but also that it uses the same standard measure. If the equation has dimensions of force on each side, and if the standard measure on the left-hand side is pounds, then the measure on the right-hand side must also be pounds and not another measure of force such as dynes.

The standard measure of force in the British system of units is the *pound.* One pound of force is defined as being 0.45359237 times the gravitational force exerted on a standard kilogram mass of platinum-iridium, the physical standard of which is in the possession of the International Committee of Weights and Measures at Sèvres, France. The measurement of the force must take place at a point where the gravitational acceleration is 32.174 ft/sec^2 at conditions of absolute rest. Since this is most difficult to obtain, it is correct to say that the pound is not exactly defined.

The standard measure of time is *seconds.* One second is defined as 1/31,556,925.9747 of the tropical year 1900. The standard measure of length in the British system is *feet.* Three feet constitute 1 yard, and the yard in turn is equal to 3600/3937 of 1 meter. A meter is defined as 1,650,763.73 wavelengths of the orange-red line of krypton 86. Adoptions of the definitions of seconds and meters were made at the Eleventh General Conference on Weights and Measures held in October 1960.

2

Kinematics

Kinematics is the study of the geometry of motion of bodies. In kinematics we are interested in the problem of how to describe the motion of a body as it moves through space; we are not concerned with the forces that cause the motion. In this chapter we shall consider the kinematics of particles. More will be said about the kinematics of rigid bodies in Chapter 8.

2-1. RECTILINEAR MOTION

Description of the motion. First we shall consider a particle that is constrained to move along a straight-line path. This one-dimensional motion is called *rectilinear motion.*

In order to describe the position of the particle as it moves along the straight line, we must first define a reference point. The reference point is the point O in Fig. 2–1. It would be impossible to define the position of P without specifying a reference, so it is apparent that the position of a particle may be defined only in a relative manner.

Once the reference point O has been chosen, the position of P may be specified as a distance from O. It is customary to define distance as being positive to the right and negative to the left. Thus, if it is said that the displacement of the particle is a -4, that would indicate that the particle is four units to the left of O.

The position of the particle will vary as it moves along the path, and therefore the position of the particle is said to be a function of time. If we let the variable x define the position of the particle, then we may say that x is a function of time.

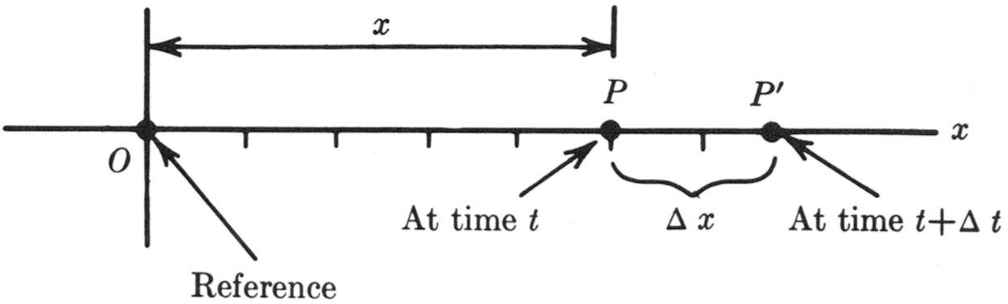

Figure 2-1

We are interested not only in the position of the particle as a function of time, but also in the manner in which it moves. In a given increment of time, Δt, the particle will move a distance Δx from P to P'. As a measure of the rapidity with which the particle moves from P to P', we define the average velocity during this interval as

$$v_{\text{avg}} = \frac{\Delta x}{\Delta t} \tag{2.1}$$

where Δx is length, Δt is time, and v is length per time, or feet per second (fps).

In general, the velocity of a body will change, so that it also will be a function of time. Therefore, instead of talking about an average velocity, we define an instantaneous velocity at a point or instant in time. The velocity of the particle at point P may be determined by taking the limit of the average velocity as the time increment approaches zero. Thus,

$$v = \lim_{t \to 0} \frac{\Delta x}{\Delta t} \tag{2.2}$$

However, this is just the definition of the derivative of the position with respect to time.

$$\boxed{v = \frac{dx}{dt}} \tag{2.3}$$

If the velocity is a function of time, it also will change by an amount Δv during the time increment Δt. Knowing this, we can also measure the change in velocity by defining the average acceleration during the time t as

$$a_{\text{avg}} = \frac{\Delta v}{\Delta t} \tag{2.4}$$

Since the dimensions of Δv are feet per second and Δt is in seconds, it follows that the dimensions of acceleration are feet per square second.

Upon examination of the definition of the average acceleration, it is apparent that a particle with a large acceleration is changing its velocity very rapidly in comparison to a particle with a small acceleration. An automobile that accelerates from rest to 60 mph in 10 sec is said to have a larger acceleration than an automobile that takes 20 sec to accelerate from rest to 60 mph.

Acceleration also may change with time, and we may define an instantaneous acceleration at a point or instant in time. The instantaneous acceleration at point P may be obtained by taking the limit of the average acceleration as t approaches zero:

$$a = \lim_{t \to 0} \frac{\Delta v}{\Delta t} \tag{2.5}$$

But this is merely the derivative of the velocity:

$$\boxed{\begin{aligned} a &= \frac{dv}{dt} \\ a &= \frac{d^2x}{dt^2} \end{aligned}} \tag{2.6}$$

If the displacement is given as a function of time, the velocity may be obtained by differentiating the displacement. The acceleration may be found in turn by differentiating the velocity.

Example 2–1. The velocity of a particle moving in a straight-line path is given as $v(t) = 8t^3 + 12t$ fps. If at $t = 0$, the displacement of the particle is 4 ft, determine the acceleration at time equal to two seconds.

Solution: The acceleration of the particle may be obtained by differentiating the velocity:

$$a = \frac{dv}{dt}$$

$$= 24t^2 + 12 \text{ ft/sec}^2$$

At time equal to two seconds,

$$a = 24(2)^2 + 12$$

$$= 108 \text{ ft/sec}^2$$

The inverse problem. Now consider the problem where the acceleration may be given as a function of not only time but also velocity or displacement. The case where the acceleration is a function of all three, or of a combination of the three, is not uncommon, but it does generally require the solution of a differential equation. Here we shall consider only three special cases.

Acceleration given as a function of time. $a = a(t)$. Consider the acceleration as given in Eq. 2.6. We integrate both sides with respect to time:

$$\begin{aligned} \int_{t_0}^{t} a(t)\,dt &= \int_{t_0}^{t} \frac{dv}{dt}\,dt \\ &= \int_{t_0}^{t} dv = v(t) - v(t_0) \end{aligned} \tag{2.7}$$

Now the velocity may be written as

$$v = v_0 + \int_{t_0}^{t} a(t)\,dt \tag{2.8}$$

where v_0 is the velocity at time t_0. The displacement may be obtained by taking the velocity, $v = dx/dt$, and integrating both sides with respect to time:

$$\begin{aligned} \int_{t_0}^{t} v(t)\,dt &= \int_{t_0}^{t} \frac{dx}{dt}\,dt \\ &= \int_{t_0}^{t} dx = x(t) - x(t_0) \end{aligned} \tag{2.9}$$

Thus,

$$x = x_0 + \int_{t_0}^{t} v(t)\,dt \tag{2.10}$$

Here x_0 is the displacement of the particle at time t_0.

Acceleration given as a function of velocity. $a = a(v)$. If acceleration is given as a function of velocity, we may write

$$a = \frac{dv}{dt} = a(v) \tag{2.11}$$

By separating variables and integrating,

$$\int_{v_0}^{v} \frac{dv}{a(v)} = \int_{t_0}^{t} dt = t - t_0 \tag{2.12}$$

This gives velocity as a function of time.

Acceleration given as a function of displacement. $a = a(x)$. If the acceleration is given as a function of displacement, we use the relationship $v = dx/dt$ and write

$$dt = \frac{v}{dx} \tag{2.13}$$

Thus,

$$a = \frac{dv}{dt} = \frac{dv}{v\,dx} = a(x) \tag{2.14}$$

Integrating,

$$\int_{v_0}^{v} \frac{dv}{v} = \int_{x_0}^{x} a(x)\,dx$$

$$\frac{v^2}{2} - \frac{v_0^2}{2} = \int_{x_0}^{x} a(x)\,dx \tag{2.15}$$

This integration gives velocity as a function of displacement.

Example 2–2. An accelerometer mounted in an automobile records magnitude of acceleration of the accelerating vehicle. The recorded acceleration as a function of time is recorded as $a(t) = 10 - 0.06t$ ft/sec². What is the distance that the vehicle moves in 10 sec, and what is the velocity at that instant? The automobile starts from rest.

Solution: The velocity is obtained by integrating the acceleration:

$$v = v_0 + \int (10 - 0.06t)\,dt$$

$$v(t) = 10t - 0.03t^2 \quad \text{fps}$$

The displacement is a function of time:

$$x = x_0 + \int (10t - 0.03t^2)\,dt$$

$$x(t) = 5t^2 - 0.01t^3 \quad \text{ft}$$

At 10 sec, the velocity is

$$v = 10(10) - 0.03(10)^2$$
$$= 97 \text{ fps}$$

and the displacement is

$$x = 5(10)^2 - 0.01(10)^3$$
$$= 490 \text{ ft}$$

Example 2–3. The acceleration of the mass of a spring-mass system is given as a function of the displacement: $a(x) = -(k/m)x$. If the system is started from rest at a displacement of $-p$, determine the velocity of the mass as a function of the displacement.

Solution: The initial conditions are $v_0 = 0$ and $x_0 = -p$. The integration, where a is given as a function of x, may be accomplished by referring to Eq. 2.15 and the accompanying discussion. Thus,

$$\frac{v^2}{2} - \frac{v_0^2}{2} = \int_{-p}^{x} \left(-\frac{k}{m}\right) x\,dx$$

and it follows that

$$v^2 = \left(\frac{k}{m}\right)(p^2 - x^2)$$

Motion with a constant acceleration. It is a very common problem in dynamics to have a particle moving with a constant acceleration. A body in free fall under the influence of gravitational force will accelerate toward the surface of the earth with an acceleration of 32.2 ft/sec². In other types of problems, a great deal of useful information may be obtained by assuming a constant acceleration situation when data concerning the motion as a function of time are unavailable.

If the acceleration is constant, then the velocity is

$$v = v_0 + \int_0^t a\,dt$$

$$= v_0 + at \tag{2.16}$$

and the displacement is

$$x = x_0 + \int_0^t a\,dt$$

$$= x_0 + \int (v_0 + at)\,dt \tag{2.17}$$

$$= x_0 + v_0 t + \frac{at^2}{2}$$

The velocity as a function of the displacement may be obtained by eliminating time between Eqs. 2.16 and 2.17:

$$v^2 - v_0^2 = 2a(x - x_0) \tag{2.18}$$

If the original velocity and displacement is equal to zero, then

$$v = \sqrt{2ax} \tag{2.19}$$

It would be a good idea for the student to memorize these equations. It should be emphasized, however, that these equations apply only to those cases where the acceleration is constant.

Example 2–4. An automobile is traveling with a speed of 60 mph when the driver observes a stop light 600 ft away. Assume that it takes the driver $\frac{1}{2}$ sec to react and apply the brakes, and assume that after he applies them, he will decelerate at a constant rate and come to rest at the stop light. Calculate the constant acceleration that the automobile is experiencing.

Solution: First it is necessary to determine the distance that the car traveled before the brakes were applied. The speed of 60 mph corresponds to 88 fps. Therefore, the distance that the car traveled in the $\frac{1}{2}$ sec is 44 ft. As the brakes are applied and the car starts decelerating, the velocity of the car is 88 fps, and the total distance that the car will move is

$$x = 600 - 44 = 556 \text{ ft}$$

Consider Eq. 2.18:

$$v^2 - v_0^2 = 2a(x - x_0)$$

The original displacement x_0 is equal to zero, and the final velocity v is equal to zero. Solving for the acceleration:

$$a = \frac{-v_0^2}{2x}$$

$$= \frac{-(88)^2}{2(556)}$$

$$= -6.93 \text{ ft/sec}^2$$

The minus acceleration indicates that the car is decelerating.

Graphical kinematics. Experimental kinematical data are often given in graphical form and expressed as acceleration, velocity, or displacement as a function of time. Since graphical integration may be performed by measuring the area under a curve, the change in velocity between any two points may be determined by direct measurement of A_1, as shown in Fig. 2–2. The velocity curve may be constructed from the acceleration curve in this manner. However, one should certainly want to take much smaller time increments than those shown in the figure. Figure 2–2 also illustrates how to obtain the displacement from the velocity curve and how to obtain the velocity curve from the displacement cnrve by measuring slopes of the curve at each point.

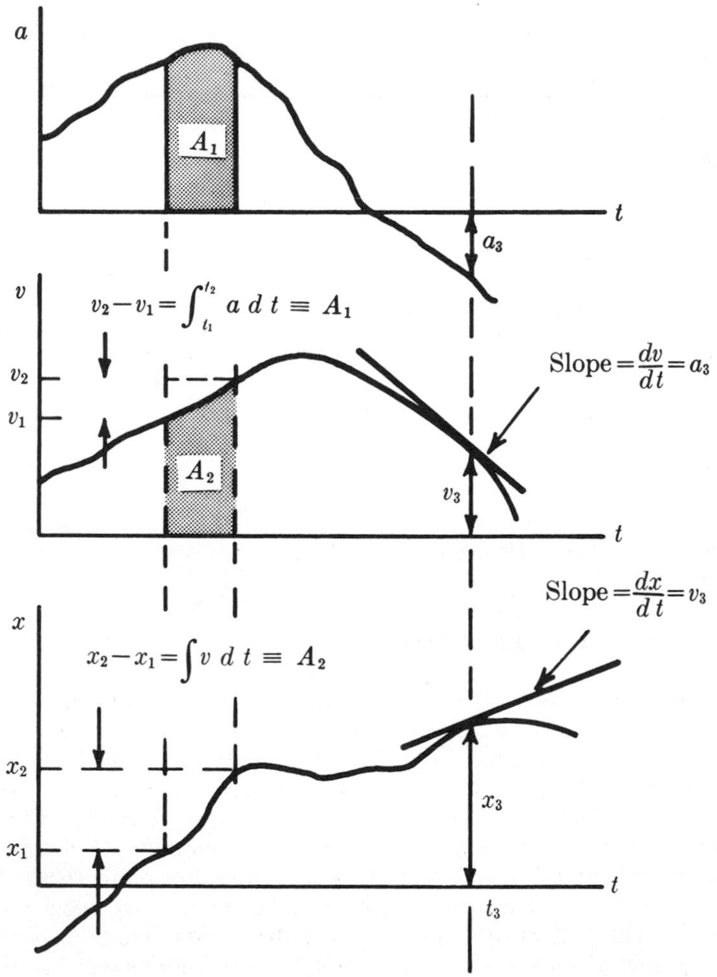

Figure 2-2

Example 2–5. The velocity of a particle is shown graphically in Fig. 2-3. What is the displacement of the particle at time equal to 5 sec if the initial displacement of the particle is equal to 4 ft? What is the acceleration of the particle at time equal to 8 sec?

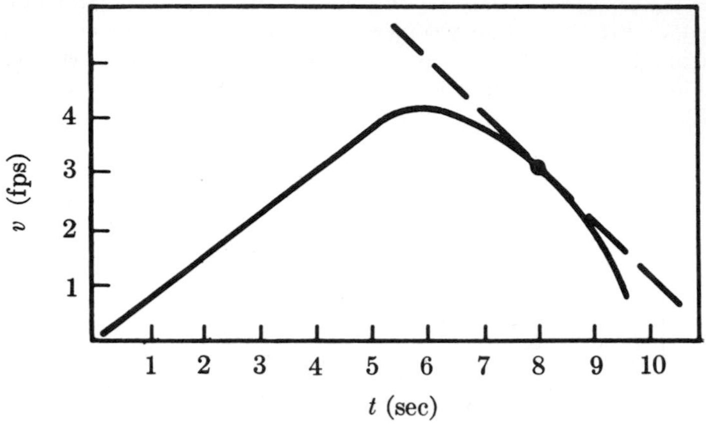

Figure 2-3

Solution: The change in displacement from $t = 0$ to 5 sec is just the area under the velocity-time curve. This is equal to $\frac{1}{2}(4)(5)$. Since the initial displacement of the particle was equal to 4, the total displacement of the particle given as

$$x = x_0 + \int_0^5 v\, dt$$

is equal to

$$x = 4 + 10 = 14 \text{ ft}$$

The acceleration at 8 sec is just the slope of the velocity curve at that time. The slope is equal to -0.9, and therefore the acceleration at 8 sec is -0.9 ft/sec^2.

2–2. CARTESIAN COORDINATES

Position. Assuming now that we are able to establish a fixed point or reference in space, we must attempt to find some sort of scheme for describing position and motion. The French mathematician René Descartes proposed a method for defining a point in space by use of a *coordinate system*, now called the *Cartesian coordinate system*. Although the student is quite familiar with this scheme, briefly it consists of defining three mutually orthogonal lines intersecting at a common point O, as shown in Fig. 2–4. A point P in space may then be defined by specifying three quantities, the projections on each of the three lines. These lines are called the x, y, and z axes, respectively, and the projections are the distances x, y, and z from the point O.

The coordinate system, or frame of reference, is now thought of as

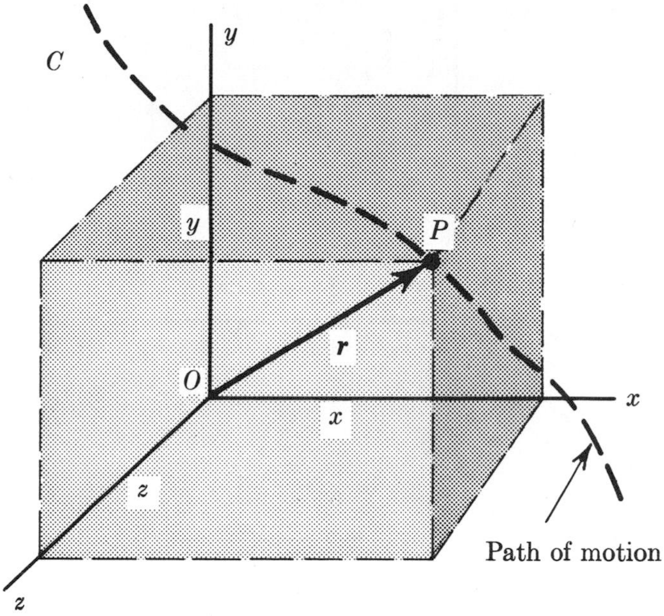

Figure 2-4

being fixed in space. The particle, or point P, is moving through space and thus moving relative to the fixed system. This implies that the distances x, y, and z are not constant distances, but are functions of time. Thus,

$$\begin{aligned} x &= x(t) \\ y &= y(t) \\ z &= z(t) \end{aligned} \tag{2.20}$$

where, given any value of the parameter t (time), a unique x, y, and z may be determined, thus defining the position of the particle. It might also be pointed out that this so-called *parametric relationship* is probably the most convenient method of defining a curve in three-dimensional space. Equation 2.20 defines a curve in space, and this curve is referred to as the *path of motion* of the point or particle.

The position P of the particle in space may be thought of as a vector. This position-vector or radius-vector is defined as a vector $\boldsymbol{r}$ drawn from the point O to the point P. In vector form:

$$\boxed{\boldsymbol{r}(t) = x(t)\bar{\boldsymbol{i}} + y(t)\bar{\boldsymbol{j}} + z(t)\bar{\boldsymbol{k}}} \tag{2.21}$$

The vectors $\bar{\boldsymbol{i}}$, $\bar{\boldsymbol{j}}$, and $\bar{\boldsymbol{k}}$ are defined as vectors of unit length, directed along the x, y, and z axes, respectively. The student will recall that these are nothing more than labels that define or specify the direction of the scalar quantity that multiplies them (Fig. 2–5).

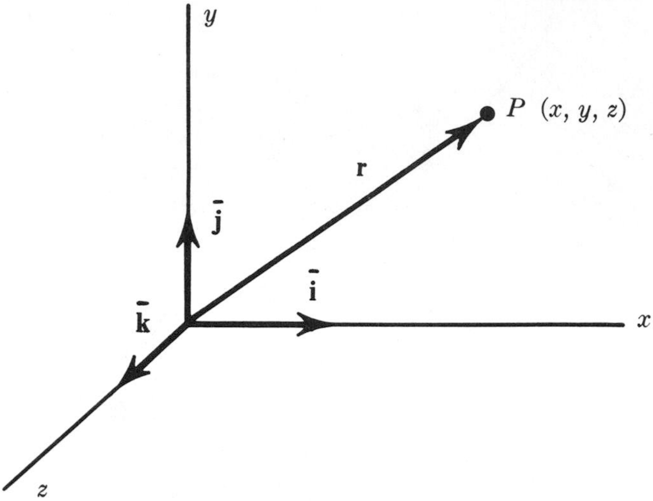

Figure 2-5

Thus we are able to describe the position of a point or particle as it moves through space by simply specifying the vector $\boldsymbol{r}$. Now we shall investigate means of describing the motion of the particle.

Velocity. Consider now the motion of a particle as it moves along the curve C. Suppose at time t the particle is at position A, and at some small increment of time later (say, $t + \Delta t$), the particle is at position B. The distance that the particle moves in time Δt is $\Delta \boldsymbol{r}$, and by the rules of vector addition, the vector describing the new position of the particle is $\boldsymbol{r} + \Delta \boldsymbol{r}$.

The average velocity as the particle moves from A to B is defined as the displacement during Δt per Δt, or

$$v_{\text{avg}} = \frac{\Delta \boldsymbol{r}}{\Delta t} \tag{2.22}$$

and the velocity at a point (in this case point A, which corresponds to time t) is defined as

$$\boldsymbol{v}(t) = \lim_{\Delta t \to 0} \frac{\Delta \boldsymbol{r}}{\Delta t} \tag{2.23}$$

But we recognize the right-hand side of the above expression as simply the time differentiation of the radius vector, and of course this implies that the velocity itself is a vector quantity. Thus,

$$\boldsymbol{v}(t) = \frac{d\boldsymbol{r}}{dt} \tag{2.24}$$

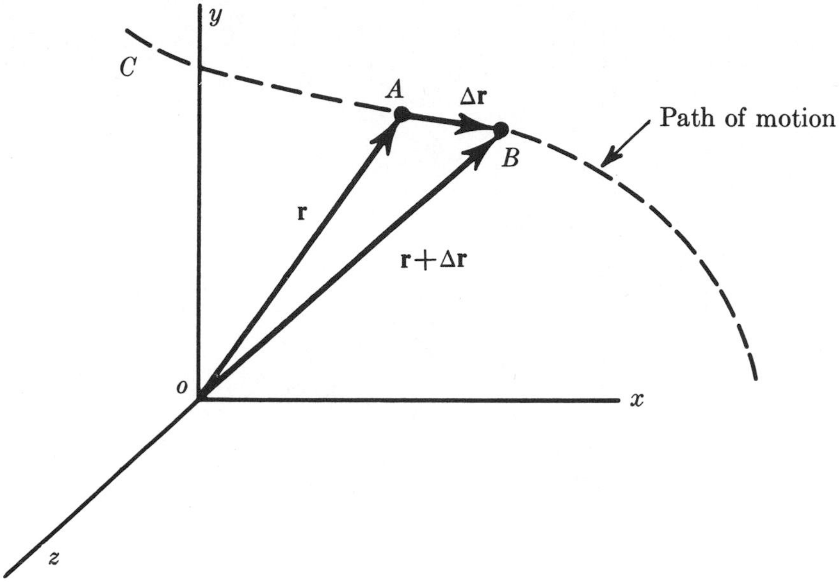

Figure 2-6

Upon differentiation of the radius vector of Eq. 2.21, to obtain the velocity, we get

$$\boldsymbol{v}(t) = \dot{x}(t)\bar{\boldsymbol{i}} + \dot{y}(t)\bar{\boldsymbol{j}} + \dot{z}(t)\bar{\boldsymbol{k}} \tag{2.25}$$

The dot that appears above the x, y, and z terms indicates in shorthand notation the differentiation of those quantities.

The velocity $\dot{x}$ is the velocity of the particle in the x direction, $\dot{y}$ is the velocity of the particle in the y direction, and $\dot{z}$ is the velocity of the particle in the z direction. This shorthand scheme of writing time derivatives is reported to have been started by Isaac Newton.

The *speed* of a particle is defined as the magnitude of the velocity. If the velocity is given as a vector quantity, then the magnitude of the velocity is nothing more than the length of the velocity vector. Therefore the speed is the length of the velocity vector. Thus,

$$v = \sqrt{\dot{x}^2 + \dot{y}^2 + \dot{z}^2} \tag{2.26}$$

Acceleration. It is possible to construct a Cartesian reference system where the three orthogonal axes define the three components of the velocity, as shown in Fig. 2–7. The velocity of the particle at time t is defined as a point A in this so-called *velocity space*. As the particle moves through space, the velocity of the particle changes, and at $t + \Delta t$, the

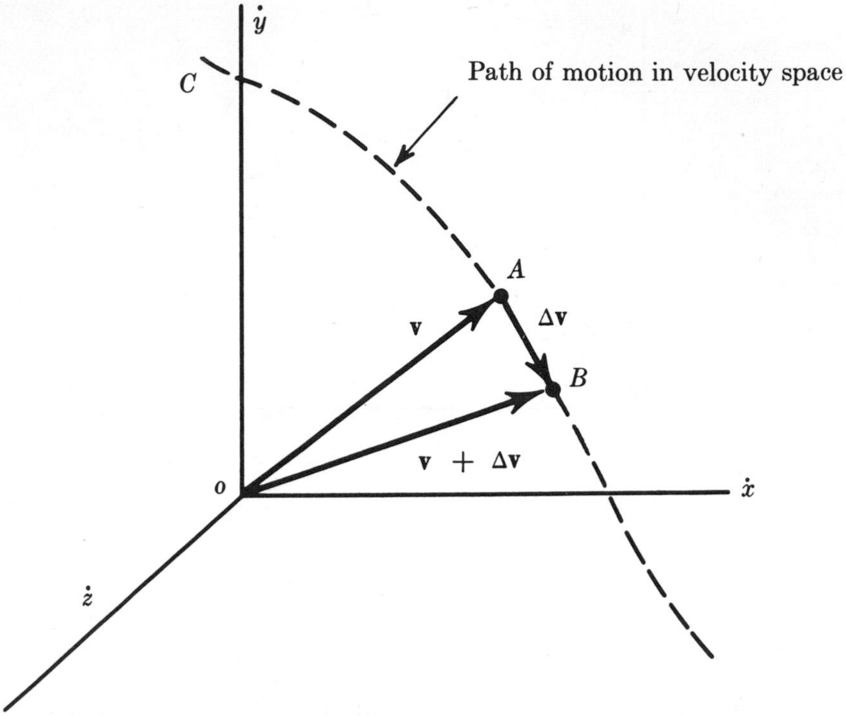

Figure 2-7

velocity of the particle is defined by point B. The change in velocity during the increment of time Δt is given by the vector $\Delta \boldsymbol{v}$ (Fig. 2–7).

The average acceleration of the particle as the velocity changes is defined as

$$a_{\text{avg}} = \frac{\Delta \boldsymbol{v}}{\Delta t} \tag{2.27}$$

and the acceleration of the particle at time t (point A) is

$$\boldsymbol{a}(t) = \lim_{\Delta t \to 0} \frac{\Delta \boldsymbol{v}}{\Delta t} \tag{2.28}$$

But the term on the right-hand side of Eq. 2.28 is nothing more than the definition of the time derivative of the velocity vector, which implies that *acceleration (like velocity) is a vector quantity*. Thus,

$$\boldsymbol{a}(t) = \frac{d\boldsymbol{v}}{dt} \tag{2.29}$$

and since the velocity is the time derivative of the radius vector, then

$$\boldsymbol{a}(t) = \frac{d^2\boldsymbol{r}}{dt^2} \tag{2.30}$$

By differentiating the velocity vector (given by Eq. 2.25), we obtain the acceleration:

$$\boxed{\boldsymbol{a}(t) = \ddot{x}(t)\bar{\boldsymbol{i}} + \ddot{y}(t)\bar{\boldsymbol{j}} + \ddot{z}(t)\bar{\boldsymbol{k}}} \tag{2.31}$$

Thus it is seen that if we know the displacement or position of a particle as a function of time, we can determine the velocity and acceleration as a function of time simply by performing the required differentiations.

The magnitude of the acceleration a is nothing more than the length of the acceleration vector:

$$a = \sqrt{\ddot{x}^2 + \ddot{y}^2 + \ddot{z}^2} \tag{2.32}$$

Units. The units of velocity are L/T, or *feet per second*, and the units of acceleration are L/T^2, or *feet per square second.*

Example 2–6. Given the displacement of a particle in space as a function of time:

$$x = x(t) = 4t^3$$
$$y = y(t) = 3t^2$$
$$z = z(t) = 6t$$

Determine the velocity and acceleration of the particle when $t = 2$ sec. Also determine the magnitude of the velocity and acceleration at the same instant of time.

Solution: In vector form, the displacement is

$$\boldsymbol{r} = \boldsymbol{r}(t) = (4t^3)\bar{\boldsymbol{i}} + (3t^2)\bar{\boldsymbol{j}} + (6t)\bar{\boldsymbol{k}}$$

The velocity is obtained by differentiating the displacement with respect to time:

$$\boldsymbol{v} = \frac{d\boldsymbol{r}}{dt} = (12t^2)\bar{\boldsymbol{i}} + (6t)\bar{\boldsymbol{j}} + 6\bar{\boldsymbol{k}}$$

and the acceleration in turn is obtained by differentiating the velocity with respect to time:

$$\boldsymbol{a} = \frac{d\boldsymbol{v}}{dt} = (24t)\bar{\boldsymbol{i}} + 6\bar{\boldsymbol{j}}$$

At $t = 2$ sec,

$$\boldsymbol{r} = 32\bar{\boldsymbol{i}} + 12\bar{\boldsymbol{j}} + 12\bar{\boldsymbol{k}}$$
$$\boldsymbol{v} = 48\bar{\boldsymbol{i}} + 12\bar{\boldsymbol{j}} + 6\bar{\boldsymbol{k}}$$
$$\boldsymbol{a} = 48\bar{\boldsymbol{i}} + 6\bar{\boldsymbol{j}}$$

The magnitude of the velocity (speed) at $t = 2$ is

$$v = \sqrt{48^2 + 12^2 + 6^2} = 50$$

The magnitude of the acceleration at $t = 2$ is

$$a = \sqrt{48^2 + 6^2} = 48.2$$

The inverse problem. It was shown in Sec. 2–1 that when the acceleration is given as a function of time, the velocity may be obtained by performing a time integration. It may be easily shown that Eq. 2.8, written for motion in one direction, may be used to construct the similar expression for three-dimensional motion:

$$\boxed{\boldsymbol{v} = \boldsymbol{v}_0 + \int \boldsymbol{a}\, dt} \qquad \textbf{(2.33)}$$

Similarly, expansion of Eq. 2.10 results in the vector equation for the displacement:

$$\boxed{\boldsymbol{r} = \boldsymbol{r}_0 + \int \boldsymbol{v}\, dt} \qquad \textbf{(2.34)}$$

Thus, if the vector acceleration is given as a function of time, it may be integrated once to obtain the velocity and twice to obtain the displacement.

Example 2–7. The acceleration of a particle is given as $\boldsymbol{a} = 7\bar{\imath} - 3t\bar{\jmath} + t^2\bar{k}$. It is desired to determine the displacement of the particle at $t = 2$ sec. The velocity and displacement of the particle at $t = 0$ is

$$\boldsymbol{v}_0 = -4\bar{\imath} + 2\bar{\jmath} + \bar{k}$$
$$\boldsymbol{r}_0 = 4\bar{\imath} + 3\bar{\jmath} - 2\bar{k}$$

Solution: The velocity of the particle is obtained by integrating the acceleration with respect to time:

$$\begin{aligned}\boldsymbol{v} &= \boldsymbol{v}_0 + \int_0^t \boldsymbol{a}\, dt \\ &= -4\bar{\imath} + 2\bar{\jmath} + \bar{k} + \int_0^t (7\bar{\imath} - 3t\bar{\jmath} + t^2\bar{k})\, dt \\ &= (-4 + 7t)\bar{\imath} + \left(2 - \frac{3t^2}{2}\right)\bar{\jmath} + \left(1 + \frac{t^3}{3}\right)\bar{k}\end{aligned}$$

The displacement of the particle with respect to time is obtained by integrating the velocity with respect to time:

$$\begin{aligned}\boldsymbol{r} &= \boldsymbol{r}_0 + \int_0^t \boldsymbol{v}\, dt \\ &= 4\bar{\imath} + 3\bar{\jmath} - 2\bar{k} + \int_0^t (-4 + 7t)\bar{\imath} + \left(2 - \frac{3t^2}{2}\right)\bar{\jmath} + \left(1 + \frac{t^3}{3}\right)\bar{k}\, dt \\ &= \left(4 - 4t + \frac{7t^2}{2}\right)\bar{\imath} + \left(3 + 2t - \frac{t^3}{2}\right)\bar{\jmath} + \left(-2 + t + \frac{t^4}{12}\right)\bar{k}\end{aligned}$$

The displacement of the particle is evaluated at $t = 2$ sec:

$$\boldsymbol{r} = 10\bar{\imath} + 5\bar{\jmath} + 1.33\bar{k}$$

Example 2–8. A projectile is fired with an initial velocity v_0 at an angle θ with the horizontal, as shown in Fig. 2–8. Describe the motion of the flight of the projectile; that is, determine the trajectory.

Solution: We know the acceleration of the projectile and the initial velocity and position of the body; so, presumably, we are able to perform an integration to determine the velocity of the body and the path of motion of the body. Since the

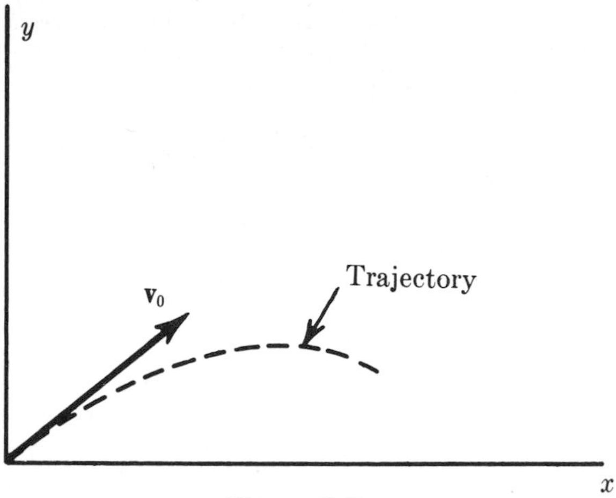

Figure 2-8

body is moving close to the surface of the earth, the body has a constant acceleration downward due to gravity. Thus,

$$\boldsymbol{a} = -g\bar{\boldsymbol{j}} \tag{2.35}$$

and the initial velocity and position of the body is

$$\begin{aligned} \boldsymbol{v}_0 &= (v_0 \cos\theta)\bar{\boldsymbol{i}} + (v_0 \sin\theta)\bar{\boldsymbol{j}} \\ \boldsymbol{r}_0 &= 0 \end{aligned} \tag{2.36}$$

The velocity of the body is determined by performing an integration of the acceleration:

$$\begin{aligned} \boldsymbol{v} &= \boldsymbol{v}_0 + \int_0^t \boldsymbol{a}\, dt \\ &= v_0 = \int_0^t -g\bar{\boldsymbol{j}}\, dt \\ &= (v_0 \cos\theta)\bar{\boldsymbol{i}} + (v_0 \sin\theta - gt)\bar{\boldsymbol{j}} \end{aligned} \tag{2.37}$$

and the displacement of the body is obtained by integrating the velocity:

$$\begin{aligned} \boldsymbol{r} &= \boldsymbol{r}_0 + \int_0^t \boldsymbol{v}\, dt \\ &= (v_0 t \cos\theta)\bar{\boldsymbol{i}} + \left(v_0 t \sin\theta - \frac{gt^2}{2}\right)\bar{\boldsymbol{j}} \end{aligned} \tag{2.37a}$$

Thus, the path of motion is given in parametric form:

$$\begin{aligned} x(t) &= v_0 t \cos\theta \\ y(t) &= v_0 t \sin\theta - \frac{gt^2}{2} \end{aligned} \tag{2.38}$$

If we eliminate t from Eq. 2.37a,

$$y = x \tan\theta - \frac{gx^2}{2v_0^2 \cos^2\theta} \tag{2.39}$$

It is seen that the path of motion of the particle will be of parabolic form. Other properties of the trajectory can be determined. The range of the motion can be found by setting $y = 0$ in Eq. 2.39:

$$0 = x\left(\tan\theta - \frac{gx}{2v_0^2\cos^2\theta}\right) \tag{2.40}$$

and, solving for x,

$$x = 0; \qquad x = R = \frac{v_0^2 \sin 2\theta}{g} \tag{2.41}$$

It may be noted that the maximum range occurs when $\theta = 45$ deg.

The time of flight can be found by setting $y = 0$ in Eq. 2.38:

$$0 = v_0 t \sin\theta - \frac{gt^2}{2} \tag{2.42}$$

Solving for t,

$$t = \frac{2v_0 \sin\theta}{g} \tag{2.43}$$

The maximum height that the projectile attains can be found by taking the equation for y as a function of t and finding the vertical distance, y_{max} when the time of flight is one-half the total time of flight:

$$y = v_0 \sin\theta t - \frac{gt^2}{2}$$

$$t = \frac{v_0 \sin\theta}{g} \quad \text{for half flight time} \tag{2.44}$$

$$y = v_0 \sin\theta\left(\frac{v_0\sin\theta}{g}\right) - \frac{g\left(\frac{v_0\sin\theta}{g}\right)^2}{2}$$

$$y_{max} = h = \frac{v_0^2 \sin^2\theta}{2g}$$

PROBLEMS

2-1. The displacement of a particle in rectilinear motion is $x = 4t^2 + 12t$ ft. Time is given in seconds. What is the displacement, velocity, and acceleration of the particle when time is equal to 3 sec?

2-2. The displacement of a particle in rectilinear motion is $x = 2t^3$ ft, where time is given in seconds. What is the acceleration of the particle when the velocity is equal to 96 fps?

2-3. The velocity of a particle in rectilinear motion is $v = 5t^4 + 3t$ fps. If at $t = 0$, the displacement is equal to 4 ft, what is the displacement and the acceleration of the particle as a function of time?

2-4. The velocity as a function of time of a projectile shot out of a cannon with an initial velocity of v_0 is equal to $v(t) = v_0 e^{-\alpha t}$. What is the displacement of the projectile of a function of time if the displacement at $t = 0$ is zero? (Assume rectilinear motion.)

2-5. A particle moving through a thin fluid will have an acceleration in a direction opposite to the motion and proportional to the velocity squared; $a = -Cv^2$. If the initial velocity is v_0, what is the velocity of the projectile as a function of time?

2-6. In a spring-mass system with a nonlinear spring, the acceleration of the mass is equal to $-C_1x - C_2x^3$. The system is started with an impulse so that, at $t = 0$, $v = V$ and $x = 0$. What is the velocity of the mass as a function of the displacement?

2-7. An automobile traveling 60 mph decelerates at a constant rate and stops in 300 ft. What is the acceleration of the automobile?

2-8. An automobile accelerates from rest to 60 mph in 10 sec. Determine the acceleration of the automobile, assuming that it is constant.

2-9. According to automotive test results, the maximum allowable acceleration for passenger comfort is roughly about 9.0 ft/sec². Using this figure as a criterion, how far would one travel after applying the brakes if the speed of the car were (a) 30 mph and (b) 60 mph?

2-10. The deceleration of an automobile skidding to an emergency stop is roughly the same, regardless of the speed of the vehicle. If this is true, show that by doubling the speed of an automobile, you will increase by four times the distance needed to stop.

2-11. In general, the displacement as a function of time for the spring-mass system shown in Fig. P.2-11 is given as $x = A \cos 2t + B \sin 2t$, where A and B are arbitrary constants that must be determined from the initial conditions. If, at $t = 0$, the displacement is equal to 4 and the velocity is equal to -4, determine the acceleration of the mass as a function of time.

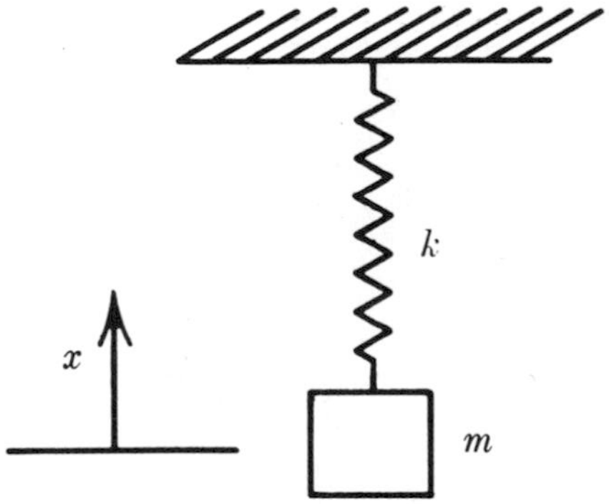

Figure Prob. 2-11

2-12. A monkey wrench is dropped by a workman working on a television tower on the top of a 20 story (220 ft) office building. Assuming that the force of the air friction is negligible, what is the velocity of the wrench when it hits the ground?

2-13. A rocket sled accelerates on a straight-line track at a rate of $0.42t$ ft/sec². What is the acceleration of the sled after it has traveled a distance of 2 miles if the sled started from rest? What is the velocity of the sled at this point?

2-14. A rocket is fired vertically. The thrust given to the rocket by its engines produces a net acceleration upward of 12 ft/sec². How long will it take the rocket to attain an altitude of 20,000 ft, and what is the velocity of the rocket at this height?

2-15. An automobile with an accelerometer mounted in the car starts from rest and moves along a straight test track. The acceleration of the automobile as a function of time is read out on a strip chart, as shown in Fig. P.2–15. Draw a sketch of the velocity and displacement of the automobile as a function of time.

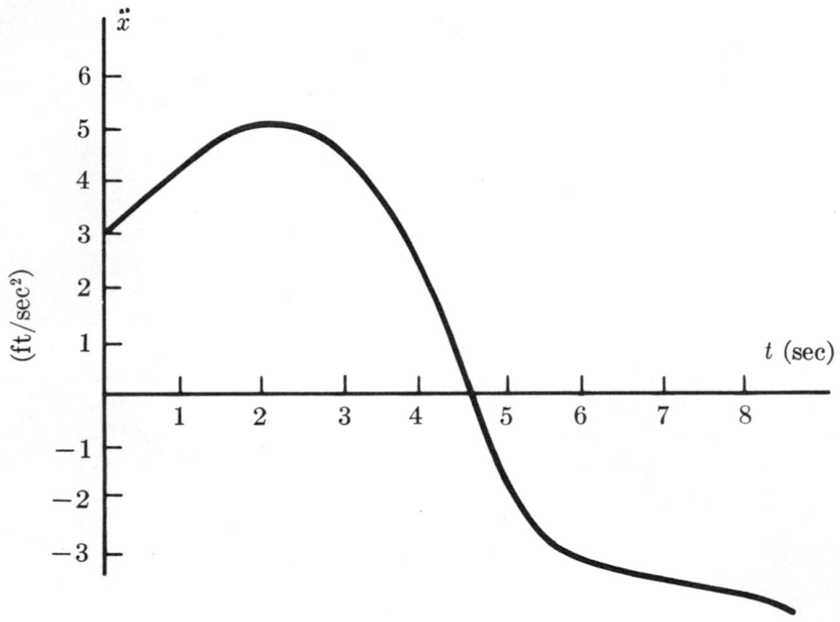

Figure Prob. 2-15

2-16. An automobile starts from point A and travels with an average velocity of 50 mph. Another car starts from the same point, 4 hr later, and travels with an average velocity of 60 mph. How long will it take the second car to overtake the first?

2-17. At a certain time, train A, moving to the right with a constant velocity of 40 fps, has its engine a distance of 5 miles from the intersection. Train B is also moving toward the intersection. Its engine is a distance of 4 miles from the intersection. What may be the maximum velocity of train B so that A may pass the intersection first? Train A is 2000 ft long and train B is 2400 ft long.

2-18. For Problem 2–17, determine the maximum velocity of train B so that B will pass the intersection before A.

2-19. The maximum speed for a given elevator is 20 fps and the maximum acceleration (and deceleration) is 4.0 ft/sec². What would be the time required for an elevator to descend from the fourteenth floor to the second floor if there were an

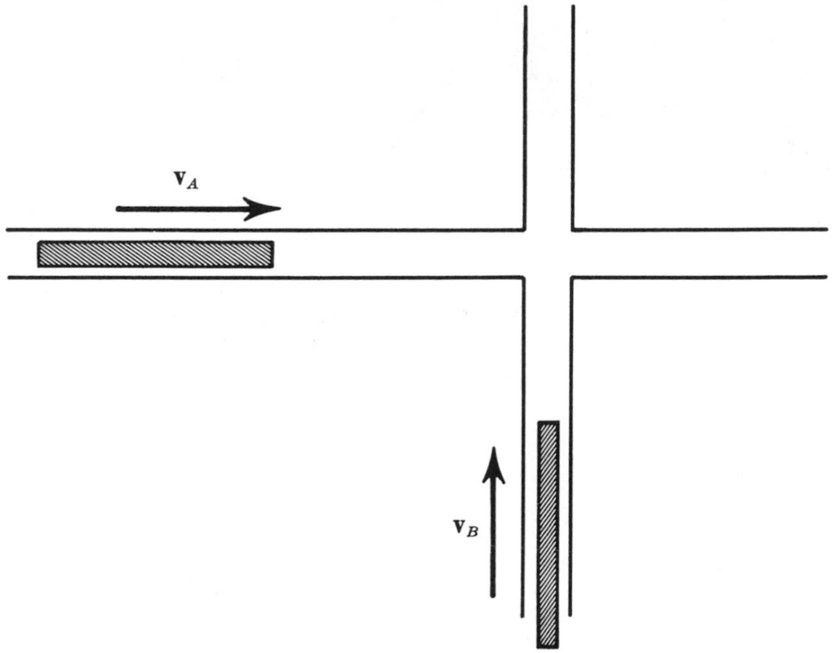

Figure Prob. 2-17

average of 13 ft per floor? (Assume in the calculations that the acceleration is a constant.)

2-20. Consider the preceding problem. Determine the time required for the elevator to move from the fourteenth floor to the eighth floor. Note that here the elevator will not be able to attain its maximum speed, and here also we have a situation of passenger discomfort due to the sudden change in acceleration.

2-21. A portion of a bus timetable is shown in the table here. What is the average velocity (in mph) of the bus in the total journey? (Figure a 10-min stop at each town.) What is the average velocity of the bus when it is on the road?

Town:	*A*		*B*		*C*		*D*		*E*		*F*
Departure:	7:05 A.M.		7:40 A.M.		8:30 A.M.		9:25 A.M.		11:50 A.M.		1:00 P.M.
Distance: (miles)		20		42		37		122		64	

2-22. A body starts at $t = 0$ at point (3,6) and moves with the velocity as shown in Fig. P.2–22. Determine (a) the speed of the particle at $t = 5$ sec, (b) the magnitude of the acceleration of the particle at $t = 2$ sec, and (c) the displacement of the body when $t = 5$ sec.

2-23. Given $x = 4t$, $y = t^3$, and $z = t^4$ (the description of the motion of the particle in parametric form) determine (a) the velocity and acceleration of the particle when $t = 2$ sec, (b) the magnitude of the velocity and acceleration of the particle when $t = 2$ sec, and (c) the acceleration of the particle in the z direction when the velocity in the y direction is equal to $\frac{1}{8}$.

2-24. The motion of a particle moving on a spiral path is given parametrically as

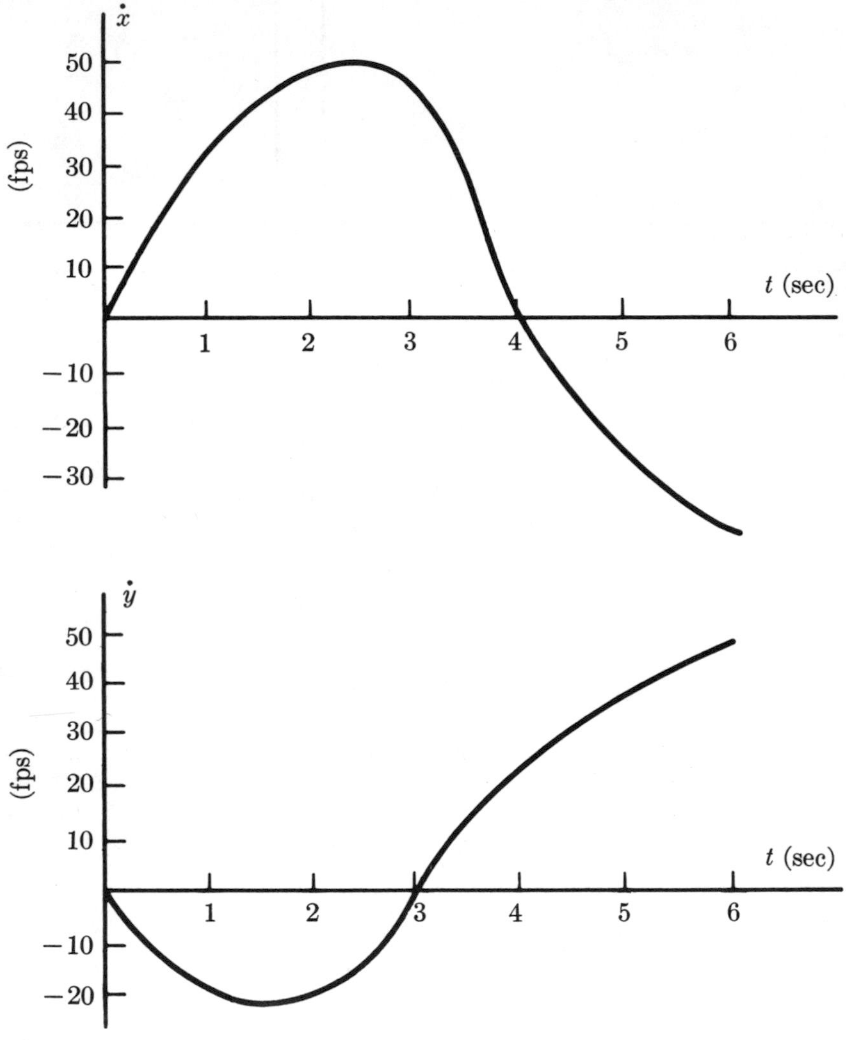

Figure Prob. 2-22

$x = A \cos \omega t$, $y = A \sin \omega t$, and $z = -bt$. What is the velocity of the spiral when $t = \pi/\omega$? Show that the speed of the particle moving on the spiral is a constant.

2-25. Given the acceleration of a particle as a function of time as $\boldsymbol{a} = t^3\bar{\boldsymbol{i}} - e^t\bar{\boldsymbol{j}} + \sin 4t\bar{\boldsymbol{k}}$. Determine the displacement of the particle when $t = 2$ sec if the velocity at $t = 0$ is $\boldsymbol{v}_0 = 2\bar{\boldsymbol{i}} + 6\bar{\boldsymbol{j}} - 3\bar{\boldsymbol{k}}$ and the displacement at $t = 0$ is $\boldsymbol{r}_0 = -\bar{\boldsymbol{i}} + \bar{\boldsymbol{j}}$. (Leave the answer in terms of exponential and sine functions.)

2-26. If the acceleration of a particle in the x direction is $\ddot{x} = kt$, what is the displacement as a function of the velocity if $\dot{x}_0$ is the original velocity and x_0 is the original displacement?

2-27. If the velocity of a particle moving in two-dimensional space is $v = 6t\bar{i} - 3t^2\bar{j}$, what is the acceleration of the particle when the displacement of the particle in the y direction is equal to 27? The original position of the particle is given as $r_0 = 0$.

2-28. A particle is moving with a velocity of $v = 3\bar{i} - 2t^2\bar{j} + (t^3 - 4t)\bar{k}$. Determine the magnitude of the acceleration of the particle when $t = 3$ sec.

2-29. For the preceding problem, determine the displacement of the particle when $t = 2$ sec if the original displacement is $r_0 = -2\bar{i} - \bar{j} + 3\bar{k}$.

2-30. For Problem 2-28, determine the speed of the particle when $t = 1$ sec.

2-31. A sky diver jumps from an airplane traveling with a velocity of 100 mph horizontally at an altitude of 6000 ft. He falls 1000 ft before he opens his parachute, and thereafter he descends vertically with a constant velocity of 20 fps. Neglecting

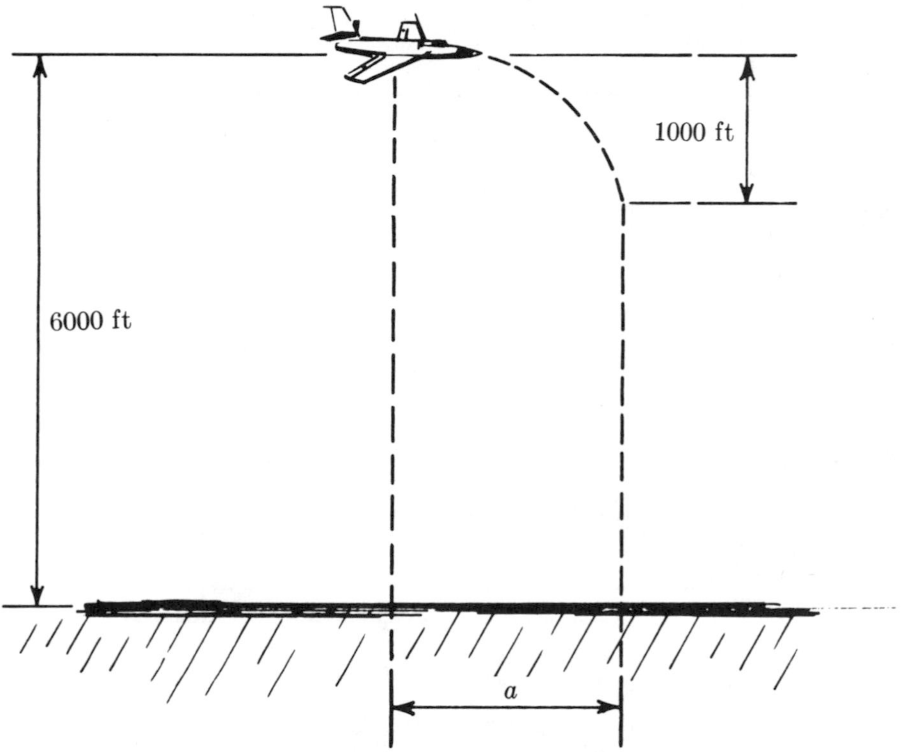

Figure Prob. 2-31

air friction in the period before he opened his parachute, determine (a) the total time of fall to the ground, and (b) the horizontal distance a that he traveled before he opened his chute.

2-32. A cannon has a muzzle velocity of 1000 fps. At what angle must the cannon

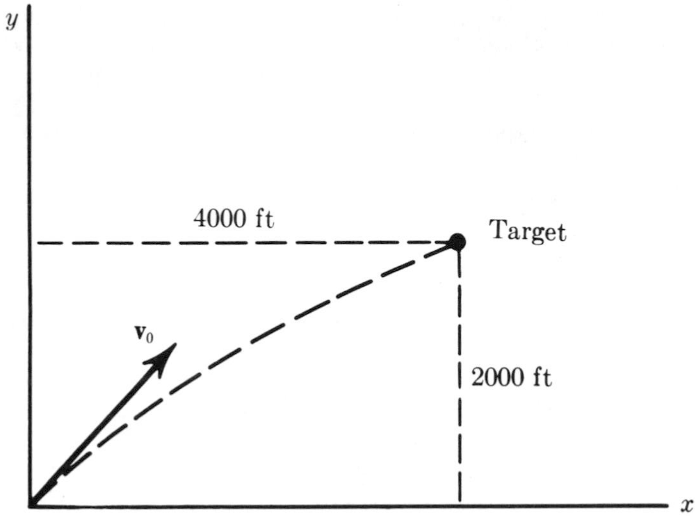

Figure Prob. 2-33

be set so that it will hit an object 4 miles away? What is the time of flight of the projectile?

2-33. A projectile is to be fired at a target in the air. The muzzle velocity of the projectile is 1000 fps. What angle should be chosen so that the projectile hits the target?

2-34. A projectile is fired with a muzzle velocity of 600 fps. Can the angle at which the projectile is fired be adjusted so that it will clear an object 1500 ft high, $1\frac{1}{2}$ miles away?

2-35. A projectile is fired from the top of a 200-ft hill with a muzzle velocity of

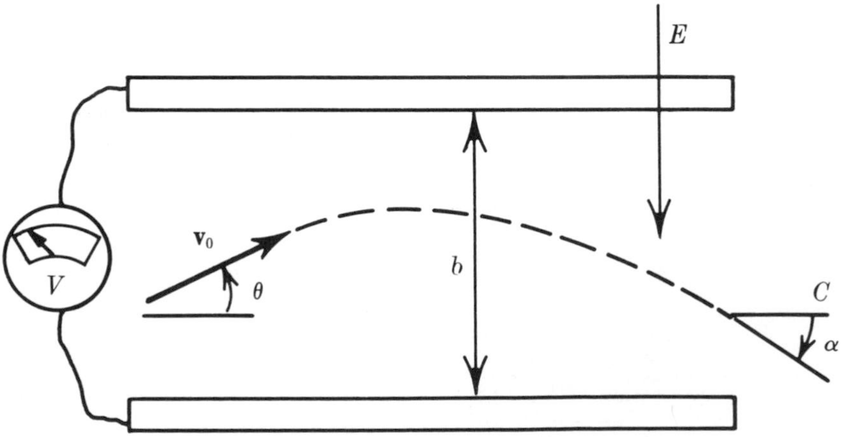

Figure Prob. 2-36

1500 fps. At what angle should the projectile be fired so that its range is a maximum? Write the equation for θ for which range is a maximum, but do not solve the equation.

2-36. The acceleration of a particle in an electric field is eE/m, where E is the magnitude of the electric field, e is the charge on the particle, and m is the mass of the particle. Derive the equation of motion of the path of the particle, $y = f(x)$, for a particle shot at an angle θ and velocity v_0 into an electric field, as shown in Fig. P.2-36.

2-37. A side view of two parallel, charged plates is shown in Fig. P.2-36. A charged electron is shot into the electric field in a direction parallel to the plates and midway between them. The value of the electric field E is given as Vb, where b is the distance that separates the plates. What value of V must be chosen so that the electron leaves the plates at point C at an angle of α degrees?

2-3. ROTATIONAL MOTION

Rotation on a circle. In Sec. 2-2 it was noted that in order to specify the position of a particle in space, three coordinates must be given. Now suppose the particle is constrained to move in a plane, and more specifically, in a circle about the point O as shown in Fig. 2-9. Since the particle is constrained to move in a circular path, only one coordinate is needed to define its position. This coordinate may be the angle θ, shown in

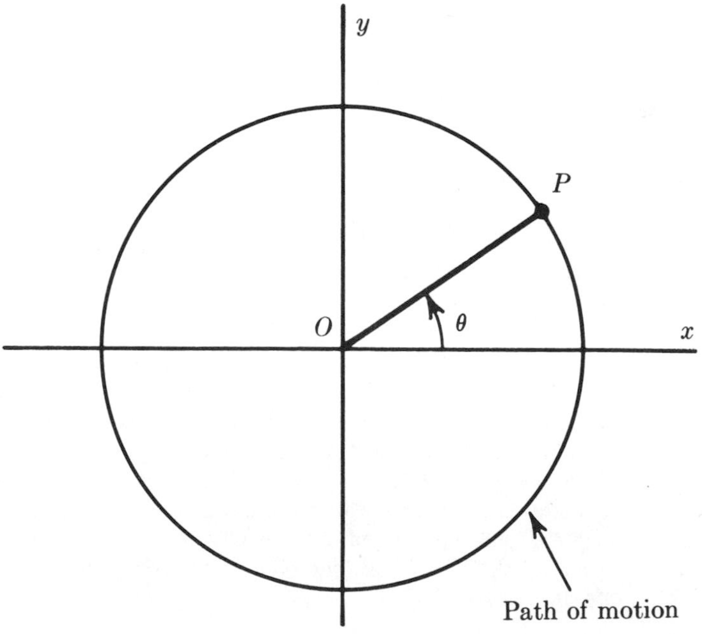

Figure 2-9

the figure and defined as the angle measured positive counterclockwise from the x axis to the line joining the points O and P. If the particle P is moving, then the angle θ will be a function of time.

We may also think of θ as defining the angular position of the line OP. If, for instance, the line OP were scribed on a rigid body rotating about the fixed axis (defined by the point O), then the angle θ would be used to measure the angular position of the body. If the particle P is moving in a circular path, we may talk about its rate of motion in terms of the angle θ. If during a small amount of time Δt, the angle θ changes by an amount of $\Delta\theta$, then we may define the average angular velocity over this period of time as

$$\omega_{\text{avg}} = \frac{\Delta\theta}{\Delta t} \tag{2.45}$$

where ω (omega) represents angular velocity. The angular velocity at a point or instant in time is just the limit of the average velocity as Δt approaches zero:

$$\omega = \lim_{\Delta t \to 0} \frac{\Delta\theta}{\Delta t} \tag{2.46}$$

But the right-hand side of Eq. 2.46 is just the time derivative of θ. Thus,

$$\boxed{\omega = \frac{d\theta}{dt}} \tag{2.47}$$

Similarly, the *angular acceleration* is just the time rate of change of angular velocity (change in angular velocity per change in time), so that the angular acceleration is just the time derivative of the angular velocity. Thus,

$$\boxed{\dot{\omega} = \frac{d\omega}{dt} = \frac{d^2\theta}{dt^2}} \tag{2.48}$$

where $\dot{\omega}$ represents the angular acceleration.

It is seen that the definitions of angular velocity and acceleration correspond to the definitions of linear velocity and acceleration.

Relationship between arc length and angle. It is desired to determine a relationship between the linear distances along an arc or the circumference of a circle and the angle θ. The distance s, as shown in Fig. 2–10, is the distance measured along the path of motion or, in this case, the circle. Thus we should like to establish a relationship between s and r.

It is known that the circumference of a circle is equal to $2\pi r$, which implies that one can write

$$s = 2\pi r\theta \tag{2.49}$$

where θ is the angle given in revolutions.

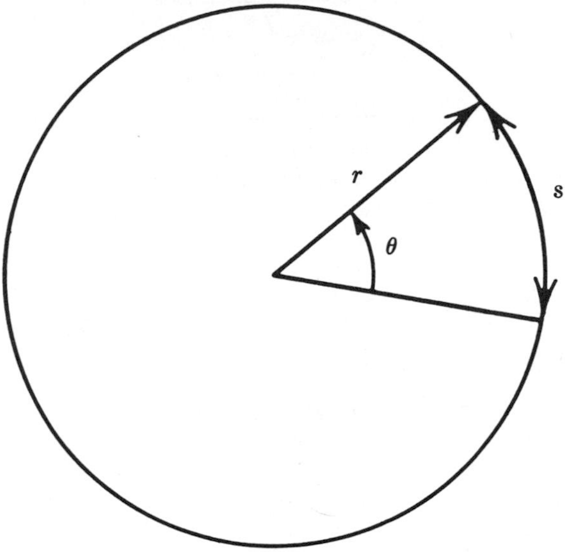

Figure 2-10

By changing the measure of θ properly, we may write Eq. 2.49 as

$$\boxed{s = r\theta} \tag{2.50}$$

where θ must be now measured in a new unit, commonly known as the *radian*. It is apparent by observation of Eqs. 2.49 and 2.50 that the radian must be defined in the following manner:

$$\theta \text{ (radians)} = 2\pi\theta \text{ (revolutions)} \tag{2.51}$$

If one revolution is 360 deg, then one radian would be $360/2\pi$, or about 57.3 deg.

Equation 2.50 is the well-known *arc formula* and will be employed often throughout this text.

The inverse problem. The inverse problem is, given the angular acceleration, what is the angular velocity and angular displacement? This problem is analogous to the case of rectilinear motion. The angular velocity is obtained by integrating the acceleration with respect to time, and the angular displacement is obtained by integrating the angular velocity with respect to time. Thus,

$$\boxed{\omega = \omega_0 + \int_0^t \dot{\omega}\, dt} \tag{2.52}$$

and

$$\boxed{\theta = \theta_0 + \int_0^t \omega \, dt} \tag{2.53}$$

Units. Angles are commonly measured in units of degrees, revolutions, or radians. All, in a dimensional sense, are unitless. Generally it is more convenient to use radian measure, particularly when we are dealing with problems where we are concerned with arc lengths involving the arc formula. However, the unit of angular velocity of revolutions per minute (rpm) is not at all uncommon. The units of angles are dimensionless radians, revolutions, or degrees; the units of angular velocity, (L/T) *radians per second*, or rpm; the units of angular acceleration, (L/T^2) *radians per square second.*

Vector definition of angular velocity. Shown in Fig. 2–11 is a body that is spinning about a line or axis at an instant of time. It is possible that the orientation of the axis of rotation will change with time. The angular velocity of the body is defined as a vector whose magnitude is equal to the magnitude of the angular velocity at that instant. Its direction is given by the right-hand rule, by which the fingers of the right hand are curled in the direction of rotation and the position of the thumb denotes the direction of the vector.

The angular velocity vector is similar to the moment vector in that it is a pseudovector; it does not represent a motion or action in the given direction, but it is rather arbitrarily defined. To understand physically what the angular velocity vector represents, one has to recall the definition.

One might be tempted to try to define angular rotation or position by a vector similar to the angular velocity vector. By using the right-hand rule to define rotations about reference axes of a given body, one can show that the rotations do not commute. That is to say, a 90-deg rotation of the body about an x axis plus a 90-deg rotation about the y axis does not result in the same position that you would get if you performed the rotations in an inverse order.

Example 2–9. A flywheel rotating with an angular velocity of 200 rpm accelerates with a constant angular acceleration to 800 rpm in 12 sec. The radius of the flywheel is 6 in. Determine (a) the angular acceleration of the flywheel, (b) the number of rotations that the flywheel makes in the 12 sec, and (c) the total distance moved by a point on the periphery.

Solution: It is customary, but not necessary, to express the angular acceleration in terms of radians per second. Since there are 2π radians in one revolution and 60 secs in 1 min, it follows that

$$200 \text{ rpm} = (200)\left(\frac{2\pi}{60}\right) = 20.9 \text{ radians/sec}$$

$$800 \text{ rpm} = (800)\left(\frac{2\pi}{60}\right) = 83.8 \text{ radians/sec}$$

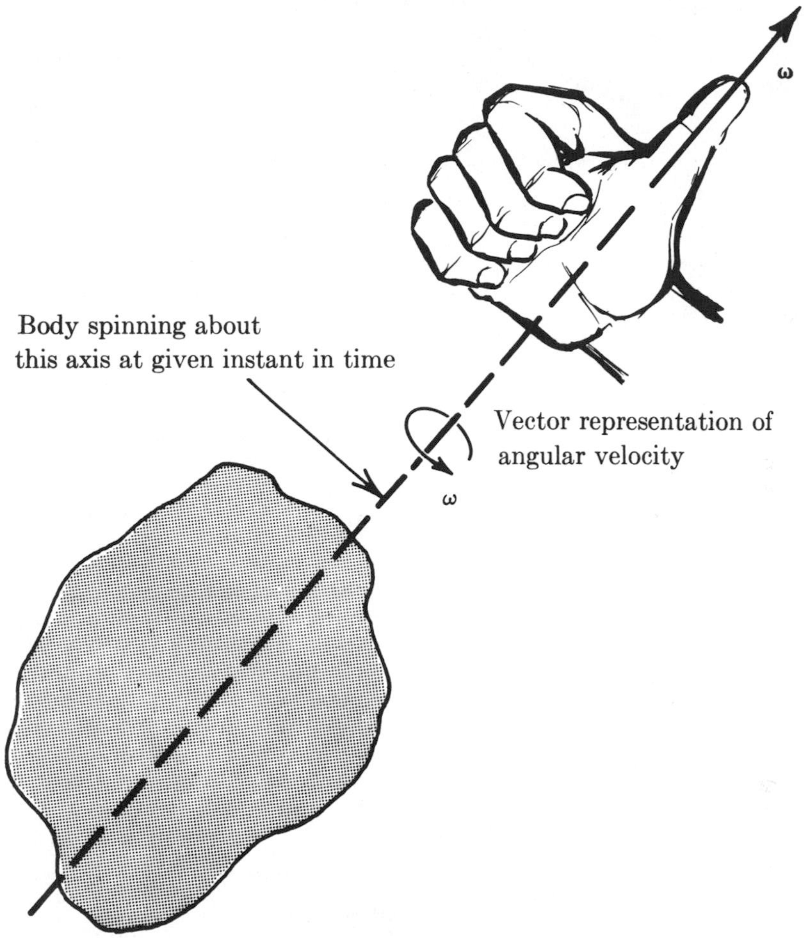

Figure 2-11

If the angular acceleration $\dot{\omega}$ is a constant, it follows that

$$\omega = \omega_0 + \dot{\omega}t$$

and

$$83.8 = 20.9 + \dot{\omega}(12)$$
$$\dot{\omega} = 5.24 \text{ radians/sec}^2$$

Since the angular acceleration is a constant,

$$\theta = \theta_0 + \omega_0 t + \frac{\dot{\omega}t^2}{2}$$

and

$$\theta = (20.9)(12) + \frac{(5.24)(12)^2}{2}$$
$$= 629 \text{ radians}$$
$$= \frac{629}{2\pi} = 100 \text{ revolutions}$$

The total distance moved by the point on the periphery is $s = r\theta$, or

$$s = (6)(629) = 3774 \text{ in.}$$

Example 2–10. Write the angular velocity vector for a top (Fig. 2-12) as it spins about its fixed axis AO. The magnitude of the angular velocity is $\omega = 24$ radians/sec.

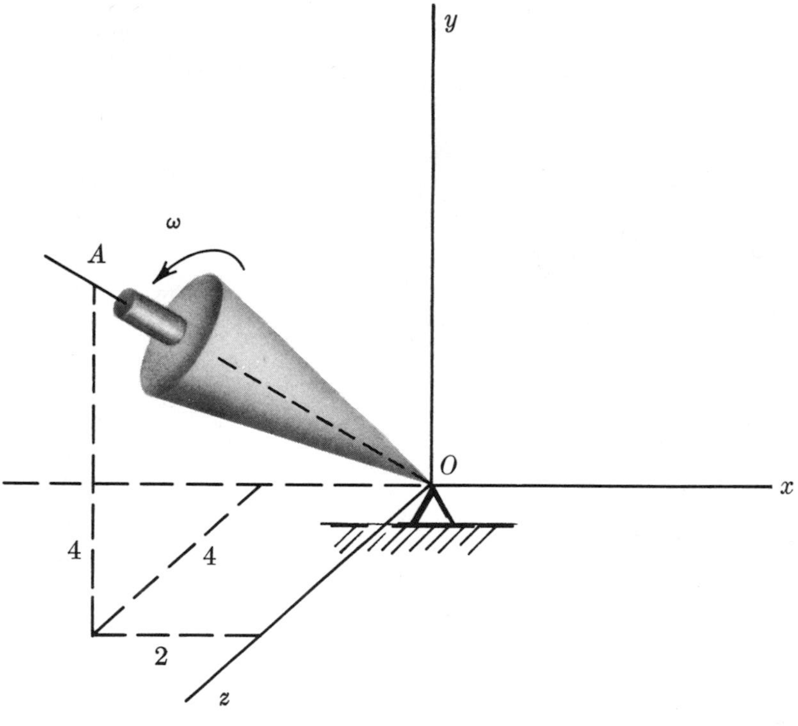

Figure 2-12

Solution: By noting the definition of the angular velocity vector, it is observed from the diagram that the vector will lie along line OA in the direction from O to A. The distance OA (Fig. 2–13) is

$$OA = \sqrt{4^2 + 4^2 + 2^2} = 6$$

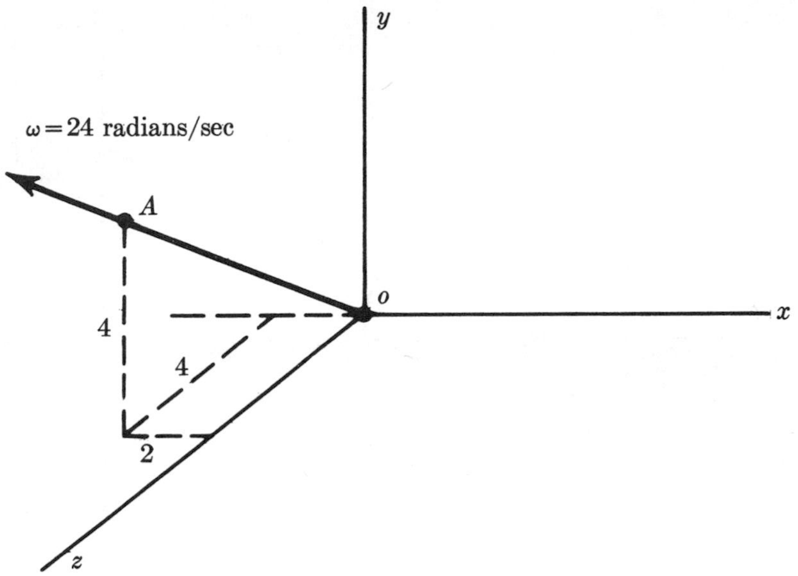

Figure 2-13

Therefore

$$\omega_x = -24(\tfrac{2}{6}) = -8$$
$$\omega_y = 24(\tfrac{4}{6}) = 16$$
$$\omega_z = 24(\tfrac{4}{6}) = 16$$

so that

$$\boldsymbol{\omega} = -8\bar{i} + 16\bar{j} + 16\bar{k}$$

PROBLEMS

2-38. The angular velocity of the radius vector to a particle moving on a circle is given as $\omega = Ae^{-2t}$, where A is an arbitrary constant that must be determined from the initial conditions. If at $t = 0$, the angular displacement is equal to 4 and the angular velocity is equal to 3, determine the angular displacement and acceleration of the particle as a function of time.

2-39. A flywheel has an angular acceleration of $\dot{\omega} = 4t + 10$ radians/sec^2. If the flywheel starts from rest, determine (a) the angular velocity of the flywheel, at $t = 4$ sec, in radians per second, (b) the angular velocity of the flywheel, at $t = 4$ sec, in revolutions per minute, and (c) the number of revolutions that the flywheel has made at the end of 4 sec.

2-40. A flywheel starts from rest and accelerates to 2000 radians/sec in 60 sec with a constant acceleration. What is the angular acceleration of the flywheel?

2-41. A body is rotating with an angular velocity of 3000 rpm. What constant acceleration (in radians per square second) is required so that the body will rotate with an angular velocity of 5000 rpm in 5 sec?

2-42. The armature of an electrical machine has an angular acceleration of

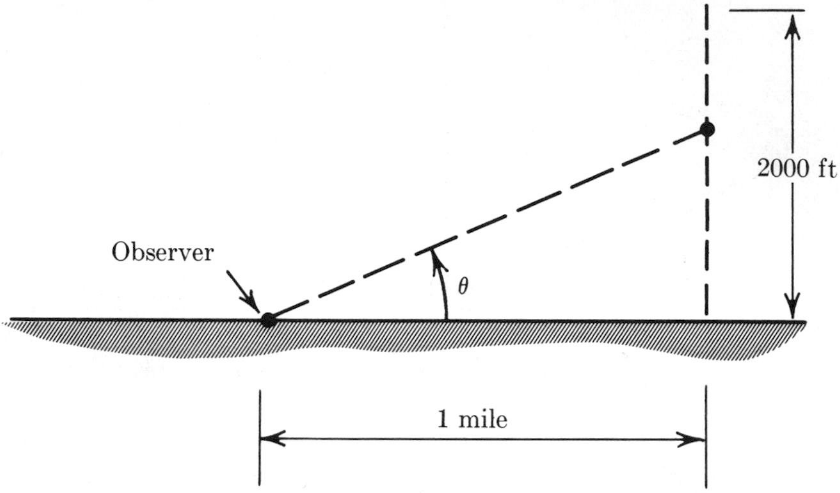

Figure Prob. 2-44

$\dot{\omega} = 3 + 10t - 2t^2$ radians/sec^2 until such a time that the acceleration is zero. Then the armature will rotate with a constant velocity. If the armature starts from rest, what is the constant velocity that the armature assumes, and how long does it take the armature to attain this velocity?

2-43. For the preceding problem, determine the velocity and acceleration of the armature after it has made ten revolutions.

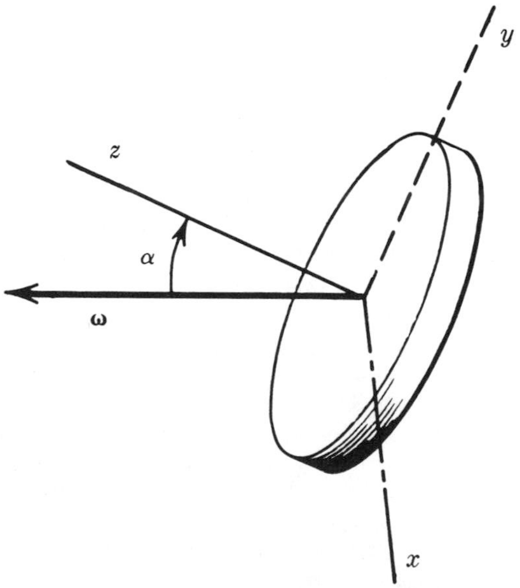

Figure Prob. 2-49

2-44. A falling object is observed from the ground, 1 mile away (Fig. P.2–44). If the object is dropped from a height of 2000 ft, what is the rate of change of the angle θ, with respect to time, 4 sec after the body has been released?

2-45. The earth rotates about the sun in a nearly circular orbit with an average radius of about 93 million miles. If the earth makes one revolution in every 365-day period, determine (a) the angular velocity of the radius vector from the sun to the earth in radians per second, and (b) the speed of the center of the earth as it moves in circular orbit.

2-46. If the earth's polar axis were assumed to be fixed in space, what would be the speed ($\dot{s}$) of points on the earth's surface as a function of the longitude ϕ? The angular velocity of the earth is one revolution per day and the radius of the earth is approximately 4000 miles.

2-47. The angular velocity of a body referred to axes that are fixed in space is $\omega = 4\bar{i} + 3\bar{j}$. Describe the motion of the body and determine the magnitude of the angular velocity of the body.

2-48. A moment free-body has an angular velocity of $\boldsymbol{\omega} = A \cos \lambda t\bar{i} + A \sin \lambda t\bar{j} + B\bar{k}$, where the unit vectors are defined along axes that are fixed in the body and moving with the body. Show that the magnitude of the angular velocity of the body is a constant.

2-49. The angular velocity of the body shown in Fig. P.2–49 is a constant and has the direction shown in the figure. Write the angular velocity as a vector, $\boldsymbol{\omega}$, in the moving system fixed to the wheel where the unit vectors are now defined along the moving axes.

2-50. The angular motion of the flywheel shown in Fig. P.2-50 consists of an

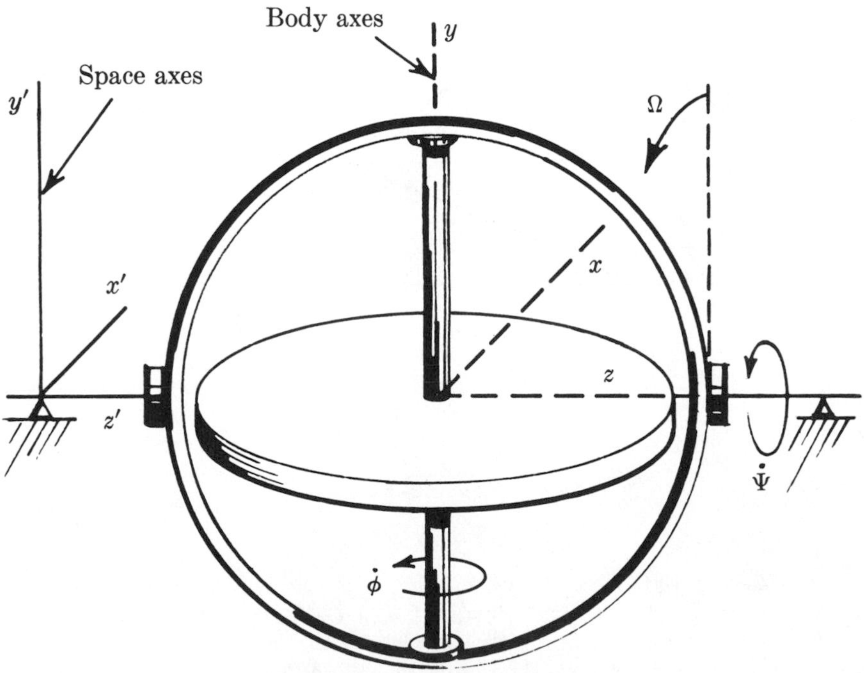

Figure Prob. 2-50

angular velocity of spin $\dot{\phi}$ and the angular velocity of precession $\dot{\Psi}$. Write the total angular velocity vector in terms of the space-fixed coordinates shown in the figure as a function of the angle Ω, and in terms of the coordinates fixed to the frame (the y axis lies always along the axis of spin, and the z axis lies on the axis of precession).

2-4. POLAR COORDINATES

Velocity and acceleration. Often it is more convenient to express the motion of a body in coordinates other than in Cartesian coordinates. This is true when the particle is moving on a circular path or on a path that is easily expressible in terms of polar coordinates. At this point, we shall restrict the motion of the particle to the plane.

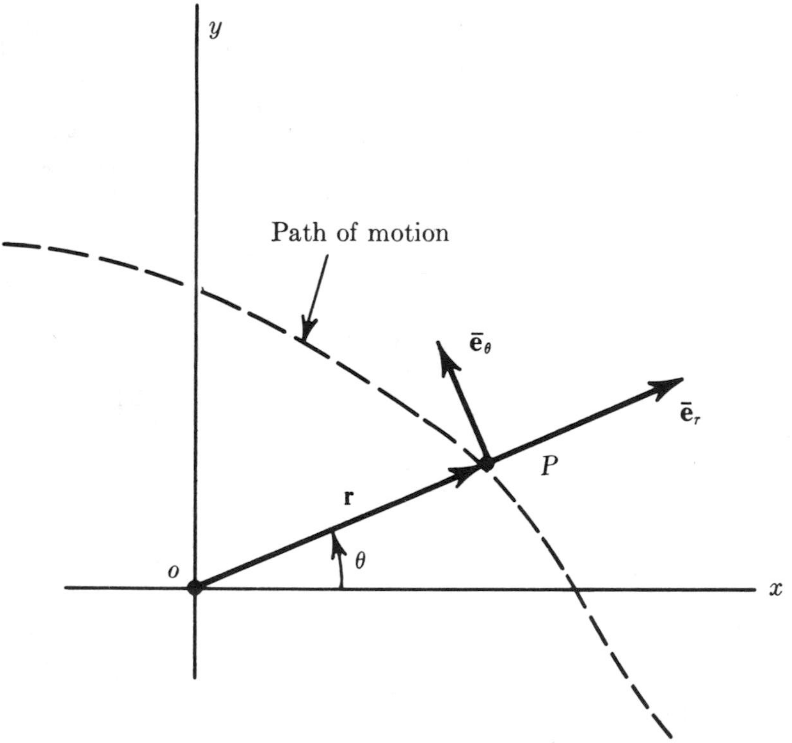

Figure 2-14

Consider a particle P moving along a prescribed path of motion as shown in Fig. 2–14. In polar coordinates, a Cartesian frame of reference is used, but instead of defining the point in terms of its projections on the horizontal and vertical axes, the point P is defined in terms of its distance r

from the origin and the angle that it makes with the horizontal axis θ, counterclockwise θ being defined as positive. Therefore the coordinate representing the point is (r,θ) instead of (x,y).

In polar coordinates a new set of unit vectors for indicating direction must be defined. The two unit vectors in polar coordinates are $\bar{\boldsymbol{e}}_r$ and $\bar{\boldsymbol{e}}_\theta$, and they are defined as follows:

$\bar{\boldsymbol{e}}_r$ = a unit vector always in the direction of the vector *from* point O to point P.

$\bar{\boldsymbol{e}}_\theta$ = a unit vector always perpendicular to $\bar{\boldsymbol{e}}_r$ and positive in a counterclockwise sense to $\bar{\boldsymbol{e}}_r$ (see Fig. 2–14).

These unit vectors now have the property that they may rotate in the plane. Looking at Fig. 2–14, we note that as the particle moves along the path of motion, $\bar{\boldsymbol{e}}_r$ (which by definition is in the direction of the line OP) must change its direction because the direction of the line OP is changing. The position of the particle may be expressed very simply in polar coordinates as

$$\boldsymbol{r}(t) = r(t)\bar{\boldsymbol{e}}_r \tag{2.54}$$

where it must be assumed that the direction of $\bar{\boldsymbol{e}}_r$ is known. It might be pointed out here that the direction of $\bar{\boldsymbol{e}}_r$ could be specified by the angle θ, but this point will not be elaborated because we are primarily interested in description of the velocity and the acceleration.

The velocity of the particle is obtained by differentiating the radius vector with respect to time:

$$\begin{aligned} \boldsymbol{v} &= \frac{d\boldsymbol{r}}{dt} \\ &= \dot{r}\bar{\boldsymbol{e}}_r + r\dot{\bar{\boldsymbol{e}}}_r \end{aligned} \tag{2.55}$$

Note that upon differentiating the position vector of the particle, we have assumed that the unit vector $\bar{\boldsymbol{e}}_r$ has a time derivative, which is different from zero. At first this might seem surprising, particularly in view of the fact that we know that $\bar{\boldsymbol{e}}_r$ by definition has a constant unit magnitude. A time derivative of a vector exists if (1) the vector is changing in magnitude, or (2) the vector is changing in direction. In this case it is seen that the unit vector $\bar{\boldsymbol{e}}_r$ is changing direction (in general), so that presumably it should have a time derivative.

To show why the time derivative of a rotating vector exists, and to find the value of the time derivative of the vector, consider Fig. 2–15. The vectors $\bar{\boldsymbol{e}}_r$ and $\bar{\boldsymbol{e}}_\theta$ for a particle are shown at some instant of time. Later, during a small increment of time Δt, the particle P moves along the path of motion to a new position; during this motion, the angle θ changes by amount $\Delta\theta$. Now say that the motion is such that the change in θ becomes positive, and the unit vectors have a different orientation, defined in Fig. 2–15 by $\bar{\boldsymbol{e}}_r'$ and $\bar{\boldsymbol{e}}_\theta'$, so that $\bar{\boldsymbol{e}}_r'$ may be expressed as the vector sum of $\bar{\boldsymbol{e}}_r$ and the change in $\bar{\boldsymbol{e}}_r$, which is given as $\Delta\bar{\boldsymbol{e}}_r$ in Fig. 2–15. Since the vectors have a unit magnitude, we may draw the circle of unit magnitude as

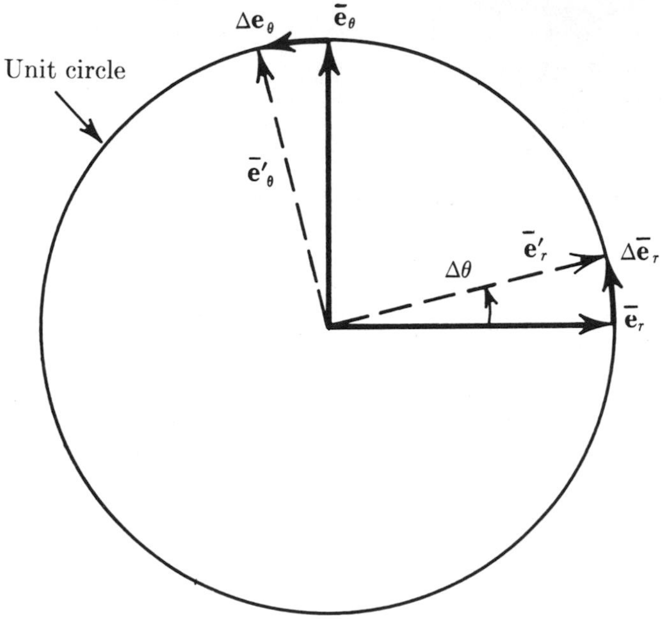

Figure 2-15

shown. Consider now $\Delta\bar{e}_r$. By the arc formula (Eq. 2.50), the magnitude of this vector is equal to (1) $\Delta\theta$. Since $\Delta\bar{e}_r$ is in the $\bar{e}_\theta$ direction,

$$\Delta\bar{e}_r = \Delta\theta\bar{e}_\theta \qquad (2.56)$$

Dividing both sides of the equation by the change in time, Δt,

$$\frac{\Delta\bar{e}_r}{\Delta t} = \frac{\Delta\theta}{\Delta t}\bar{e}_\theta \qquad (2.57)$$

and upon taking the limits of both sides of Eq. 2.57 as Δt approaches zero, we get the definitions of the time derivatives:

$$\dot{\bar{e}}_r = \dot{\theta}\bar{e}_\theta \qquad (2.58)$$

In a similar fashion, it may be shown that

$$\dot{\bar{e}}_\theta = -\dot{\theta}\bar{e}_r \qquad (2.59)$$

Now we are able to write the velocity of the particle in terms of the unit vectors. Substituting Eq. 2.58 into Eq. 2.55, we get for the velocity:

$$\boxed{v = \dot{r}\bar{e}_r + r\dot{\theta}\bar{e}_\theta} \qquad (2.60)$$

This says, then, that the velocity of a particle is a combination of a component directed away from the origin of the Cartesian reference system of magnitude dr/dt, and a component at right angles to the radius vector

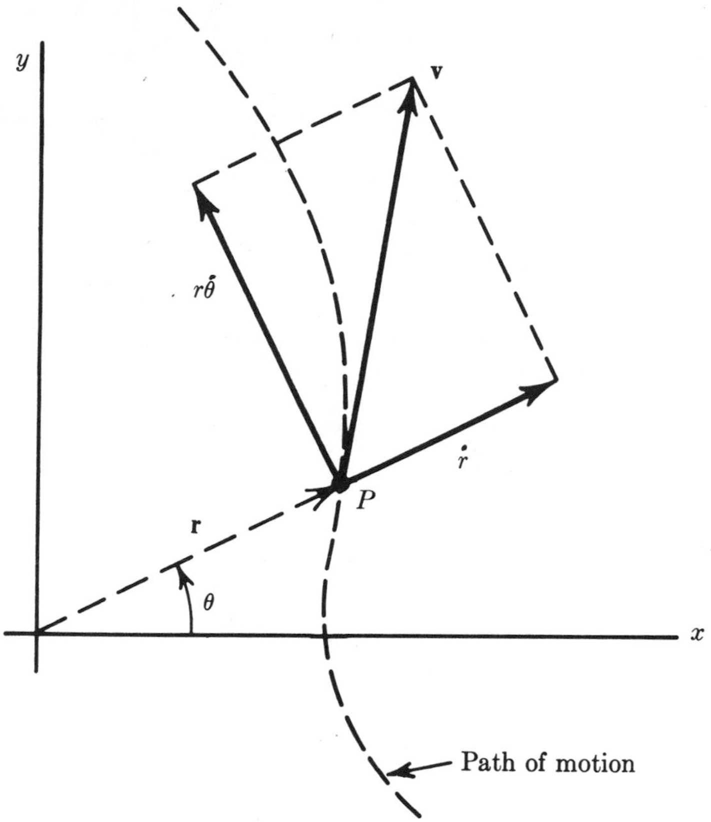

Figure 2-16

of magnitude $r\dot{\theta}$, as shown in Fig. 2–16. The acceleration in turn is obtained by differentiating the velocity:

$$\boldsymbol{a} = \ddot{r}\bar{\boldsymbol{e}}_r + \dot{r}\dot{\bar{\boldsymbol{e}}}_r + \dot{r}\dot{\theta}\bar{\boldsymbol{e}}_\theta + r\ddot{\theta}\bar{\boldsymbol{e}}_\theta + r\dot{\theta}\dot{\bar{\boldsymbol{e}}}_\theta$$

By substituting the values of the time derivatives of the unit vectors, the acceleration in polar form becomes

$$\boxed{\boldsymbol{a} = (\ddot{r} - r\dot{\theta}^2)\bar{\boldsymbol{e}}_r + (r\ddot{\theta} + 2\dot{r}\dot{\theta})\bar{\boldsymbol{e}}_\theta} \tag{2.61}$$

and the two components of acceleration are as shown in Fig. 2–17.

Motion of a particle in a circle. A special, yet very common, example of the use of polar coordinates is the description of the motion of a particle in a circular path. When the particle is moving in a circle, $\dot{r} = 0$, and the velocity becomes

$$\boldsymbol{v} = r\dot{\theta}\bar{\boldsymbol{e}}_\theta \tag{2.62}$$

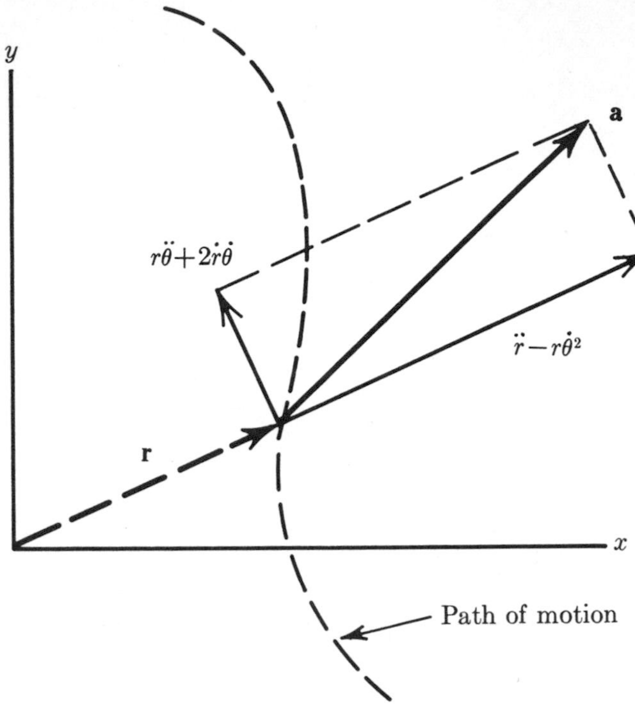

Figure 2-17

This says that the velocity of a particle moving in a circle is of magnitude $r\dot{\theta}$. The direction of the velocity of the particle is *always* tangent to the path of motion.

On the other hand, the acceleration for $\dot{r} = 0$ becomes

$$\boldsymbol{a} = -r\dot{\theta}^2\bar{\boldsymbol{e}}_r + r\ddot{\theta}\bar{\boldsymbol{e}}_\theta \tag{2.63}$$

This says that for a particle moving in a circle, the acceleration of the particle has two components. The particle has an acceleration of magnitude $r\dot{\theta}^2$ directed inward toward the center of the circle. In addition, the particle has another acceleration component; this one is directed tangent to the path of motion and is of magnitude $r\ddot{\theta}$ (Fig. 2–18).

Example 2–11. A particle moves on a path defined parametrically as

$$r = t^4 - 2t^2 \text{ ft} \quad \theta = t^3 \text{ radians}$$

Determine the velocity and the acceleration when $t = 2$ sec.

Solution: The polar equations for the velocity and the acceleration are, respectively,

$$\boldsymbol{v} = \dot{r}\bar{\boldsymbol{e}}_r + r\dot{\theta}\bar{\boldsymbol{e}}_\theta$$
$$\boldsymbol{a} = (\ddot{r} - r\dot{\theta}^2)\bar{\boldsymbol{e}}_r + (r\ddot{\theta} + 2\dot{r}\dot{\theta})\bar{\boldsymbol{e}}_\theta$$

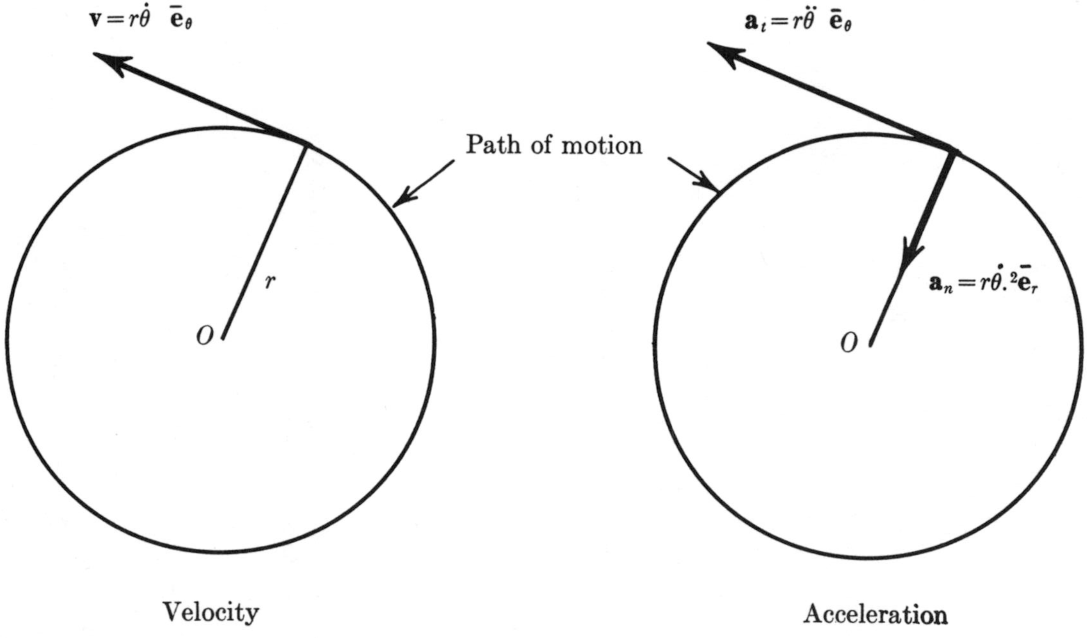

$\mathbf{v} = r\dot{\theta}\ \bar{\mathbf{e}}_\theta$
$\mathbf{a}_t = r\ddot{\theta}\ \bar{\mathbf{e}}_\theta$
Path of motion
r
O
O
$\mathbf{a}_n = r\dot{\theta}^2\bar{\mathbf{e}}_r$
Velocity
Acceleration

Figure 2-18

The values of r and θ and their time derivatives are

$$\begin{aligned} r &= t^4 - 2t^2 & \theta &= t^3 \\ \dot{r} &= 4t^3 - 4t & \dot{\theta} &= 3t^2 \\ \ddot{r} &= 12t^2 - 4 & \ddot{\theta} &= 6t \end{aligned}$$

At $t = 2$,

$$\begin{aligned} r &= 8 & \theta &= 8 \\ \dot{r} &= 24 & \dot{\theta} &= 12 \\ \ddot{r} &= 44 & \ddot{\theta} &= 12 \end{aligned}$$

The vector form of the velocity is

$$\begin{aligned} \boldsymbol{v} &= 24\bar{\boldsymbol{e}}_r + 8(12)\bar{\boldsymbol{e}}_\theta \\ &= 24\bar{\boldsymbol{e}}_r + 96\bar{\boldsymbol{e}}_\theta \text{ fps} \end{aligned}$$

and the magnitude of the velocity is

$$v = \sqrt{24^2 + 96^2} = 99 \text{ fps}$$

The acceleration in vector form is

$$\boldsymbol{a} = -1108\bar{\boldsymbol{e}}_r + 672\bar{\boldsymbol{e}}_\theta$$

and the magnitude of the acceleration is

$$a = \sqrt{1108^2 + 672^2} = 1300 \text{ ft/sec}^2$$

Example 2–12. A body starts from rest and moves in a circle, of radius 10 ft, with a constant angular acceleration of 2 radians/sec². What is the linear velocity and acceleration at $t = 3$ sec?

Solution: For motion on a circular path, the velocity and acceleration equations in polar form become

$$\begin{aligned} \boldsymbol{v} &= r\dot{\theta}\boldsymbol{e}_\theta \\ \boldsymbol{a} &= -r\dot{\theta}^2\bar{\boldsymbol{e}}_r + r\ddot{\theta}\bar{\boldsymbol{e}}_\theta \end{aligned}$$

The only unknown term in the equations is the angular velocity. This can be determined by integrating the acceleration:

$$\dot{\theta} = \dot{\theta}_0 + \int_0^t \ddot{\theta}\, dt = \int_0^t 2dt = 2t$$

and at $t = 3$, the angular velocity $\dot{\theta} = 6$ radians/sec.

Therefore the velocity is

$$\boldsymbol{v} = 60\bar{\boldsymbol{e}}_\theta$$

and the acceleration is

$$\boldsymbol{a} = -360\bar{\boldsymbol{e}}_r + 20\bar{\boldsymbol{e}}_\theta$$

The magnitude of the acceleration is

$$a = \sqrt{360^2 + 20^2} = 361 \text{ ft/sec}^2$$

Example 2–13. A pin on the end of a retractable arm slides in the slot as shown in Fig. 2–19. Suppose the arm moves from A to B with a constant angular velocity $\dot{\theta} = 0$. Write the acceleration in polar vector form as a function of the angle θ.

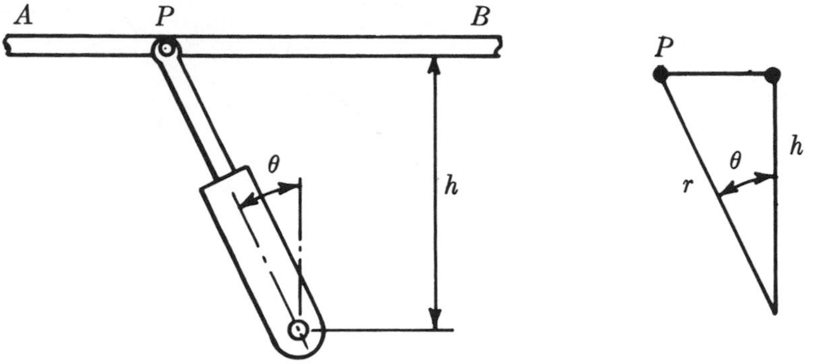

Figure 2-19

Solution: By a trigonometric identity, the radial distance to the pin can be written as a function of θ.

$$r = h \sec \theta$$

The first time derivative of r is

$$\dot{r} = h \sec \theta \tan \theta \frac{d\theta}{dt}$$

Noting that

$$\frac{d\theta}{dt} = \dot{\theta} = c$$

$\dot{r}$ becomes

$$\dot{r} = hc \sec \theta \tan \theta$$

Similarly, the second time derivative of r is

$$\ddot{r} = hc^2 \sec \theta \,(\tan^2 \theta + \sec^2 \theta)$$

The acceleration equation is

$$\boldsymbol{a} = (\ddot{r} - r\dot{\theta}^2)\overline{\boldsymbol{e}}_r + (r\ddot{\theta} + 2\dot{r}\dot{\theta})\overline{\boldsymbol{e}}_\theta$$

But $\ddot{\theta} = 0$, so that

$$\boldsymbol{a} = \{hc^2 \sec \theta(\tan^2 \theta + \sec^2 \theta) - hc^2 \sec \theta\}\overline{\boldsymbol{e}}_r + \{2hc^2 \sec \theta \tan \theta\}\overline{\boldsymbol{e}}_\theta$$

or

$$\boldsymbol{a} = \{2hc^2 \sec \theta \tan^2 \theta\}\overline{\boldsymbol{e}}_r + \{2hc^2 \sec \theta \tan \theta\}\overline{\boldsymbol{e}}_\theta$$

PROBLEMS

2-51. Given the motion of a particle in parametric form as $\theta = Ae^{kt}$ and $r = B \cos kt$, write the velocity and acceleration of the particle as a function of time in polar vector form.

2-52. The motion of a particle is given as $\dot{\theta} = t(3 + t)$ and $\ddot{r} = 7$. If at $t = 0$, $\theta = 2$, $\dot{r} = -2$, and $r = 3$, what is the velocity and the acceleration of the particle at $t = 4$? Give the answer in polar vector form and determine the magnitudes also.

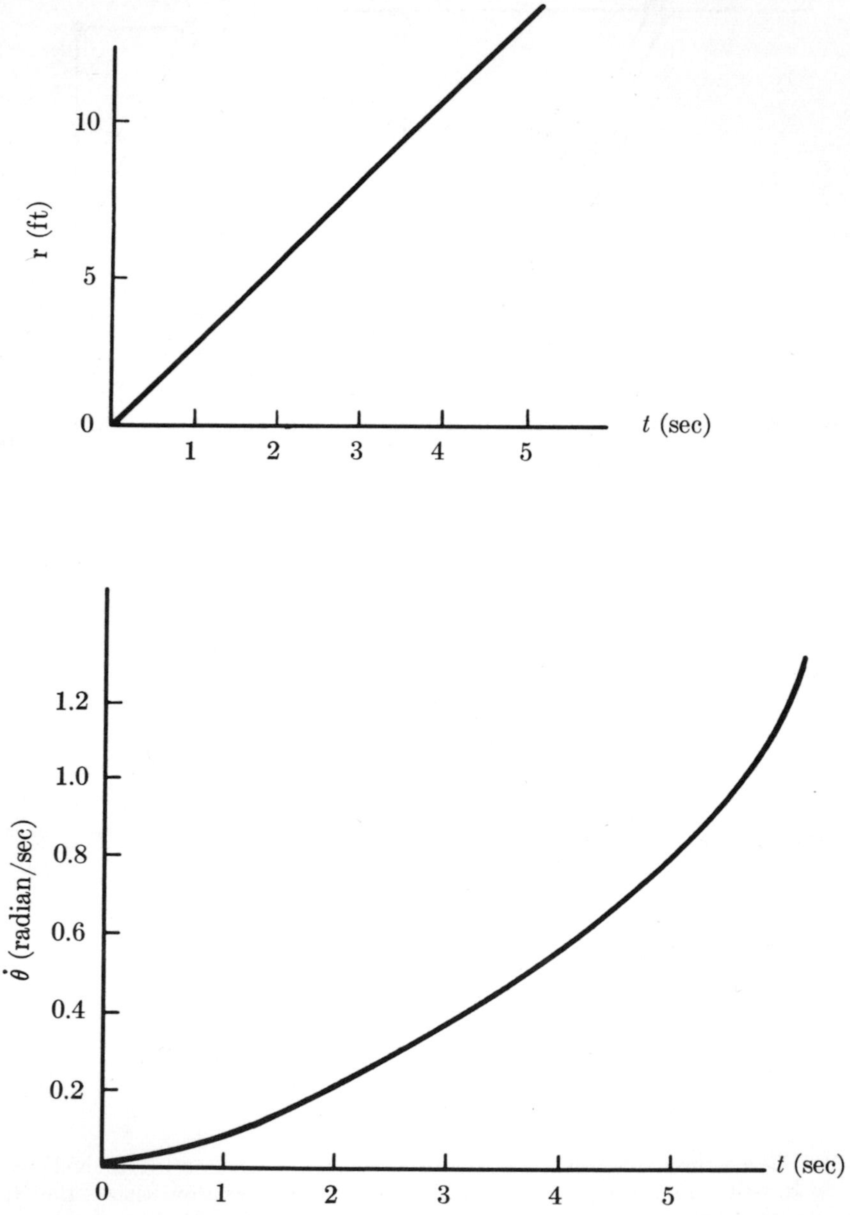

Figure Prob. 2-59

2-53. If the position of a particle is given as $r = A \cos \theta$, where $\theta = Bt$, write the acceleration as a function of θ.

2-54. The angular position of a pendulum in small oscillations is given as $\theta = \theta_0 \sin \omega t$. Write the angular velocity and acceleration of the pendulum as a function of time. Then determine as a function of time the velocity and acceleration of the mass attached to the end of the cord.

2-55. A particle is resting on the periphery of a 6-ft diameter flywheel. The flywheel is rotating with an angular velocity of 2.0 radians/sec counterclockwise and an angular acceleration of 10.0 radians/sec^2 clockwise. What is the total acceleration of the particle? Sketch on a diagram the vector acceleration and determine the magnitude of the acceleration.

2-56. Consider a particle on the edge of a flywheel moving in a horizontal plane. The radius of the flywheel is 4 ft. If the flywheel starts from rest and has a constant angular acceleration of 0.4 radian/sec^2, draw a sketch of the magnitude of the acceleration as a function of time for the first 4 sec of time.

2-57. For the preceding problem, determine (a) the speed of the particle at $t = 3$ sec, and (b) the total acceleration of the particle at $t = 6$ sec.

2-58. A fly is sitting on a large rotating turntable of radius 16 ft. The turntable starts from rest and has an angular acceleration of $0.2t - 0.3t^2$ radian/sec^2. The fly, which originally is only 5 ft from the axis of rotation of the wheel, starts walking outward along the radius of the wheel with a velocity of 0.1 fps when the wheel starts to move. What is the velocity and acceleration of the fly after 6 sec have elapsed?

2-59. The polar coordinates of a particle are given graphically in Fig P.2-59. Determine the velocity and acceleration of the particle, in polar vector form, at $t = 6$ sec.

2-60. Draw the curves of $\dot{r}$, $\ddot{r}$, and $\ddot{\theta}$ as a function of time for the preceding problem.

2-61. The motion of a point is given in parametric form as $\dot{\theta} = 1 + t$ and $\dot{r} = 6t$. At $t = 2$ sec, write the position, velocity, and acceleration of the particle as vectors in the Cartesian reference system. At $t = 0$, $r = 4$ and $\theta = 1$.

2-62. Determine the velocity and acceleration of a particle on the surface of the earth as a function of the longitude ψ (Fig. P.2-62). Assume that the polar axis of the earth is fixed in space. The radius of the earth is 4000 miles and the angular velocity of rotation of the earth is one revolution per day. Express the answer in terms of feet and seconds.

2-63. The earth rotates about the sun in a nearly circular orbit with an average radius of 93 million miles. The period of rotation is roughly 365 days. What is the angular velocity of the radius vector (in radians per second) from the sun to the earth, and what is the acceleration of the center of the earth (assuming that the sun is absolutely fixed in space)?

2-64. An artificial earth satellite is moving in a circular orbit about the earth with a constant velocity. It makes one revolution about the earth every 1 hr and 53 min. If the satellite is at an altitude of 600 miles above the earth's surface, what is the acceleration of the satellite? The radius of the earth is 4000 miles.

2-65. The arm shown in Fig. P.2-65 is moving with a velocity of 3.0 radians/sec counterclockwise in the position shown. The pin, which moves along the curve BC,

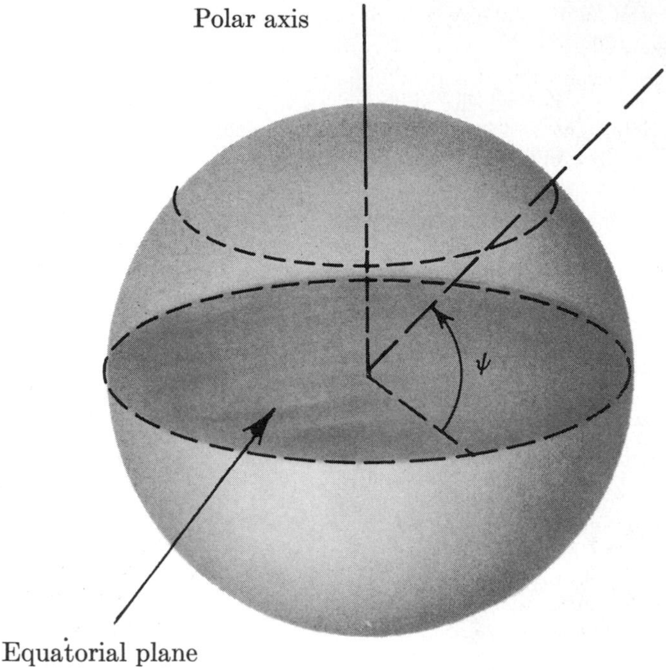

Figure Prob. 2-62

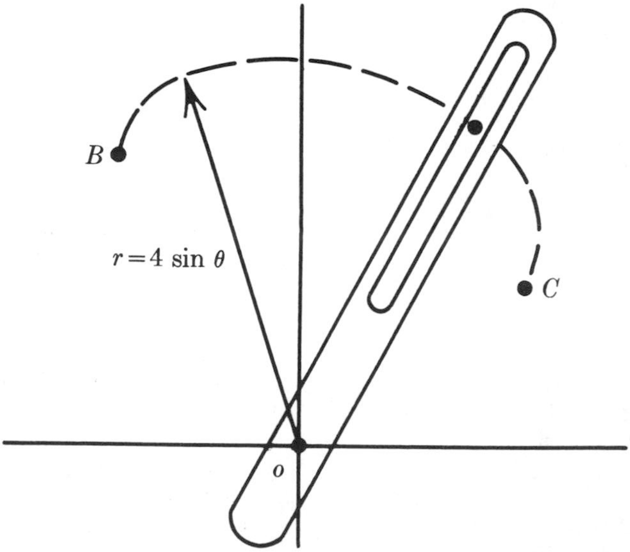

Figure Prob. 2-65

is also free to move in the slot. What is the acceleration of the pin when the angle θ is equal to 90 deg?

2-66. Determine for the preceding problem the acceleration of the pin when the angle is equal to 75 deg.

2-67. The bar shown in Fig. P.2-67 is oscillating sinusoidally. The equation for the angle θ as a function of time is $\theta_0 \sin \omega t$. Determine the acceleration of the pin as a function of the angle θ.

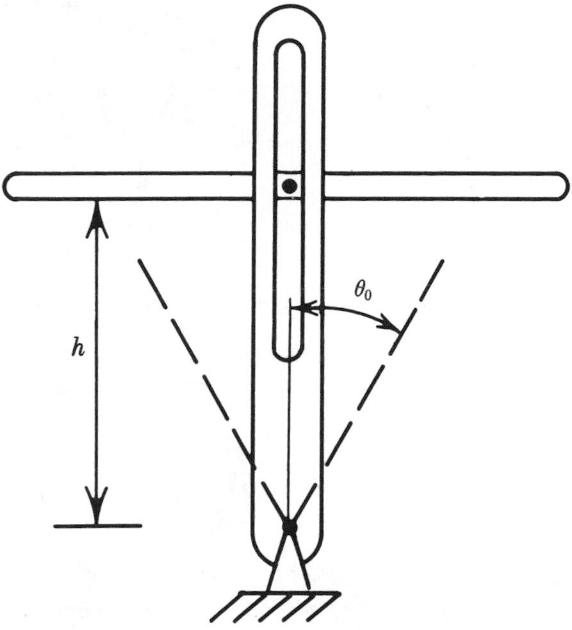

Figure Prob. 2-67

2-5. NORMAL AND TANGENTIAL COORDINATES

In some cases of a particle moving on a curve in two-dimensional space, it is most convenient to express the motion of the particle in terms of *normal and tangential* components. This is particularly true when the particle is moving on a curve where y is given as a function of x. Consider the particle moving on the curve as shown in Fig. 2–20. The two unit vectors are:

$\bar{e}_n \equiv$ a unit vector defined so that it is always normal or orthogonal to the path of motion and is positive outward from the curvature.

$\bar{e}_t \equiv$ a unit vector defined so that it is always directed along the path of motion and is thus perpendicular to $\bar{e}_n$.

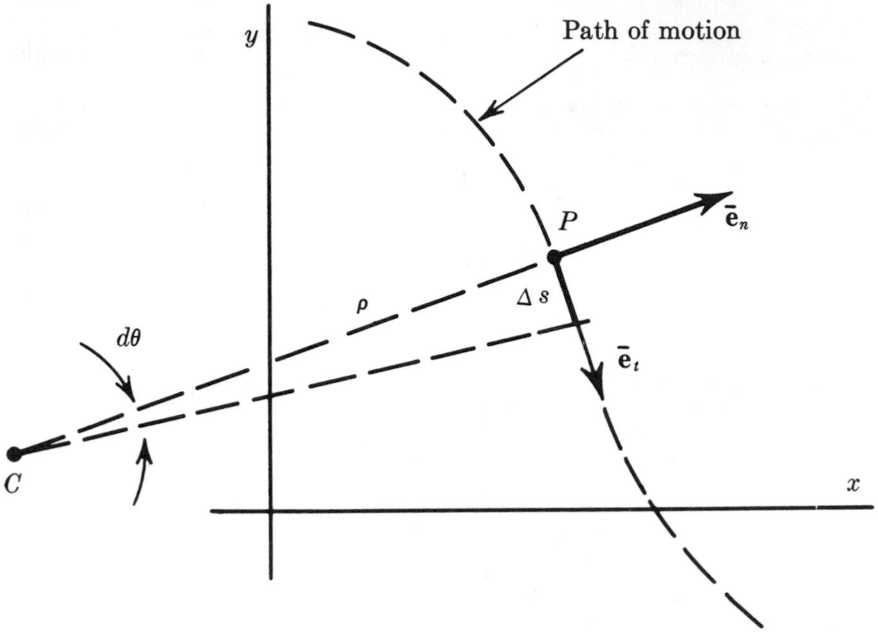

Figure 2-20

Here, again, we notice that both unit vectors will be changing direction as the particle moves along the path of motion, and hence they will have time derivatives.

The point c in Fig. 2–20 represents the *center of curvature* of the path of motion at point P; the distance ρ is the *radius of curvature;* and the distance measured along the path of motion, the arc distance, is given by the letter s.

There is no convenient method for expressing the position of P in terms of these unit vectors normal and tangential to the path of motion. However, since it is known that the velocity of a particle is always in the direction of the motion of the particle, the velocity can be written as

$$\boxed{\boldsymbol{v} = v\bar{\boldsymbol{e}}_t} \tag{2.64}$$

The acceleration is then determined by differentiating the velocity with respect to time:

$$\boldsymbol{a} = \frac{dv}{dt}\,\bar{\boldsymbol{e}}_t + v\dot{\bar{\boldsymbol{e}}}_t \tag{2.65}$$

The problem now is to determine the value of the time derivative of $\bar{e}_t$. Consider a small displacement of the particle ds during a small increment of time, Δt. The unit vectors will rotate through an angle $\Delta\theta$

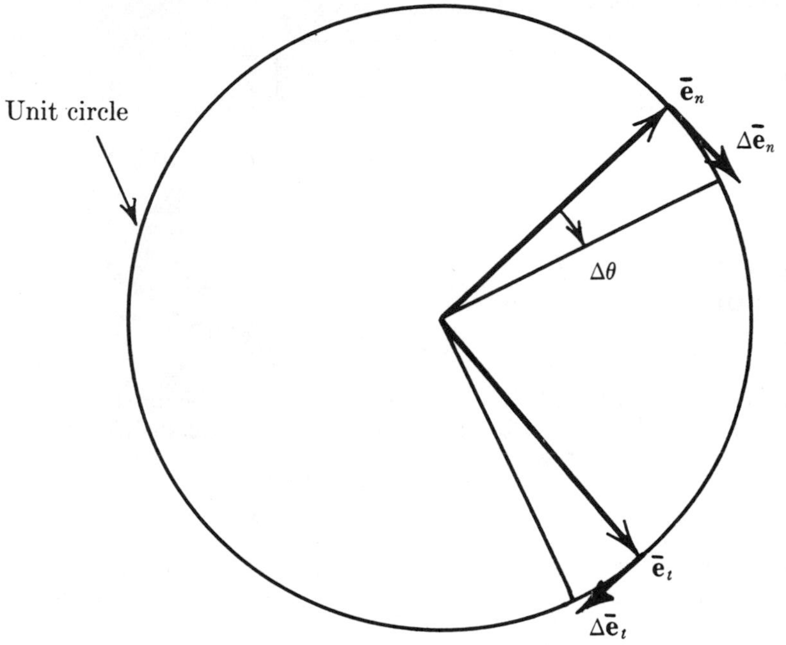

Figure 2-21

(Fig. 2–21). The magnitude of $\Delta \boldsymbol{e}_t$, from the arc formula (Eq. 2.50), is (1) $\Delta\theta$, and since $\Delta\bar{e}_t$ is in the $-\bar{e}_n$ direction,

$$\Delta\bar{e}_t = -\Delta\theta\bar{e}_n \tag{2.66}$$

By dividing both sides by Δt and taking the limit as Δt approaches zero, we get

$$\dot{\bar{e}}_t = \dot{\theta}\bar{e}_n \tag{2.67}$$

From Fig. 2–20 it is noted that

$$\Delta s = \rho\,\Delta\theta \tag{2.68}$$

so that

$$\dot{s} = v = \rho\dot{\theta} \tag{2.69}$$

and

$$\dot{\bar{e}}_t = \frac{-v}{\rho}\,\bar{e}_n \tag{2.70}$$

Finally the acceleration is

$$\boxed{\boldsymbol{a} = \frac{dv}{dt}\,\bar{e}_t - \frac{v^2}{\rho}\,\bar{e}_n} \tag{2.71}$$

The acceleration in the direction of the motion of the particle is often called the *tangential acceleration* and is denoted by the symbol a_t. The acceleration normal to the path is called the *normal acceleration* and is denoted by the symbol a_n. Thus,

$$\boxed{\boldsymbol{a} = a_t\bar{\boldsymbol{e}}_t + a_n\bar{\boldsymbol{e}}_n} \tag{2.72}$$

where

$$a_t = \frac{dv}{dt} \qquad \text{(time rate of change of speed)} \tag{2.73}$$

$$a_n = \frac{-v^2}{\rho}$$

The magnitude of the acceleration is

$$a = \sqrt{a_t^2 + a_n^2} \tag{2.74}$$

In two dimensions, the radius of curvature ρ can be determined if y is given as a function of x. A textbook on differential calculus will show that the radius of curvature is

$$\rho = \frac{[1 + (dy/dx)^2]^{3/2}}{dy^2/dx^2} \tag{2.75}$$

Consider again the motion of a particle on a circular path. The normal and tangential components of the acceleration are as shown in Fig. 2–22.

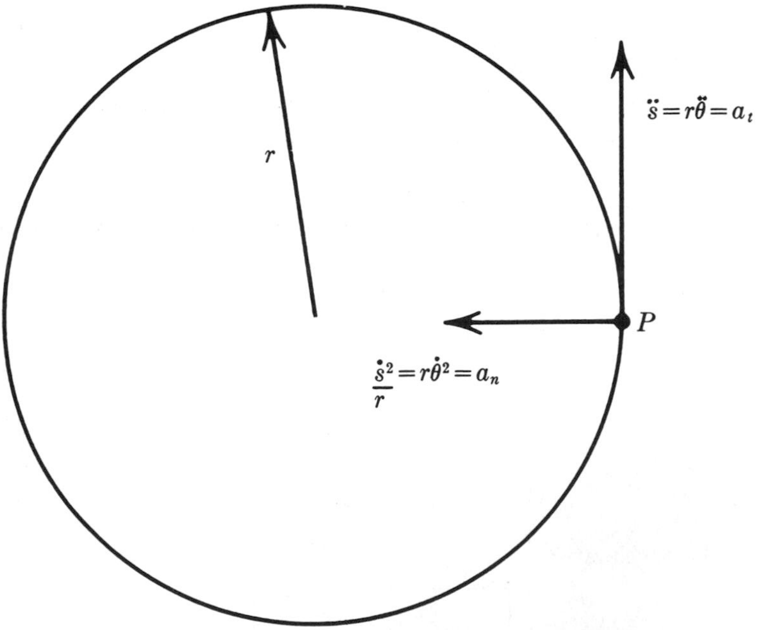

Figure 2-22

From the discussion on angular motion recall that $s = r\theta$, $\dot{s} = r\dot{\theta}$ and $\ddot{s} = dv/dt = r\ddot{\theta}$, so that the acceleration in the direction of the path of motion becomes $r\ddot{\theta}$, and the acceleration component directed toward the center of rotation is $r\dot{\theta}^2$. We note that this result is the same as that obtained in the preceding section.

Example 2–14. A car rounds a curve at a constant 30 mph. An accelerometer mounted in the car records a maximum acceleration of 4 ft/sec² at one point. What is the radius of curvature of the curve at this one point?

Solution: The total acceleration is

$$a = 4 \text{ ft/sec}^2$$

The tangential acceleration is zero because the velocity is constant, so that

$$\frac{dv}{dt} = 0$$

and

$$a = a_n$$

But

$$a_n = -\frac{v^2}{\rho}$$

and the velocity is

$$v = 30 \text{ mph} = 44 \text{ fps}$$

or

$$4 = \frac{(44)^2}{\rho}$$

The radius of curvature is

$$\rho = 484 \text{ ft}$$

Example 2–15. A body moves on a curve from point A to point B with a constant acceleration. The velocity of the particle at A is 10 ft/sec and 10 seconds later at B it is 50 ft/sec. What is the total acceleration of the particle at point B?

Solution: The acceleration of the particle is given in vector form as

$$\mathbf{a} = \frac{dv}{dt}\bar{\mathbf{e}}_t - \frac{v^2}{\rho}\bar{\mathbf{e}}_n$$

Since the velocity at A and B are known and the time for the particle to move from A to B is known, the acceleration along the path can be determined from an integration:

$$v = v_0 + \int_0^t a_t\, dt$$

Since the tangential acceleration is a constant,

$$50 = 40 + a_t(10)$$

from a direct integration and substitution, and the tangential acceleration becomes

$$a_t = 4 \text{ ft/sec}^2$$

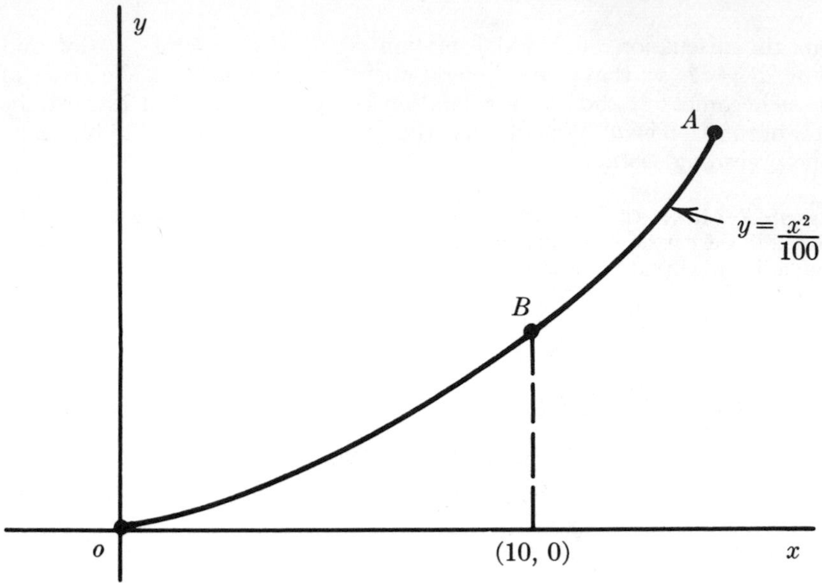

Figure 2-23

The radius of curvature can be determined from the standard form:

$$\rho = \frac{[1 + (y')^2]^{3/2}}{y''}$$

The first and second time derivatives of y with respect to x are

$$y' = \frac{x}{50}$$

$$y'' = \frac{1}{50}$$

so that the radius of curvature becomes

$$\rho = \frac{[1 + (x/50)^2]^{3/2}}{(1/50)}$$

At $x = 10$,

$$\rho = \frac{[1 + (1/5)^2]^{3/2}}{(1/50)}$$

Solving for ρ,

$$\rho = 53 \text{ ft}$$

Now, at point B, the velocity of the particle is 50 fps; therefore acceleration of the particle becomes

$$\boldsymbol{a} = 4\bar{\boldsymbol{e}}_t - \frac{(50)^2}{53}\bar{\boldsymbol{e}}_n$$

or

$$\boldsymbol{a} = 4\bar{\boldsymbol{e}}_t - 47.2\bar{\boldsymbol{e}}_n$$

and the magnitude of the acceleration is

$$a = \sqrt{4^2 + 47.2^2} = 47.3 \text{ ft/sec}^2$$

PROBLEMS

2-68. A particle starts from rest and moves in a circle, of radius 10 ft, with a constant linear acceleration along the path of 0.5 ft/sec². What is the total acceleration of the particle after 8 sec have elapsed?

2-69. A particle is moving on a curve, $y = 2x^3$, with a constant velocity of 10 fps. What is the acceleration of the particle when y is equal to 2 ft?

2-70. An automobile starts from rest on a circular test track and accelerates with a constant acceleration along the track from rest to 60 mph in 14 sec. What is the total acceleration of the car after 4 sec have elapsed if the radius of the track is 200 ft?

2-71. Consider the automobile of the preceding problem. Suppose that an accelerometer mounted in the automobile measures the magnitude of the total acceleration. At a certain point on the track, the accelerometer reads an acceleration of 5.0 ft/sec². Determine, (a) the speed of the automobile at that point, and (b) the time elapsed since the automobile started from rest.

2-72. An automobile traveling on a highway enters a curve at 60 mph. The automobile accelerates at a constant rate, and 15 sec later the auto is moving with a velocity of 70 mph. If an accelerometer mounted in the car reads 10.0 ft/sec², 5 sec after the car starts to accelerate, what is the radius of curvature of the highway?

2-73. If the maximum acceleration at which man can retain consciousness is 3 g, what would be the smallest radius of curvature that an airplane could make when pulling out of a dive if it were traveling with a velocity of 500 mph?

2-74. The velocity of an automobile on a circular test track is determined experimentally and recorded on a chart (Fig. P.2-74). If the radius of the track is 450 ft, what is the total acceleration of the automobile 10 sec after it starts from rest?

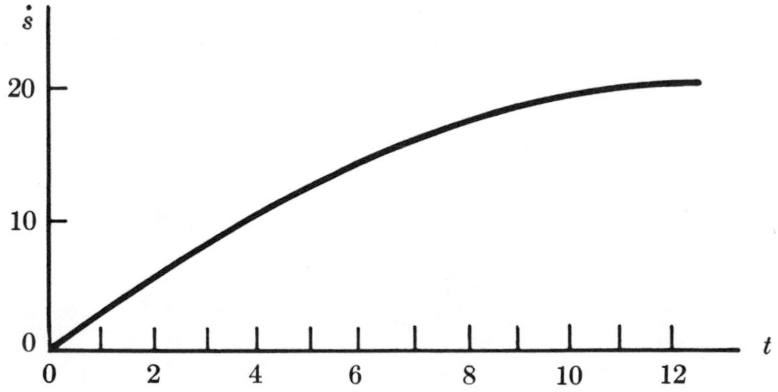

Figure Prob. 2-74

2-75. A particle is moving on the curve $y = \sin(\pi x/L)$ with a constant velocity of v. Determine the acceleration of the particle when it is at the point $x = L/2$ and the point $x = L$.

2-76. Show that the time derivative of the unit vector $\bar{e}_n$ is equal to $\dot{\theta}\bar{e}_t$.

2-77. An automobile on a curved test track accelerates with a constant acceleration from rest to 50 mph in 10 sec. What is the radius of curvature of the track if an accelerometer measures an acceleration of 8.0 ft/sec^2 at a point where the car has traveled 100 ft from its original position?

2-78. An accelerometer is mounted on the edge of a flywheel and reads an acceleration of 10 ft/sec^2 at a time when the flywheel is rotating with a constant angular velocity of 30 rpm. What is the linear velocity of a point on the edge of the flywheel?

2-79. An artificial earth satellite is moving in a circular orbit with a velocity of 17,000 mph. What is the acceleration of the satellite if its altitude is 700 miles? The radius of the earth is 4000 miles.

2-80. A projectile is fired with an initial velocity of v_0 at an angle of θ_0 with the horizontal. What is the radius of curvature of the trajectory at the midpoint?

2-81. A projectile is fired at a 45 deg angle with an initial velocity of 500 fps. What is the radius of curvature of the path 5 sec after the body has been fired?

3

Relative Motion

One class of kinematics problem that was not considered in Chapter 2 is the problem of determining the absolute velocity and acceleration of a body when it is measured by an observer who is also moving. In this chapter we shall attempt to establish a general approach for solving this type of kinematic problem.

3-1. RELATIVE MOTION IN A PLANE

Relative velocity and acceleration. In this section we shall consider the relative motion of particles or points in a plane.

In order to determine the velocity and acceleration of points on bodies moving in some prescribed manner, we employ what is known as a *moving reference system*. Shown in Fig. 3–1 are two sets of Cartesian reference axes, an inertially fixed (X,Y) system to which absolute velocity and acceleration are referred, and an (x,y) system that is moving relative to the inertial system. The unit vectors $\bar{i}$ and $\bar{j}$ are defined in the moving system.

We shall restrict the moving system to move in such a manner that the x, y axes remain parallel to the X, Y axes at all times. The problem now is, given the motion of point O and the motion of point P relative to O, what is the velocity and acceleration of point P?

From Fig. 3–1 it can be seen that the displacement of the particle $\boldsymbol{r}$

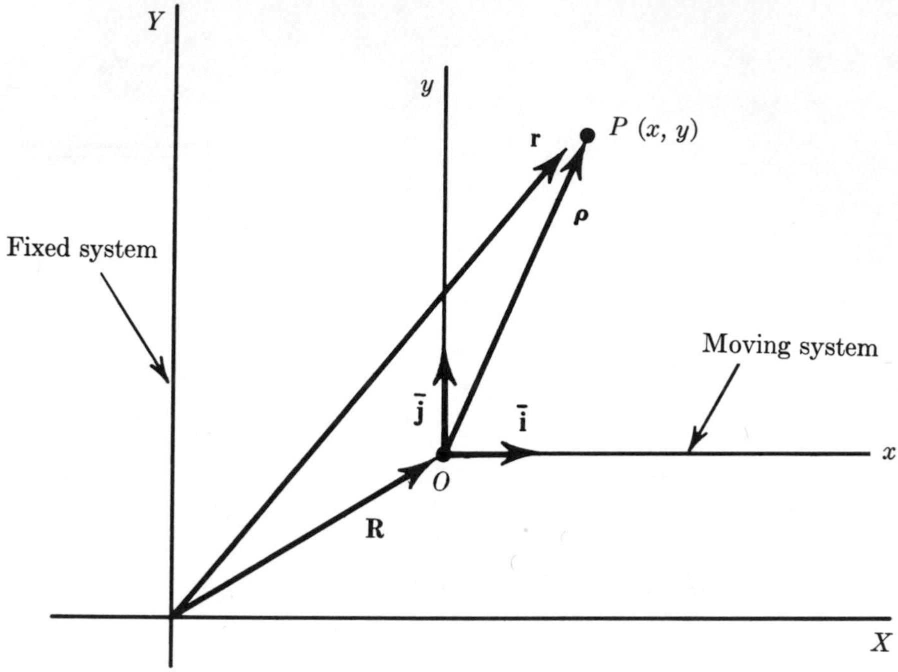

Figure 3-1

may be written in terms of the displacement of the origin of the moving system $\boldsymbol{R}$ and the displacement of the particle relative to the origin of the moving system $\boldsymbol{\rho}$, by simply performing a vector addition:

$$\boldsymbol{r} = \boldsymbol{R} + \boldsymbol{\rho} \tag{3.1}$$

The velocity of the point P is obtained by differentiating the displacement vector:

$$\boldsymbol{v}_P = \dot{\boldsymbol{R}} + \dot{\rho} \tag{3.2}$$

The vector $\dot{\boldsymbol{R}}$ may be interpreted as the velocity of the point O and may be written as $\boldsymbol{v}_0$. We shall consider now the vector $\dot{\boldsymbol{\rho}}$. From Fig. 3–1 it can be seen that the vector $\boldsymbol{\rho}$ defined in the moving coordinate system may be written as

$$\boldsymbol{\rho} = x\bar{\boldsymbol{i}} + y\bar{\boldsymbol{j}} \tag{3.3}$$

and the time derivative of this vector is

$$\dot{\boldsymbol{\rho}} = \dot{x}\bar{\boldsymbol{i}} + x\dot{\bar{\boldsymbol{i}}} + \dot{y}\bar{\boldsymbol{j}} + y\dot{\bar{\boldsymbol{j}}} \tag{3.4}$$

It was assumed upon differentiation that the unit vectors $\bar{\boldsymbol{i}}$ and $\bar{\boldsymbol{j}}$ have time derivatives. We know that vectors have time derivatives if they are changing in magnitude or direction, but since these unit vectors are defined in a coordinate system that is not changing direction, then the time derivatives are zero. Thus the time derivative of $\boldsymbol{\rho}$ becomes

$$\dot{\boldsymbol{\rho}} = \dot{x}\bar{\boldsymbol{i}} + \dot{y}\bar{\boldsymbol{j}}$$

The term $\dot{\boldsymbol{\rho}}$ may now be interpreted as the velocity of the point P relative to the point O; that is, the velocity of point P as seen by an observer at point O. It may be written as $\boldsymbol{v}_{P/O}$. Thus, the velocity may be written as

$$\boxed{\boldsymbol{v}_P = \boldsymbol{v}_O + \boldsymbol{v}_{P/O}} \tag{3.5}$$

where: $\boldsymbol{v}_P \equiv$ absolute velocity of the particle P.
$\boldsymbol{v}_O \equiv$ absolute velocity of point O, the origin of the moving coordinate system.
$\boldsymbol{v}_{P/O} \equiv$ velocity of point P with respect to O, the velocity of P as observed from the moving system.

The acceleration at point P is obtained by differentiating the velocity:

$$\boldsymbol{a} = \ddot{\boldsymbol{R}} + \ddot{\boldsymbol{\rho}} \tag{3.6}$$

The term $\ddot{\boldsymbol{R}}$ may be interpreted as the acceleration of point O and may be written as $\boldsymbol{a}_O$. The term $\ddot{\boldsymbol{\rho}}$, in terms of the moving coordinate system, becomes

$$\ddot{\boldsymbol{\rho}} = \ddot{x}\bar{\boldsymbol{i}} + \ddot{y}\bar{\boldsymbol{j}} \tag{3.7}$$

which may be interpreted as the acceleration of the point P relative to the point O (that is, the acceleration of point P as seen by an observer at point O) and may be written as $\boldsymbol{a}_{P/O}$. Thus,

$$\boxed{\boldsymbol{a}_P = \boldsymbol{a}_O + \boldsymbol{a}_{P/O}} \tag{3.8}$$

where: $\boldsymbol{a}_P \equiv$ absolute acceleration of point P.
$\boldsymbol{a}_O \equiv$ absolute acceleration of point O, the origin of the moving coordinate system.
$\boldsymbol{a}_{P/O} \equiv$ the acceleration of point P with respect to point O, the acceleration of P as seen by an observer in the moving system.

At this point, it will be most instructive to consider the relative velocity and acceleration of a point on a moving rigid bar. The bar shown in Fig. 3–2 is both translating and rotating in a plane in some arbitrary fashion. In order to determine the velocity of point B with respect to point A, we imagine ourselves stationed at point A and watching point B move. If we are at point A moving with the bar, we observe point B to be moving in a circular path. As far as we are concerned, B is moving in a circular path about us (in terms of polar coordinates, the velocity of B is just equal to $l\omega$) and in a direction perpendicular to the bar, as shown in Fig. 3–2. Physically, this is what we mean by relative velocity. By the same argument, the relative acceleration (the acceleration of B with respect

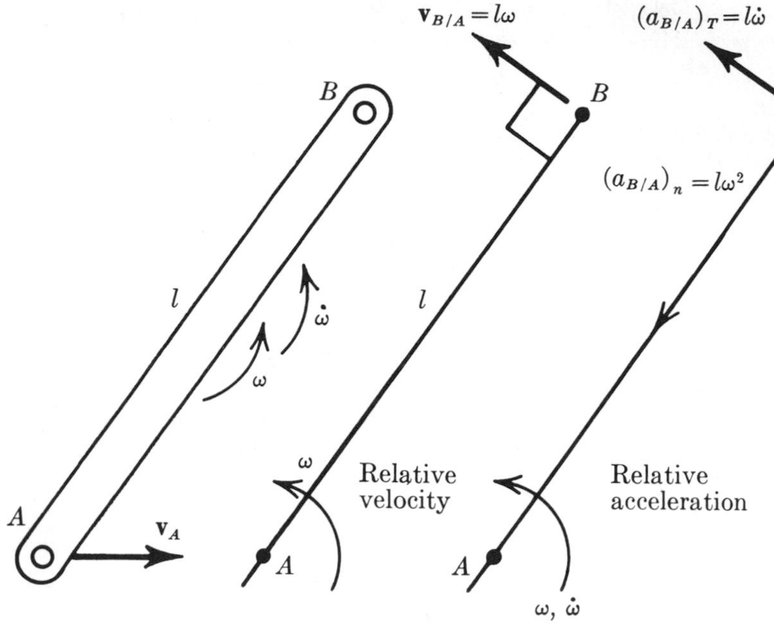

Figure 3-2

to A) has the two components, radial and tangential, of the acceleration, as shown in the figure.

Example 3–1. A passenger going down the aisle in a passenger car of a train walks with a speed of 3 fps with respect to the train and in the same direction that the train is moving. If the train itself has a speed of 40 mph, what is the absolute velocity of the passenger?

Solution: Since here we are dealing with one-dimensional motion, the vector notation may be dropped and the velocity equation can be written:

$$v_P = v_T + v_{P/T}$$

If the train is moving in positive direction,

$$v_T = +40 \text{ mph}$$

and the velocity of the passenger with respect to the train is

$$v_{P/T} = +3.0 \text{ fps}$$

$$= 3.0\left(\frac{60}{88}\right) = +2.04 \text{ mph}$$

then the total velocity of the passenger is

$$v_P = 40 + 2.04 = 42.04 \text{ mph}$$

Example 3–2. Assuming that the sun is fixed in space and an inertial coordinate system could be fixed to it, one is interested in knowing how much error would be introduced if it were assumed that the surface of the earth could be considered for the origin of an inertial coordinate system. Specifically, we should like to know what point on the earth's surface has the maximum acceleration with respect to the sun, and what is the magnitude.

Solution: The plane defined by the earth as it moves in orbit about the sun is called the *ecliptic plane*. The plane defined by the equator of the earth is the *equatorial plane*. There is an inclination of roughly 23 deg between the equatorial plane and the plane of the ecliptic, which implies that there is a similar inclination between the polar axis of the earth and a normal to the ecliptic plane. Assuming, however, that the ecliptic and the equatorial planes are coplanar, we are able to make a rough calculation of the acceleration of a point of the surface of the earth (assuming that the sun is inertially fixed). See Fig. 3–3.

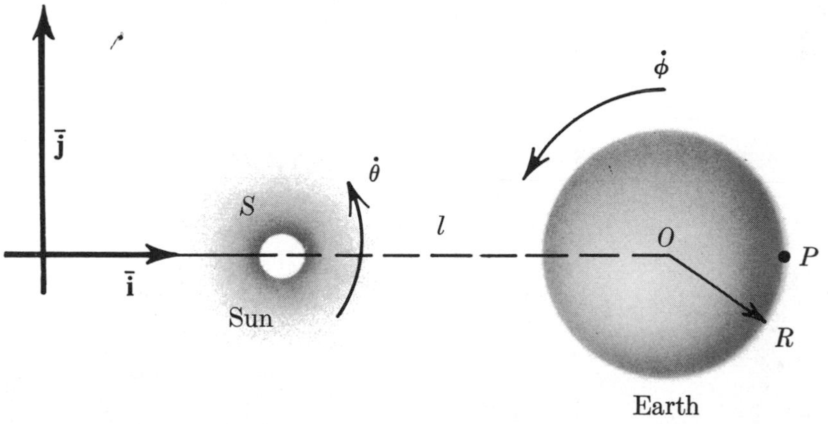

Figure 3-3. *Top view of the ecliptic plane*

The earth has a radius R of 4000 miles and an angular velocity $\dot{\phi}$ of one revolution per day. The center of the earth, point O, is moving in a circular path about the sun. The distance l is equal to 93 million miles, and the angular velocity of the line OS is equal to one revolution per 365 days. Since there is no angular acceleration involved, we note that there will be only radial acceleration. And it follows that the maximum acceleration of the point on the earth's surface will be the point P shown in Fig. 3–3. Thus,

$$\boldsymbol{a}_P = \boldsymbol{a}_O + \boldsymbol{a}_{P/O}$$

First of all we shall evaluate the acceleration of the center of the earth, point O:

$$\begin{aligned} \boldsymbol{a}_O &= -l\dot{\theta}^2\bar{i} \\ &= -[93(5280) \times 10^6]\left(\frac{2\pi}{365(24)(3600)}\right)^2 \\ \boldsymbol{a}_O &= -0.0197\bar{i} \quad \text{ft/sec}^2 \end{aligned}$$

The acceleration of P with respect to O is

$$
\begin{aligned}
\boldsymbol{a}_{P/O} &= -R\dot{\phi}^2\bar{\boldsymbol{i}} \\
&= -[4000(5280)]\left(\frac{2}{(24)(3600)}\right)^2\bar{\boldsymbol{i}} \\
&= -0.111\bar{\boldsymbol{i}} \quad \text{ft/sec}^2
\end{aligned}
$$

so that, finally,

$$
\begin{aligned}
\boldsymbol{a}_P &= -[0.0197 + 0.111]\bar{\boldsymbol{i}} \\
&= -0.131\bar{\boldsymbol{i}} \quad \text{fps}
\end{aligned}
$$

From the results we may conclude, first of all, that the effect on the acceleration of the earth moving about the sun is somewhat smaller than the effect on the acceleration of the rotation of the earth on its own axis. Secondly, we note that the total acceleration, though measurable, is very small in comparison with the acceleration due to gravity. Therefore we conclude that this acceleration may be reasonably neglected when calculating the motion of most terrestrial bodies.

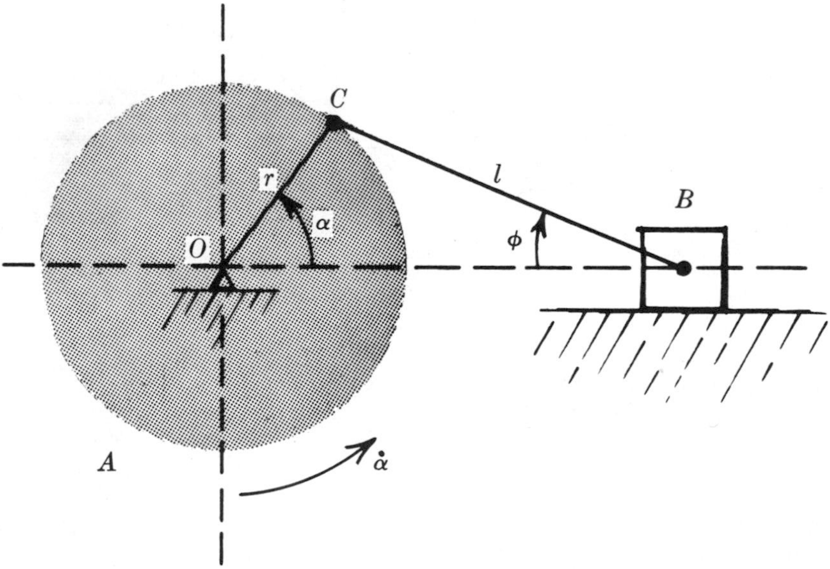

Figure 3-4

Example 3-3. Shown in Fig. 3-4 is a slider-crank mechanism. Wheel A rotates with a constant angular velocity of $\dot{\alpha}$, and the block B moves in a linear path. Determine the velocity of the block B as a function of the angle α.

Consider the vector equation

$$\boldsymbol{v}_B = \boldsymbol{v}_C = \boldsymbol{v}_{B/C}$$

By observation, it is noted that both the magnitude and direction of the velocity at point C is known. Also it is noted that the directions of both $\boldsymbol{v}_B$ and $\boldsymbol{v}_{B/C}$ are known.

Thus, even though the magnitude of v_B is not known, it may be determined by constructing a vector diagram such as Fig. 3–5.

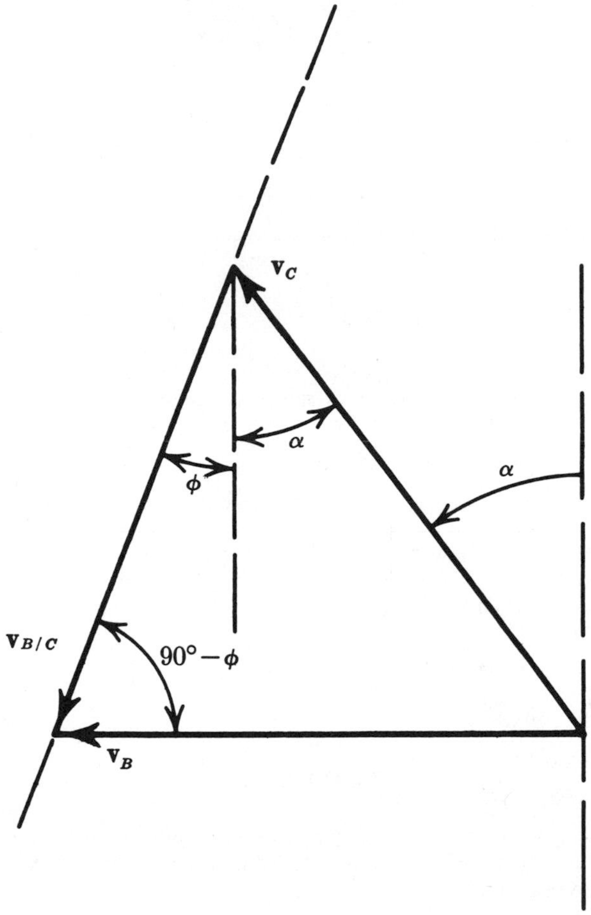

Figure 3-5

By the law of sines,

$$\frac{v_B}{\sin(\phi + \alpha)} = \frac{v_C}{\sin[(\pi/2) - \phi]}$$

and

$$v_B = v_C \frac{\sin(\phi + \alpha)}{\cos \phi}$$

After some trigonometric reduction,

$$v_B = v_C(\sin \alpha + \cos \alpha \tan \phi)$$

It would be nice to find ϕ in terms of α; this can be done by noting that

$$r \sin \alpha = l \sin \phi$$

so that

$$\sin \phi = \left(\frac{r}{l}\right) \sin \alpha$$

and

$$\cos \phi = (1 - \sin^2 \phi)^{1/2}$$

$$\tan \phi = \frac{\sin \phi}{\cos \phi}$$

Therefore, with the aid of the binomial expansion,

$$\tan \phi = \left(\frac{r}{l}\right) \sin \alpha \left[1 - \frac{1}{2}\left(\frac{r}{l}\right)^2 \sin^2 \alpha + \text{(higher-order terms)}\right]$$

or

$$\tan \phi = \left(\frac{r}{l}\right) \sin \alpha - \frac{1}{2}\left(\frac{r}{l}\right)^3 \sin^3 \alpha + \cdots$$

Now, for many situations, $r < l$, and since $\sin \alpha \gtrsim 1$, it is seen that the second term can be disregarded. Finally,

$$v_B = v_C \left[\sin \alpha + \cos \alpha \left(\frac{r}{l}\right) \sin \alpha\right]$$

and since $v_C = r\dot{\alpha}$, then

$$v_B = r\dot{\alpha} \left[\sin \alpha + \frac{1}{2}\left(\frac{r}{l}\right) \sin 2\alpha\right]$$

PROBLEMS

3-1. A passenger on a train is walking back to a club car in the rear of the train with a speed of 4.0 fps. If the train is traveling at 50 mph, what is the absolute velocity of the passenger?

3-2. An airplane traveling at 1500 mph fires one of its rockets. Radar in the plane tracks the missile and observes it to be traveling at 700 mph. What is the total absolute velocity of the missile?

3-3. Two fighter aircraft are flying toward each other. One of the planes is flying with a velocity of 1200 mph and the other has a velocity of 900 mph. If a radar unit in one of the planes spots the other when the distance between the two is 20 miles, how long will it take for the distance between the two to be equal to zero?

3-4. A radar-equipped airplane flying in an easterly direction at 30° N spots another aircraft. The radar unit that measures relative velocity indicates that the second plane is moving with components of velocity of 800 mph in a direction opposite and 60 mph in a direction to the starboard of the radar plane. What is the speed of the second plane, and in what direction with respect to the ground is it flying?

3-5. Suppose that block A in Fig. P.3–5 has a velocity and acceleration downward

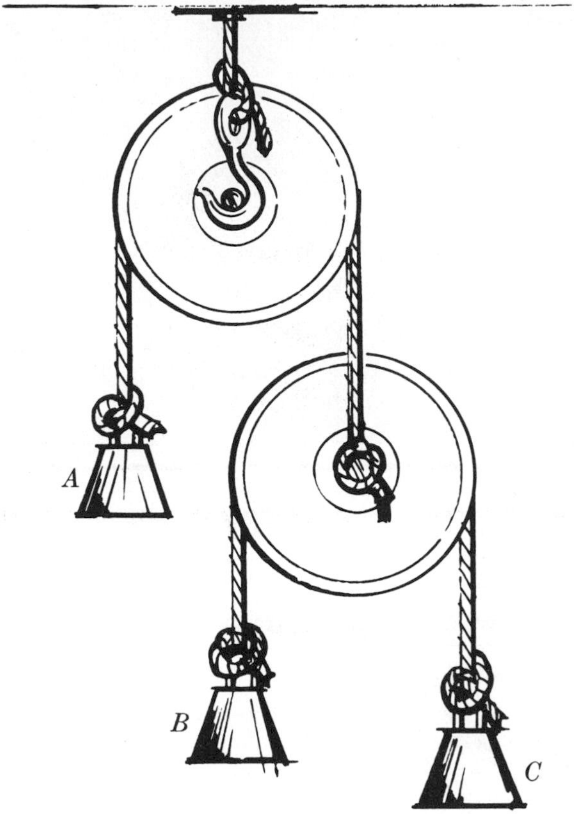

Figure Prob. 3-5

of $\boldsymbol{v}_A$ and $\boldsymbol{a}_A$, respectively. Use the relative velocity and the relative acceleration equations to show that

$$v_B + v_C = 2v_A$$
$$a_B + a_C = 2a_A$$

3-6. Consider the slider-crank mechanism discussed in Example 3–3. Suppose that the wheel turns in a 4-in. radius with an angular speed of 1000 rpm. If the distance l is 10 in., draw a sketch of the velocity of the piston as a function of the angle α for one revolution of the crank.

3-7. Bar AD in Fig. P.3-7 has a velocity to the right of 3.0 fps and an acceleration to the left of 4.0 ft/sec². The wheel rolls, without slipping, on the bar with a clockwise angular acceleration of 5.0 radians/sec² and with a counterclockwise angular velocity of 2.0 radians/sec. Determine the instantaneous velocity of points B and C in the position shown, and the instantaneous acceleration of point C.

3-8. The position of pin A (Fig. P.3-8) in the slot is given as a function of time as $x = 3 \sin 4t$. The bar AB is rotating counterclockwise with a constant angular velocity of 4.0 radians/sec. What is the velocity and the acceleration of pin B for the position shown at $t = 0$?

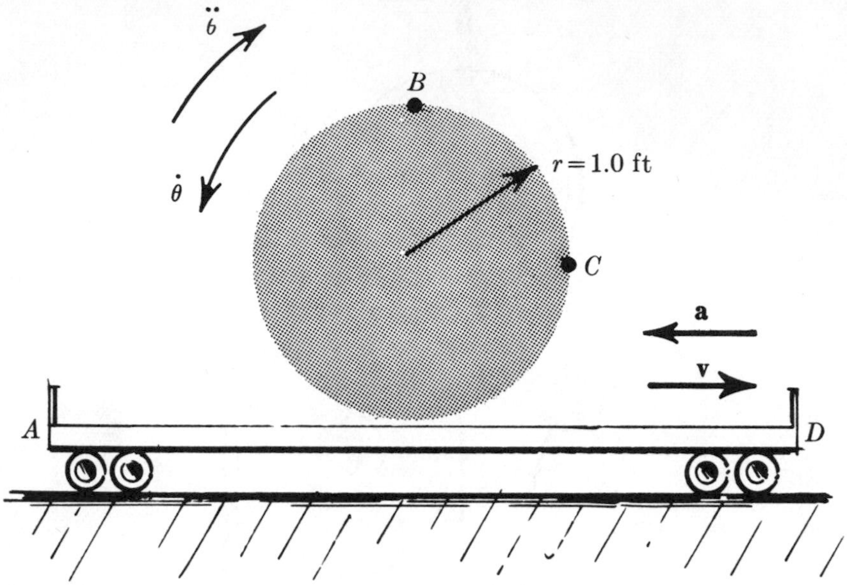

Figure Prob. 3-7

3-9. The roller A in Fig. P.3-9 has an acceleration and a velocity to the right of 4.0 in./sec^2 and 2.0 ips, respectively. Determine the velocity of B, using the relative velocity equation (Eq. 3.8).

3-10. The pitch circles of a gear train are shown in Fig. P.3-10. Gear A is the

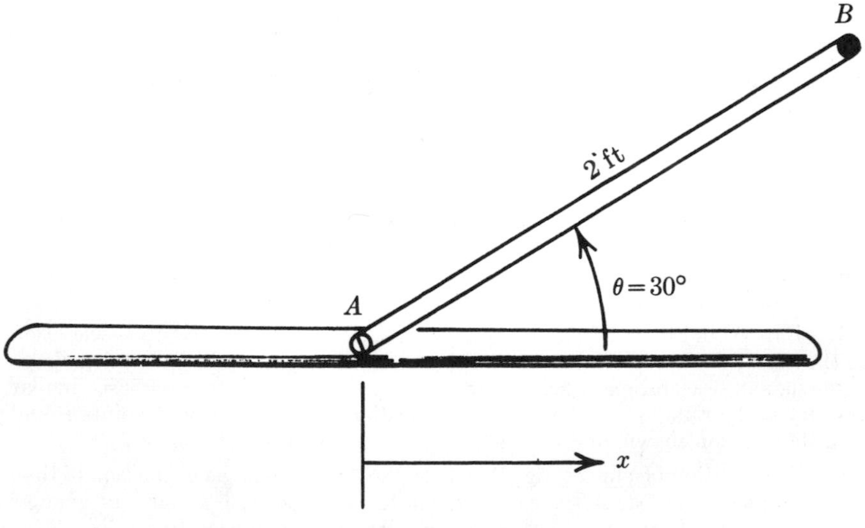

Figure Prob. 3-8

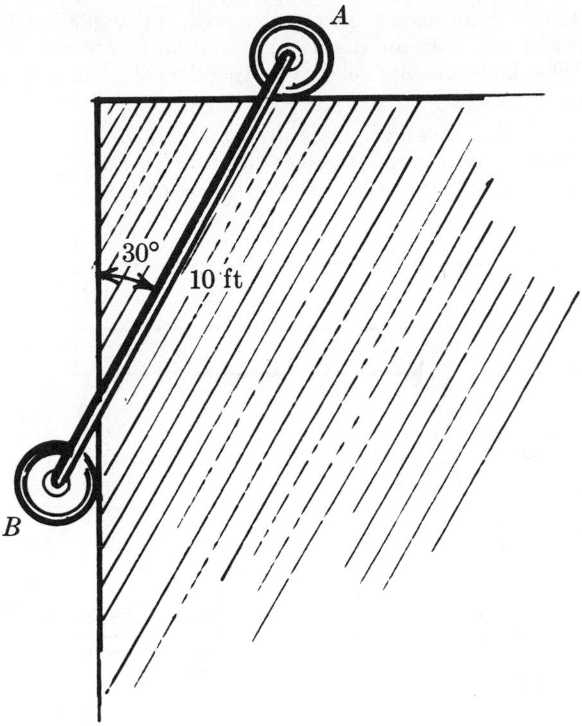

Figure Prob. 3-9

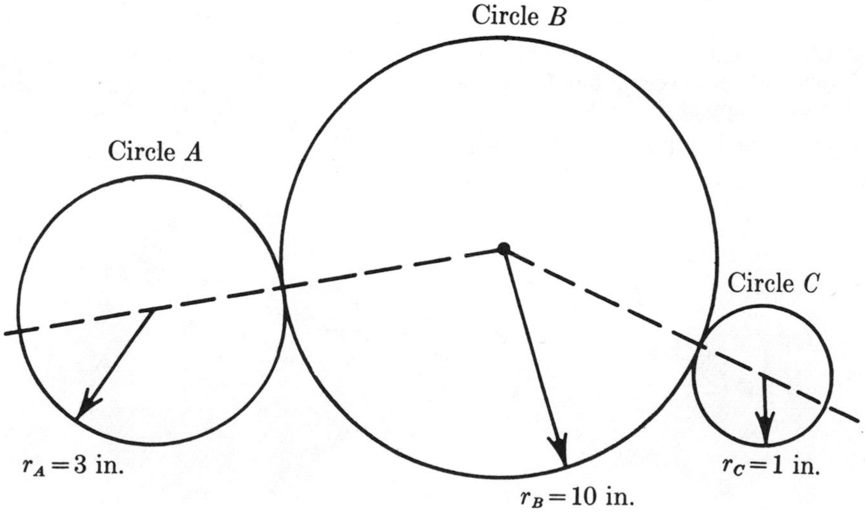

Figure Prob. 3-10

driver and, in the position shown, is rotating with an angular velocity of 6.0 radians/sec clockwise and with an angular acceleration of 2.0 radians/sec^2 in the same direction. What is the angular velocity and acceleration of gear C, and in what direction is gear C rotating?

3-11. Shown in Fig. P.3–11 is a proposed design for the mechanism of an oil-well pump. If the motor is rotating counterclockwise with an angular velocity of 2.0 radians/sec, what is the velocity and acceleration of point C in the position shown?

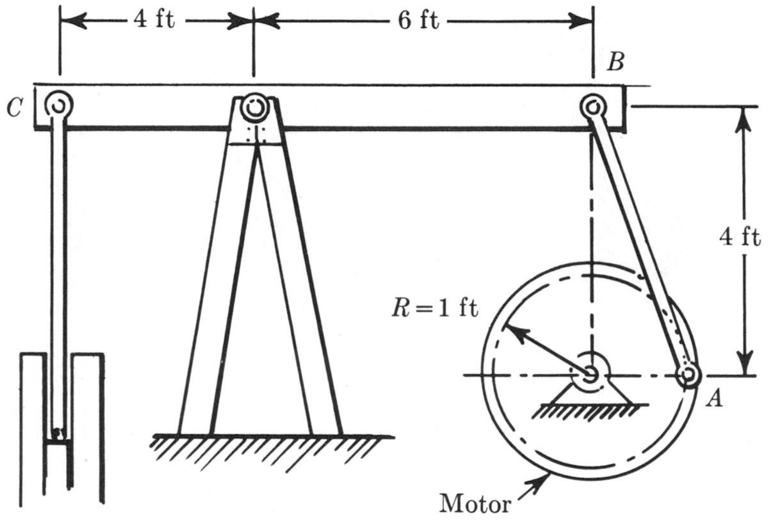

Figure Prob. 3-11

3-12. Consider the figure of the preceding problem. Determine (a) the velocity of C, and (b) the acceleration of C at the point where A has rotated 90 deg so that it is at the top of the cycle.

3-13. If an interplanetary space vehicle is to achieve a high velocity in space, the

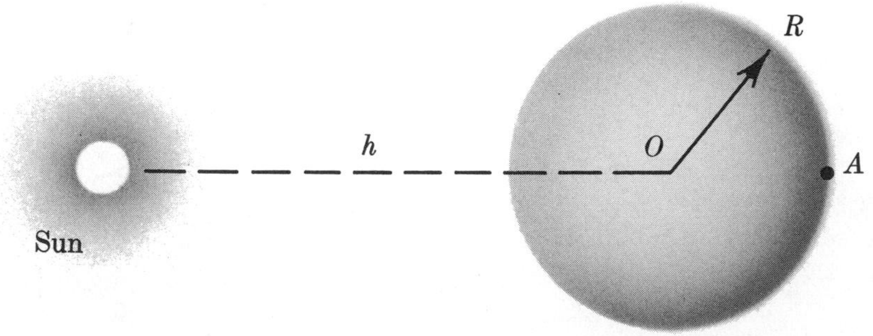

Figure Prob. 3-13. *Top view of the ecliptic plane*

vehicle should be launched in such a manner as to take advantage of the earth's spin. Assuming that the earth's polar axis is perpendicular to the plane formed by a radius vector from the sun to the earth, what is the velocity of point A shown in Fig. P.3–13 with respect to the sun, assuming that the sun is fixed in inertial space? The vehicle would then have this velocity plus any additional velocity supplied by the thrust of the rocket engines. (See Example 3–2 for the dimensions of the system.)

3-2. RELATIVE MOTION IN SPACE

Time derivative of a rotating vector. Before we can discuss the motion of a particle in space, which is referred to a coordinate system that may be both translating and rotating, we must examine some of the properties of the time derivatives of vectors. First, we shall consider a vector $\boldsymbol{\Omega}$, shown in Fig. 3–6, which is moving in such a manner that it is

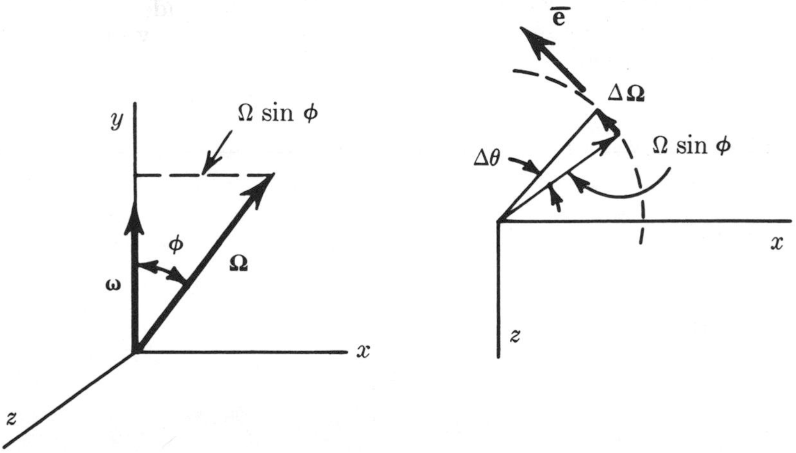

Figure 3-6

rotating about the y axis at this particular instant of time. *The length of the vector is constant.* Since the vector is changing direction, we know that it has a time derivative, and the problem here is to find that time derivative.

The angular velocity of the vector $\boldsymbol{\Omega}$ as it rotates about the y axis is described by the vector $\boldsymbol{\omega}$. This vector, $\boldsymbol{\omega}$, may itself have a time derivative because it also may be changing in magnitude or direction, but this is irrelevant, since the important thing to remember is that it represents the rotation of the vector $\boldsymbol{\Omega}$ about the y axis at this instant of time.

For top view of the system, see the right side of Fig. 3–6 and consider a small angular movement of the vector $\boldsymbol{\Omega}$. If the vector rotates through the angle $\Delta\theta$, then the change in $\boldsymbol{\Omega}$, given as $\Delta\boldsymbol{\Omega}$, can be easily determined by a consideration of the geometry of the situation. The change in $\boldsymbol{\Omega}$ may be written as

$$\Delta\boldsymbol{\Omega} = \Omega \sin \phi(\Delta\theta)\bar{\mathbf{e}} \tag{3.9}$$

noting that the unit vector $\bar{\mathbf{e}}$ has to be defined as a vector that is perpendicular to the plane formed by $\boldsymbol{\omega}$ and $\boldsymbol{\Omega}$. By dividing by Δt and taking the limit as Δt approaches zero, we get

$$\frac{d\boldsymbol{\Omega}}{dt} = \frac{d\theta}{dt}\Omega \sin \phi\bar{\mathbf{e}} \tag{3.10}$$

or

$$\dot{\boldsymbol{\Omega}} = \omega\Omega \sin \phi\bar{\mathbf{e}} \tag{3.11}$$

But by definition, this is the cross-product of $\boldsymbol{\omega}$ with $\boldsymbol{\Omega}$, so that

$$\boxed{\dot{\boldsymbol{\Omega}} = \boldsymbol{\omega} \times \boldsymbol{\Omega}} \tag{3.12}$$

Thus the time derivative of a vector of constant magnitude may be determined by taking the cross-product of the angular velocity of the vector with the vector itself. This relationship will be extremely useful in the ensuing discussions.

Time derivative of a vector defined in a moving coordinate system. Suppose now that we have a vector quantity $\boldsymbol{\Omega}$ referred to a moving coordinate system, that is, given in terms of unit vectors in a moving system. In Fig. 3-7 the XYZ system is fixed in space (inertial

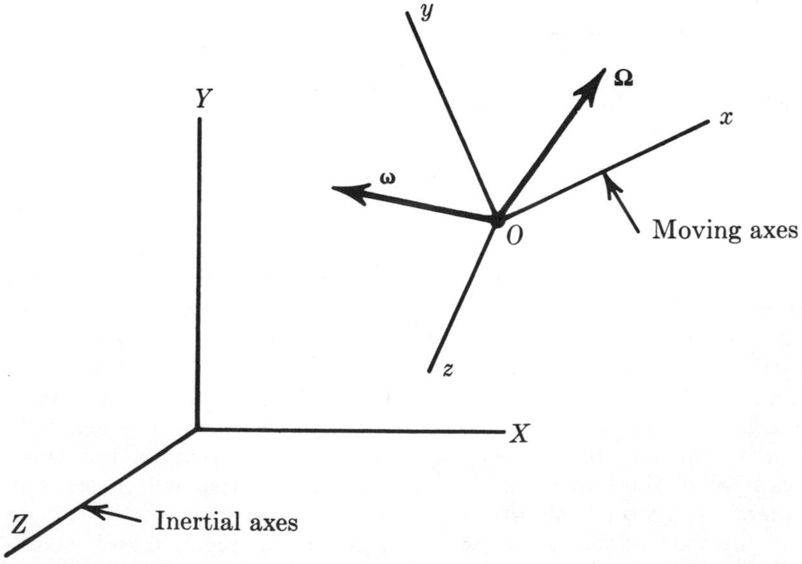

Figure 3-7

system) and the xyz system is moving in such a manner that at this particular instant of time, the angular velocity of the moving frame is given by the vector $\boldsymbol{\omega}$. The vector $\boldsymbol{\Omega}$ is given in terms of unit vectors in the moving coordinate system as

$$\boldsymbol{\Omega} = \Omega_x\bar{i} + \Omega_y\bar{j} + \Omega_z\bar{k} \tag{3.13}$$

To determine the first time derivative of $\boldsymbol{\Omega}$, it is necessary only to differentiate directly, noting that the unit vectors now have time derivatives because they are changing direction.

$$\dot{\boldsymbol{\Omega}} = \dot{\Omega}_x\bar{i} + \Omega_x\dot{\bar{i}} + \dot{\Omega}_y\bar{j} + \Omega_y\dot{\bar{j}} + \dot{\Omega}_z\bar{k} + \Omega_z\dot{\bar{k}} \tag{3.14}$$

The first, third, and fifth terms of Eq. 3.14 is nothing more than the derivative of $\boldsymbol{\Omega}$ relative to the xyz system; that is, the time derivative of $\boldsymbol{\Omega}$ that would be measured by an observer in the moving coordinate system. Thus,

$$\dot{\boldsymbol{\Omega}}_{xyz} = \dot{\Omega}_x\bar{i} + \dot{\Omega}_y\bar{j} + \dot{\Omega}_z\bar{k} \tag{3.15}$$

Further, it is noted that

$$\begin{aligned} \dot{\bar{i}} &= \boldsymbol{\omega} \times \bar{i} \\ \dot{\bar{j}} &= \boldsymbol{\omega} \times \bar{j} \\ \dot{\bar{k}} &= \boldsymbol{\omega} \times \bar{k} \end{aligned} \tag{3.16}$$

Then

$$\begin{aligned} \Omega_x\dot{\bar{i}} + \Omega_y\dot{\bar{j}} + \Omega_z\dot{\bar{k}} &= \Omega_x(\boldsymbol{\omega} \times \bar{i}) + \Omega_y(\boldsymbol{\omega} \times \bar{j}) + \Omega_z(\boldsymbol{\omega} \times \bar{k}) \\ &= \boldsymbol{\omega} \times \boldsymbol{\Omega} \end{aligned} \tag{3.17}$$

so that

$$\boxed{\dot{\boldsymbol{\Omega}}_{XYZ} = \dot{\boldsymbol{\Omega}}_{xyz} + \boldsymbol{\omega} \times \boldsymbol{\Omega}} \tag{3.18}$$

This says, then, that the derivative of $\boldsymbol{\Omega}$ with respect to the fixed XYZ axes is equal to the derivative of $\boldsymbol{\Omega}$ with respect to the moving xyz axes plus the cross-product of the angular velocity vector with the vector $\boldsymbol{\Omega}$ itself.

The general velocity and acceleration equations. Here we shall examine the velocity and acceleration of a particle that is referred to a coordinate system which is both translating and rotating in space. Consider an inertially fixed XYZ system as shown in Fig. 3–8. Moving relative to the inertial system is a moving xyz system. At the particular instant of time, the moving system has an angular velocity, $\boldsymbol{\omega}$, as shown in the figure. The vector displacements are defined as follows:

$\boldsymbol{r} \equiv$ absolute displacement of the particle.
$\boldsymbol{R} \equiv$ absolute displacement of the origin of the moving reference system.
$\boldsymbol{\rho} \equiv$ displacement of the particle as measured from the moving coordinate system.

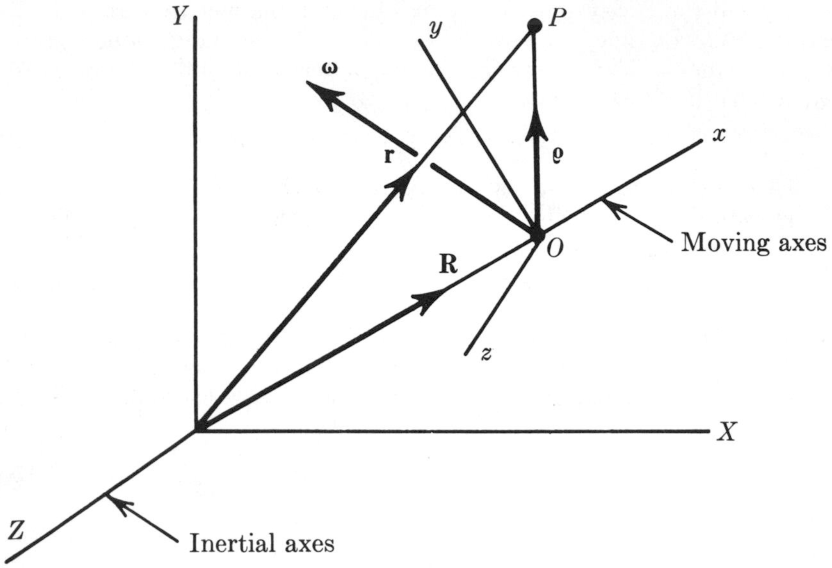

Figure 3-8

It is seen from the figure and from the rules of vector addition that the displacement vector to the particle may be written as

$$\boldsymbol{r} = \boldsymbol{R} + \boldsymbol{\rho} \tag{3.19}$$

In order to determine the velocity and acceleration of the particle, we must perform a differentiation. First, to determine the velocity, the displacement will be differentiated with respect to time:

$$\boldsymbol{v} = \dot{\boldsymbol{r}} = \dot{\boldsymbol{R}} + \dot{\boldsymbol{\rho}} \tag{3.20}$$

The vector $\dot{\boldsymbol{R}}$ may be interpreted as the velocity of the origin of the moving coordinate system and may be written as $\boldsymbol{v}_O$. The vector $\dot{\boldsymbol{\rho}}$ may be defined in terms of the unit vectors in the moving coordinate system. Now if $\boldsymbol{\rho}$ is written as

$$\boldsymbol{\rho} = x\bar{\boldsymbol{i}} + y\bar{\boldsymbol{j}} + z\bar{\boldsymbol{k}} \tag{3.21}$$

where the unit vectors are in the moving coordinate system. Then the time derivative of $\boldsymbol{\rho}$ will be equal to

$$\dot{\boldsymbol{\rho}} = \dot{\boldsymbol{\rho}}_{xyz} + \boldsymbol{\omega} \times \boldsymbol{\rho} \tag{3.22}$$

But $\dot{\boldsymbol{\rho}}_{xyz}$ (equal to $\dot{x}\bar{\boldsymbol{i}} + \dot{y}\bar{\boldsymbol{j}} + \dot{z}\bar{\boldsymbol{k}}$) may be interpreted as the velocity of the point P as seen by an observer in the moving coordinate system; therefore it is written $\boldsymbol{v}_r$ (relative velocity).

Hence the relative velocity equation becomes

$$\boxed{\boldsymbol{v} = \boldsymbol{v}_O + \boldsymbol{\omega} \times \boldsymbol{\rho} + \boldsymbol{v}_r} \tag{3.23}$$

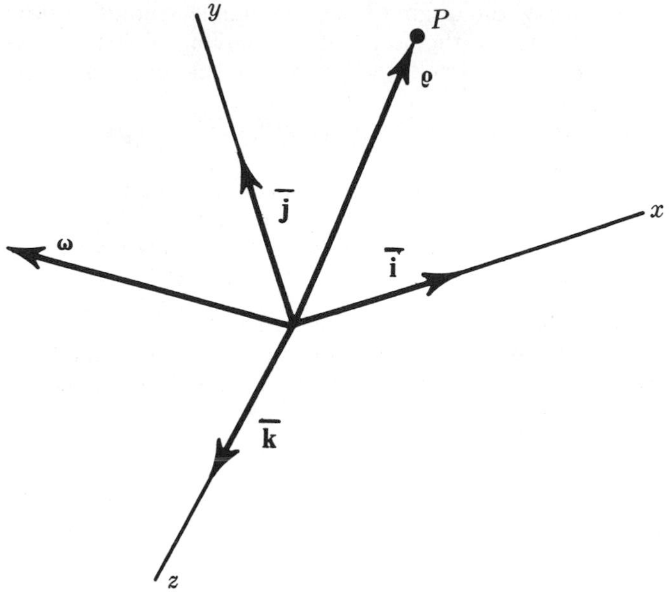

Figure 3-9

The general relative-acceleration equation may be obtained by differentiating the velocity equation with respect to time:

$$\boldsymbol{a} = \dot{\boldsymbol{v}} = \dot{\boldsymbol{v}}_O + \dot{\omega} \times \rho + \omega \times \dot{\rho} + \dot{\boldsymbol{v}}_r \tag{3.24}$$

Again, by Eq. 3.18 for the time derivative of a vector defined in a moving coordinate system,

$$\dot{\boldsymbol{v}}_r \equiv \dot{\boldsymbol{v}}_{r_{xyz}} + \boldsymbol{\omega} \times \boldsymbol{v}_r \tag{3.25}$$

where $\dot{\boldsymbol{v}}_{r_{xyz}}$ is equal to $\ddot{x}\bar{\boldsymbol{i}} + \ddot{y}\bar{\boldsymbol{j}} + \ddot{z}\bar{\boldsymbol{k}}$, which may be interpreted as the acceleration of point P as seen by an observer in the moving system and which is written as $\boldsymbol{a}_r$ (relative acceleration).

From Eq. 3.22 it is seen that

$$\boldsymbol{\omega} \times \dot{\boldsymbol{\rho}} = \boldsymbol{\omega} \times \boldsymbol{v}_r + \boldsymbol{\omega} \times (\boldsymbol{\omega} \times \boldsymbol{\rho}) \tag{3.26}$$

The term $\dot{\boldsymbol{v}}_O$ may be thought of as the acceleration of the origin of the moving system and is written as $\boldsymbol{a}_O$, so that finally the relative acceleration equation may be written as

$$\boxed{\boldsymbol{a} = \boldsymbol{a}_O + \boldsymbol{\omega} \times (\boldsymbol{\omega} \times \boldsymbol{\rho}) + \dot{\boldsymbol{\omega}} \times \boldsymbol{\rho} + 2\omega \times \boldsymbol{v}_r + \boldsymbol{a}_r} \tag{3.27}$$

At this point it is advisable to review each of the terms of the relative velocity and acceleration equations:

$\boldsymbol{v} \equiv$ absolute velocity of point P.
$\boldsymbol{a} \equiv$ absolute acceleration of point P.

$\boldsymbol{v}_O \equiv$ velocity of the origin of the moving coordinate system.
$\boldsymbol{a}_O \equiv$ acceleration of the origin of the moving coordinate system.
$\boldsymbol{\rho} \equiv$ radius vector from the origin of the moving system to the point P.
$\boldsymbol{\omega} \equiv$ angular velocity of the moving system at a particular instant of time.
$\dot{\boldsymbol{\omega}} \equiv$ time derivative of the angular velocity vector.
$\boldsymbol{v}_r \equiv$ velocity of point P as seen by an observer in the moving system.
$\boldsymbol{a}_r \equiv$ acceleration of point P as seen by an observer in the moving system.

In order to determine the velocity or acceleration of a particle, using the general velocity or acceleration equation, it is necessary to choose first an appropriate, moving, coordinate system. This reference-coordinate system should be chosen so that

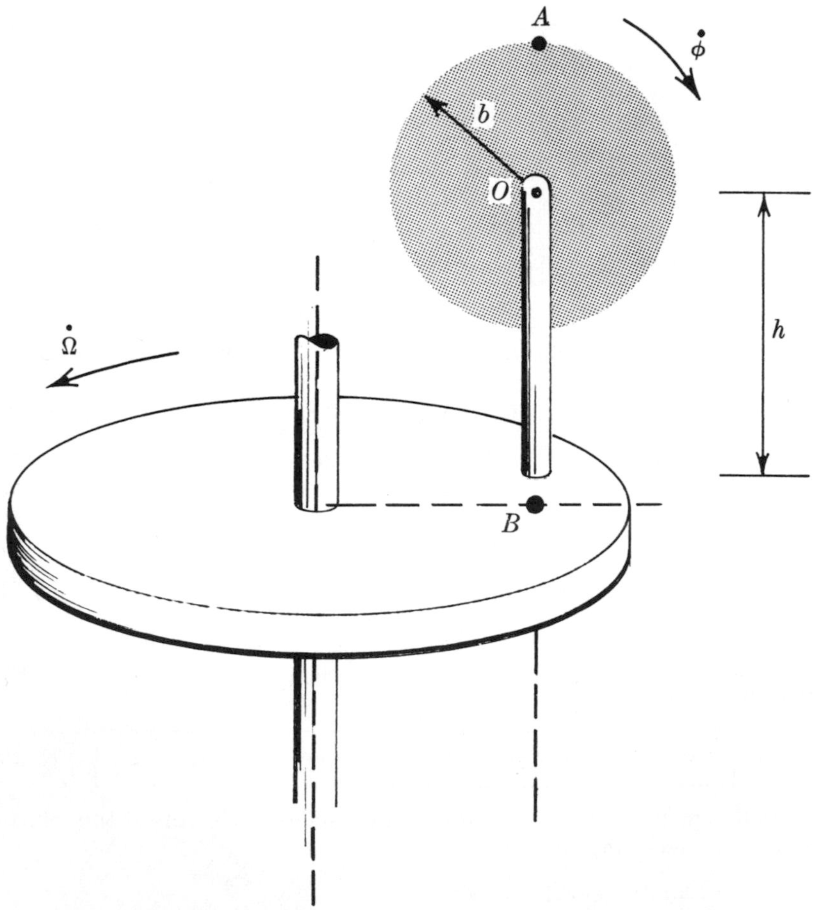

Figure 3-10

1. The velocity and acceleration of the origin of the moving system is known or easily determined.
2. The motion of the point in question is such that the velocity and acceleration of the point is easily determined by an observer on the moving frame.

Once the moving coordinate system has been established, all that is needed is to tabulate the terms of the general acceleration equation and perform the required operations in the equation, to obtain the velocity or acceleration.

Example 3–4. A disk of radius b is fixed to a rotating turntable. The disk is rotating in the radial plane of the turntable with a constant angular velocity of $\dot{\phi}$, as shown in Fig. 3–10. The turntable itself is rotating with a constant angular velocity of $\dot{\Omega}$. Determine both the velocity and acceleration of point A.

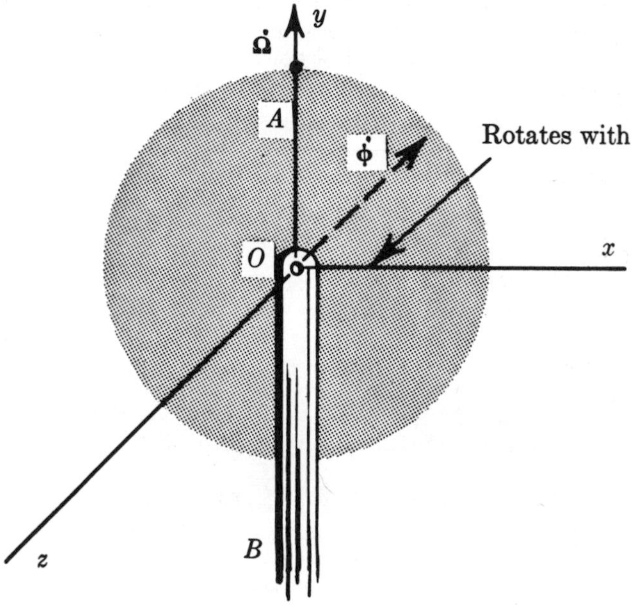

Figure 3-11

Solution: First we must define a moving coordinate system. We shall define the moving system in the following manner: The origin of the system will be placed at point O, and the axes themselves will be considered to be fixed to the disk and rotating with the disk. The following list gives a term-by-term evaluation of each quantity of the relative velocity and acceleration equation, with a short explanation of each.

$$\mathbf{v}_O = -R\dot{\Omega}\bar{k}$$

This is the absolute velocity of the origin of the moving system. (Note that all quantities are written in terms of unit vectors in the moving system.)

$$\boldsymbol{a}_O = -R\dot{\Omega}^2\bar{\boldsymbol{i}}$$

This is the absolute acceleration of the origin of the moving system.

$$\begin{aligned}\boldsymbol{\omega} &= \dot{\boldsymbol{\phi}} + \dot{\boldsymbol{\Omega}}\\ &= -\dot{\phi}\bar{\boldsymbol{k}} + \dot{\Omega}\bar{\boldsymbol{j}}\end{aligned}$$

The angular velocity of the moving system in the position shown is a combination of two rotations: a rotation about the y axis (for this position only) due to the rotation of the turntable, and a rotation about the z axis due to the spin of the disk.

$$\dot{\boldsymbol{\omega}} = \ddot{\boldsymbol{\phi}} + \ddot{\boldsymbol{\Omega}}$$

But

$$\begin{aligned}\ddot{\boldsymbol{\Omega}} &= 0\\ \ddot{\boldsymbol{\phi}} &= \dot{\boldsymbol{\Omega}} \times \dot{\boldsymbol{\phi}}\\ &= (\dot{\Omega}\bar{\boldsymbol{j}}) \times (-\dot{\phi}\bar{\boldsymbol{k}}) - \dot{\Omega}\dot{\phi}\bar{\boldsymbol{i}}\end{aligned}$$

The time derivative of the angular velocity vector is obtained by direct differentiation. The vector $\ddot{\boldsymbol{\Omega}}$ is equal to zero because $\dot{\boldsymbol{\Omega}}$ is neither changing in magnitude nor direction. But, since $\dot{\boldsymbol{\phi}}$ is changing direction by virtue of its angular velocity of rotation $\dot{\boldsymbol{\Omega}}$, it does have a time derivative, given by $\dot{\boldsymbol{\Omega}} \times \dot{\boldsymbol{\phi}}$.

$$\boldsymbol{\rho} = b\bar{\boldsymbol{j}}$$

This is the radius vector to point A.

$$\begin{aligned}\boldsymbol{v}_r &= 0\\ \boldsymbol{a}_r &= 0\end{aligned}$$

Since the moving system is fixed to the wheel, an observer in the moving system will see point A as a stationary point. Thus, the relative velocity and acceleration will be equal to zero.

Upon substituting these quantities into the relative velocity and acceleration equations, we get

$$\begin{aligned}\boldsymbol{v} &= \dot{\phi}b\bar{\boldsymbol{i}} - R\dot{\Omega}\bar{\boldsymbol{k}}\\ \boldsymbol{a} &= (-R\dot{\Omega}^2)\bar{\boldsymbol{i}} + (-b\dot{\phi}^2)\bar{\boldsymbol{j}} + (-2b\dot{\phi}\dot{\Omega})\bar{\boldsymbol{k}}\end{aligned}$$

Example 3–5. Consider the preceding example. Determine the absolute velocity and acceleration of point A. Work the example, using a coordinate system that is fixed to the rod OB. In Example 3–4, the reference system was considered as being fixed to the rotating disk. In this case, the disk is moving with respect to the reference system.

Solution: A term-by-term evaluation of all quantities of the general acceleration equation follows.

$$\begin{aligned}\boldsymbol{\omega} &= \dot{\Omega}\bar{\boldsymbol{j}}\\ \dot{\boldsymbol{\omega}} &= 0\end{aligned}$$

In this case, since the frame is not connected to the disk, the reference frame will rotate with the flywheel only.

$$\begin{aligned}\boldsymbol{v}_r &= b\dot{\phi}\bar{\boldsymbol{i}}\\ \boldsymbol{a}_r &= -b\dot{\phi}^2\bar{\boldsymbol{j}}\\ \boldsymbol{\rho} &= b\bar{\boldsymbol{j}}\\ \boldsymbol{a}_O &= -R\dot{\Omega}^2\bar{\boldsymbol{i}}\end{aligned}$$

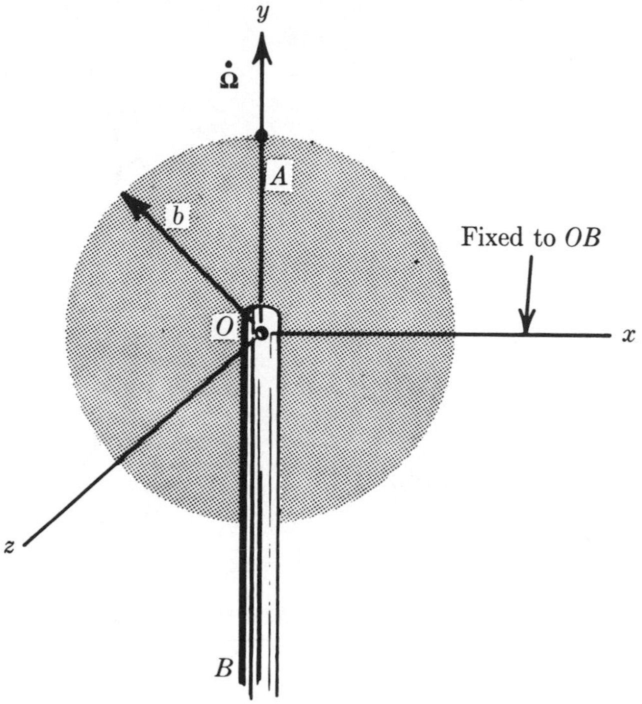

Figure 3-12

In this case, the relative velocity and acceleration are not equal to zero, since the disk is rotating with respect to the reference system. Recall that the relative velocity and acceleration of point A is the velocity and acceleration of A as seen by an observer sitting on the moving system.

Upon substitution into the general acceleration equation,

$$\boldsymbol{a} = (-R\dot{\Omega}^2)\bar{\boldsymbol{i}} - b\dot{\phi}^2\bar{\boldsymbol{j}} - 2b\dot{\phi}\dot{\Omega}\bar{\boldsymbol{k}}$$

and thus it is seen that the acceleration of point A agrees with the acceleration as determined in Example 3-4.

PROBLEMS

3-14. Using the method outlined in Sec. 3–2, determine the time derivatives of $\bar{e}_r$ and $\bar{e}_\theta$ of the polar coordinate system.

3-15. Using the method outlined in Sec. 3–2, determine the time derivatives of $\bar{e}_t$ and $\bar{e}_n$ of the normal and tangential coordinate system.

3-16. The angular velocity of spin of the body shown in Fig. P.3–16 is equal to 16 radians/sec. The y axis has a constant orientation in space. What is the velocity of point P?

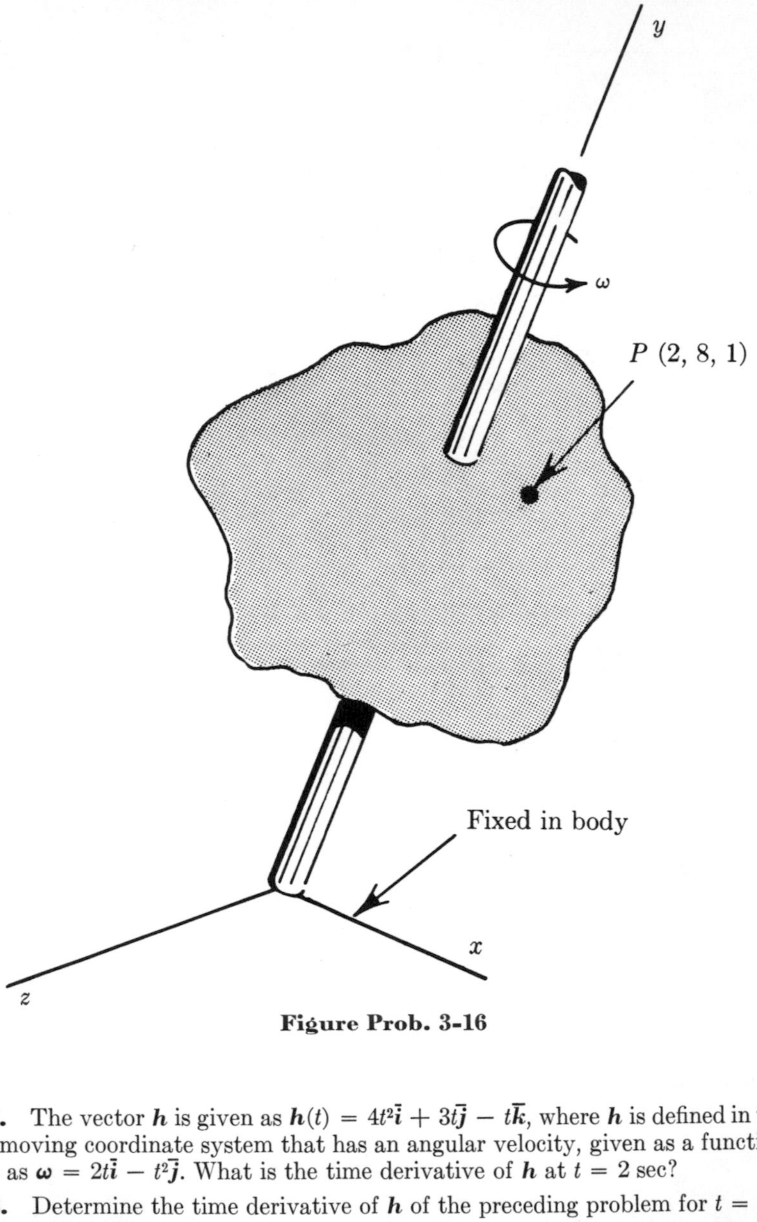

Figure Prob. 3-16

3-17. The vector $\boldsymbol{h}$ is given as $\boldsymbol{h}(t) = 4t^2\bar{\boldsymbol{i}} + 3t\bar{\boldsymbol{j}} - t\bar{\boldsymbol{k}}$, where $\boldsymbol{h}$ is defined in terms of a moving coordinate system that has an angular velocity, given as a function of time as $\boldsymbol{\omega} = 2t\bar{\boldsymbol{i}} - t^2\bar{\boldsymbol{j}}$. What is the time derivative of $\boldsymbol{h}$ at $t = 2$ sec?

3-18. Determine the time derivative of $\boldsymbol{h}$ of the preceding problem for $t = 4$ sec.

3-19. The disk shown in Fig. P.3–19 is spinning with an angular velocity of 4.0 radians/sec, in a counterclockwise sense, and with an angular acceleration of 10.0 radians/sec^2 in a clockwise sense. The bar OA is rotating clockwise with a constant angular velocity of 2.0 radians/sec. Determine the magnitude of the absolute acceleration of point P for the position shown.

3-20. Consider Example 3–4. Suppose that the flywheel has an angular acceleration of $\ddot{\Omega}$ in the same direction as its angular velocity, and suppose that the small

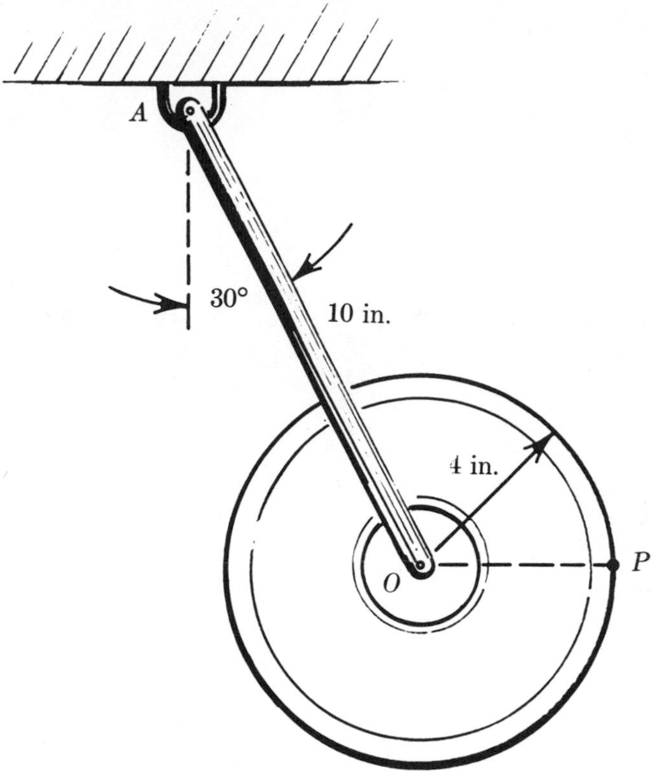

Figure Prob. 3-19

wheel has an acceleration in a direction opposite to its angular velocity of magnitude $\ddot{\phi}$. Determine the acceleration of point A.

3-21. Rod OA in Fig. P.3–21 rotates in a horizontal plane about O with an angular velocity of $\dot{\boldsymbol{\phi}}$. The disk, of radius r, travels in a radial plane and rotates with an angular velocity $\dot{\boldsymbol{\Omega}}$ as shown. Determine the acceleration of point P by considering the moving coordinate system fixed to the wheel.

3-22. Work Problem 3–21 by considering the moving system fixed to the rod OA with the origin at point O.

3-23. Determine the velocity of point O of Problem 3–21.

3-24. Consider Problem 3–21. Suppose that the direction of the angular velocity of OA is in a direction opposite to that shown in Fig. P.3–21. Determine the magnitude of the acceleration of point P if $\dot{\phi} = 2.0$ radians/sec, $l = 2.0$ ft, $r = 6.0$ in., $\dot{\Omega} = 1.0$ radian/sec clockwise, and $\ddot{\Omega} = 8.0$ radians/sec² clockwise.

3-25. The wheel shown in Fig. P.3–25 rolls on the track without slipping. The constant angular velocity of the bar OC is given as $\dot{\phi}$. Determine (a) the velocity of point A, and (b) the acceleration of point A. Choose the moving axes fixed to the wheel as shown.

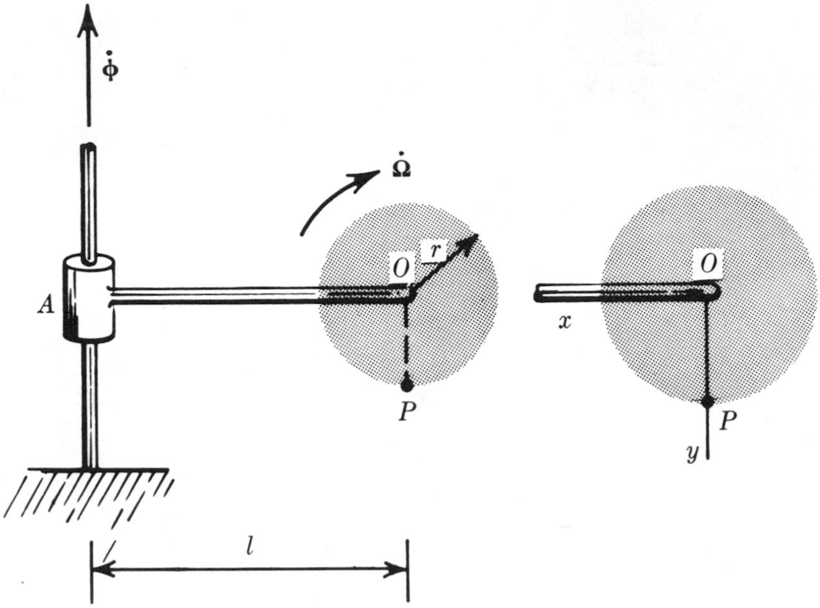

Figure Prob. 3-21

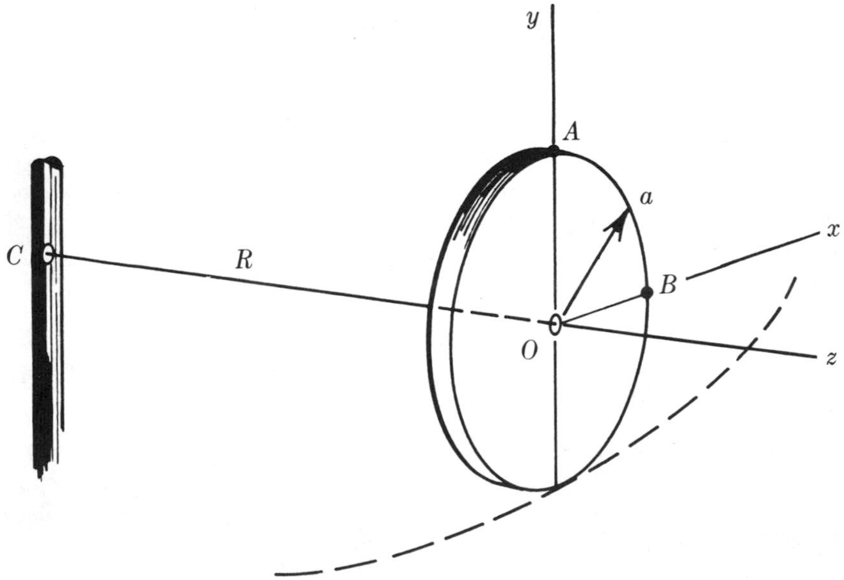

Figure Prob. 3-25

3-26. For Problem 3–25 determine the velocity and acceleration of point B for the position shown. Use a moving reference system that is fixed to OC so that the wheel moves with respect to the system.

3-27. The bar AB is rotating counterclockwise with an angular velocity of 4.0 radians/sec and an acceleration clockwise of 2.0 radians/sec². The bead is moving on the bar with a velocity of 3.0 fps outward with respect to the bar, and it has an acceleration inward of 5.0 ft/sec². What is the absolute acceleration of the bead? Fix the coordinate system to the rod in the position shown in the figure.

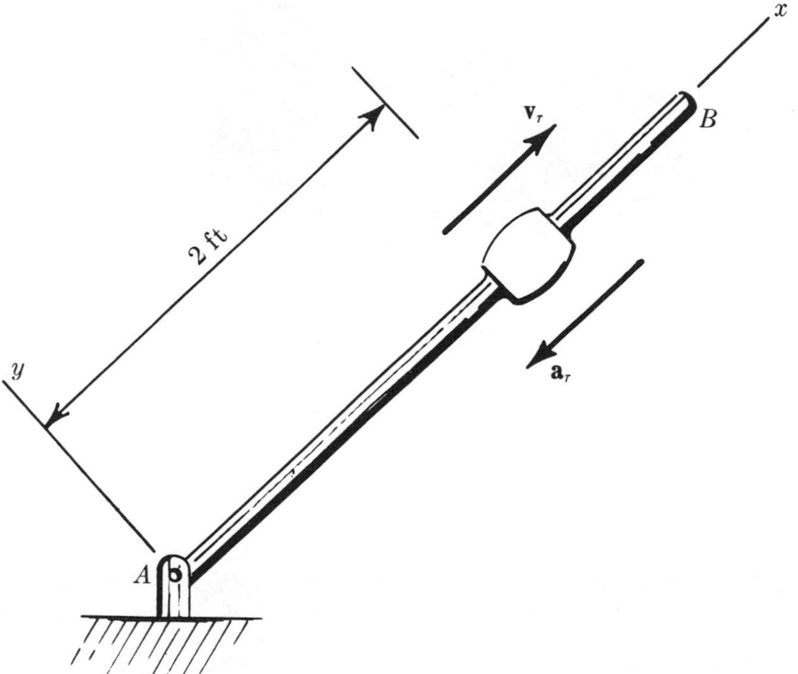

Figure Prob. 3-27

3-28. At a certain instant of time, a car is traveling around a circular horizontal path of radius 1200 ft with a speed of 60 fps and an acceleration of 1.0 ft/sec² tangent to the path. The radiator fan in the car has an angular speed of 40 radians/sec as seen by the driver and an angular acceleration of 0.80 radian/sec² in the same direction. Determine the absolute acceleration of a point on the vertical fan blade at 1 ft from the center of the shaft.

3-29. A missile is shot outward from the earth with a velocity v and an acceleration a with respect to an observer on the surface of the earth. What is the absolute

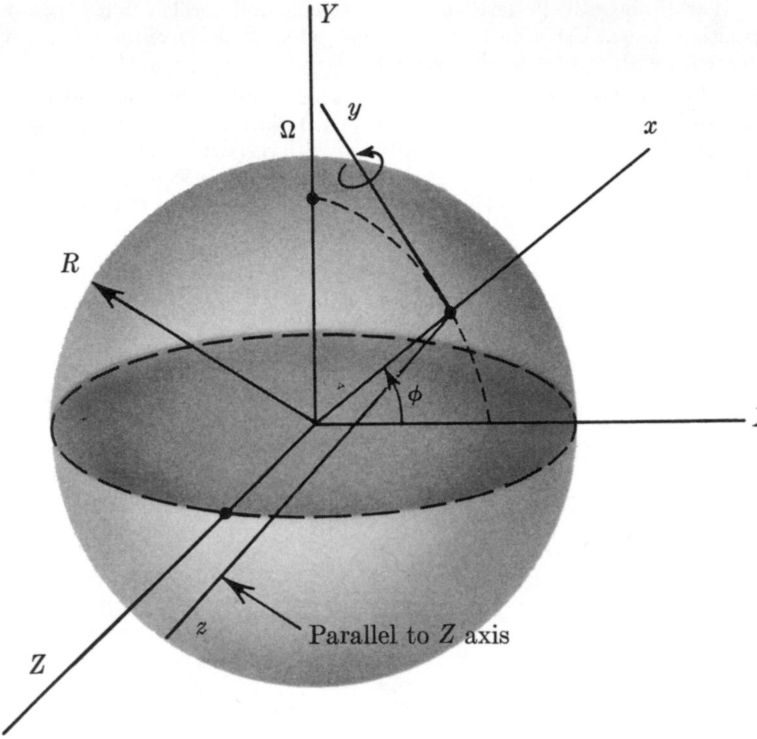

Figure Prob. 3-29

acceleration of the missile at the point of launch? (The absolute acceleration is the acceleration with reference to a coordinate system fixed to the center of the earth, but not rotating with the earth. Actually, this reference system is itself moving by virtue of the rotation of the earth about the sun. In this case, this acceleration is assumed to be zero.) Also determine the acceleration of the missile if the latitude of launch is equal to zero.

4

Kinetics of a Particle

In Chapters 2 and 3, schemes for describing the motion of a particle in space were established. Discussed were not only methods of defining the position of a particle but also the rate of motion of a particle. However, up to this point, nothing has been said about the forces that cause this motion.

In statics we saw that we could have a set of forces acting on a body in such a manner that there would be no resulting motion of that body. Recall that the condition that a body be in equilibrium was that the sum of all the forces, added vectorially, was equal to zero. If the net force on a body in any direction is equal to zero, then the body will be in a state of equilibrium. The problem we shall consider now is: What happens when the net force in any direction on the body is not equal to zero? It is intuitively obvious that a round ball, resting on a plane, will not be in equilibrium when a lateral force is applied to the body, but it is not obvious just how the ball will respond to the force. The remaining part of this chapter will be devoted to establishing relationships between the forces on a body and the resulting motion of that body. Knowing the forces that act on a body, we will be able to determine the motion of that body; and, vice versa, knowing the motion of the body, we will be able to determine the forces that are producing that motion.

4-1. NEWTON'S LAWS AND THE EQUATION OF MOTION

From the observations of Galileo and Kepler, Sir Isaac Newton formulated three principles of motion, now the well-known Newton's laws. Contained in Newton's laws of motion is the bridge between the forces on a body and the motion of that body. The three laws, which form the bases for all analytical dynamics, are discussed in the subsequent paragraphs.

Newton's first law. "A body will remain at rest or move in a straight-line path with a constant velocity unless it is acted upon by an external force." If there are no external forces acting on a body, the body must be in a state of equilibrium. If the body is at rest relative to inertial space, then the body is said to be in a state of *static equilibrium*. If this body is acted upon by a force, the body will start moving in some fashion; then, if the force is removed, the body will continue moving in a straight-line path with a constant velocity, the same velocity that the body had at the instant the force was removed. A body in this state is said to be in a state of *dynamic equilibrium*.

Newton's second law. "Change of velocity of a particle is proportional to and in the same direction of the straight line of the net external force on the body." This famous law of Newton's forms the aforementioned bridge between forces on a body and the motion of that body. The single law may be stated more explicitly by considering each implication separately:

1. The magnitude of the resultant external force is proportional to the magnitude of the resulting acceleration.
2. The direction of the resulting acceleration is the same as the direction of the resulting external force.

Newton's second law may be stated very concisely by writing the vector equation:

$$\boxed{\boldsymbol{F} = m\boldsymbol{a}} \tag{4.1}$$

where $\boldsymbol{F}$ is the vector sum of n external forces acting on the body and may be written as

$$\boldsymbol{F} = \sum_{i=1}^{n} \boldsymbol{F}_i \tag{4.2}$$

The quantity m is known as the *mass* of the body and is nothing more than the proportionality constant that relates the magnitude of the force to the magnitude of the acceleration. More is said about the mass in the next section.

Newton's third law. "Action and reaction are equal and opposite." The force of one body acting on a second body is equal in magnitude and opposite in direction to the force of the second body acting on the first. This is the well-known principle that is employed frequently in statics, and by this time it is well known to the student.

4-2. THE CONCEPT OF MASS

The proportionality constant m, which relates the forces on a body to the acceleration of the body, is known as the *mass* of the body. It is a measure of the quantity of matter of the body. Whereas the *weight*, which is defined as the force of gravitational attraction on a body, varies not only from point to point throughout the universe but also on our own planet earth, the mass of a body is a universal constant.

The mass of a body may be determined in the following manner: Regardless of the weight, a body in free fall at the surface of the earth will accelerate toward the surface of the earth with the same acceleration (g). This was reported to have been dramatically demonstrated by Galileo, who dropped a 100-lb ball and a 10-lb ball of the same size through a distance of 100 ft and observed that the two hit the ground at the same instant. The force causing the bodies to accelerate downward is the gravitational force W, which is different for each body. For the body in free fall, Newton's second law may be expressed as $W = mg$. Since g is known to be about 32.2 ft/sec^2 and the weight of the body can be measured by a spring scale, the mass may be evaluated by $m = W/g$. In weighing a body on a spring scale, the centrifugal effects of the earth's spin should be accounted for. This effect, however, is small, as demonstrated in Example 4-6.

Mass was originally defined in terms of a standard kilogram, the unit for which is kept by the International Bureau of Weights and Measures at Sèvres, France. The standard kilogram is a platinum-iridium cylinder.

The units of mass in the pound-second-foot system of units are pount-second^2 per foot. These may be easily verified by considering the units of Eq. 4.1. Since force is measured in pounds and acceleration in feet per second, mass must be measured in pound-second^2 per foot in order that Eq. 4.1 will be dimensionally homogeneous. The abbreviated form of the units of mass in pound-second^2 per foot is called a *slug*.

The slug may be expressed in terms of a kilogram. One pound of force is equal to 0.45359237 of the force exerted by the earth on the kilogram at a point where the acceleration of gravity is equal to 32.174 ft/sec^2 (it is assumed in this weighing procedure that a correction has been made for the motion of the earth). One slug is the mass for which a unit-pound force will impart a unit acceleration in feet per square second.

To determine the mass of a body in slugs, it is required to weigh the body (pounds) at any point and then divide the weight by the gravitational acceleration (ft/sec^2) at that point.

4-3. VARIOUS EXPRESSIONS OF NEWTON'S SECOND LAW

Newton's second law, expressed as an equation, is written as $\boldsymbol{F} = m\boldsymbol{a}$. Depending upon the nature of the problem, it may be convenient to use one type of coordinate system in preference to another when expressing the forces and the motion. In Fig. 4–1, forces are expressed in three types of coordinate systems, which we have already discussed. Since we have expressions for the acceleration in each of these three coordinate systems, we are easily able to express Newton's second law in each system.

The Cartesian coordinate system. Newton's second law, in terms of Cartesian coordinates, may be written as

$$F_x\bar{\boldsymbol{i}} + F_y\bar{\boldsymbol{j}} + F_z\bar{\boldsymbol{k}} = m(\ddot{x}\bar{\boldsymbol{i}} + \ddot{y}\bar{\boldsymbol{j}} + \ddot{z}\bar{\boldsymbol{k}}) \tag{4.3}$$

For this vector equation to be satisfied, the coefficients of unit vectors on each side of the equation must be the same. Thus, it follows that

$$\boxed{\begin{aligned} F_x &= m\ddot{x} \\ F_y &= m\ddot{y} \\ F_z &= m\ddot{z} \end{aligned}} \tag{4.4}$$

If the motion is rectilinear, the equation of motion may be written simply $F = ma$.

Consider the problem of a particle moving in space and being described by rectangular Cartesian coordinates. In general, the force in each of the directions is a function of not only time but also of all the other coordinates and their first and second time derivatives. Thus, the general form of the equations of motion are

$$\begin{aligned} m\ddot{x} &= F_x(x, y, z, \dot{x}, \dot{y}, \dot{z}, \ddot{x}, \ddot{y}, \ddot{z}, t) \\ m\ddot{y} &= F_y(x, y, z, \dot{x}, \dot{y}, \dot{z}, \ddot{x}, \ddot{y}, \ddot{z}, t) \\ m\ddot{z} &= F_z(x, y, z, \dot{x}, \dot{y}, \dot{z}, \ddot{x}, \ddot{y}, \ddot{z}, t) \end{aligned} \tag{4.5}$$

These equations are (in general) second-order, nonhomogeneous, and nonlinear differential equations. In general, closed-form solutions to these equations for the position and velocity of the particle are virtually impossible; however, numerical solutions to these equations are usually possible with the aid of digital computers. In this introductory text in dynamics, however, only dynamical systems with equations of motion that are readily integrable will be considered.

Polar coordinates. Newton's second law, expressed in polar coordinates, is

$$F_r\bar{\boldsymbol{e}}_r + F_\theta\bar{\boldsymbol{e}}_\theta = m[(\ddot{r} - r\dot{\theta}^2)\bar{\boldsymbol{e}}_r + (r\ddot{\theta} + 2\dot{r}\dot{\theta})\bar{\boldsymbol{e}}_\theta] \tag{4.6}$$

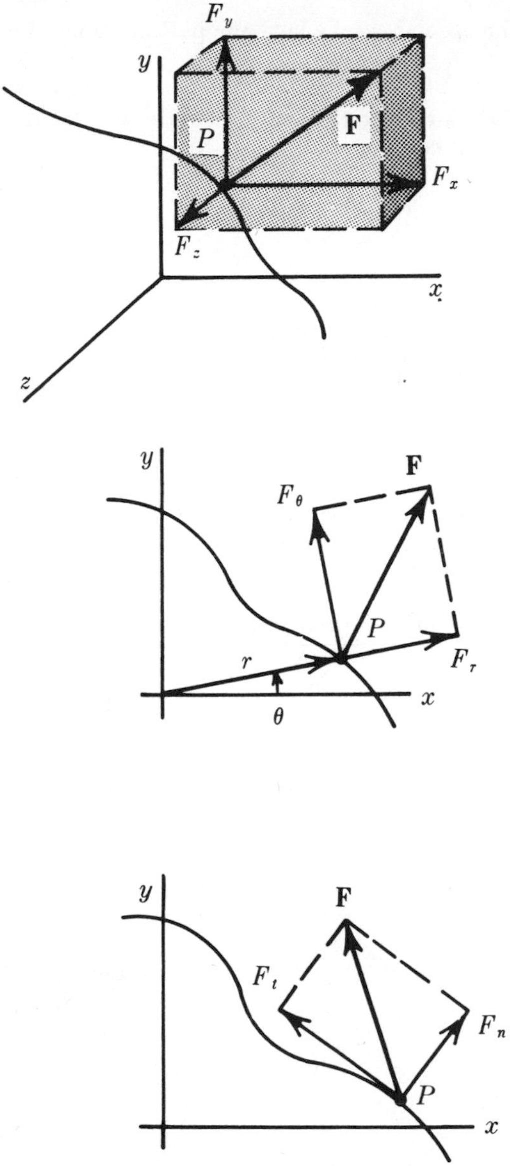

$\boldsymbol{F} = F_x\bar{\imath} + F_y\bar{\jmath} + F_z\bar{k}$

Cartesian components

$\boldsymbol{F} = F_r\bar{\mathbf{e}}_r + F_\theta\bar{\mathbf{e}}_\theta$

Polar coordinates

$\boldsymbol{F} = F_t\bar{\mathbf{e}}_t + F_n\bar{\mathbf{e}}_n$

Normal and tangential components

Figure 4-1. *Various expressions of the force on a particle*

Again, this vector equation implies the following scalar equations:

$$\boxed{\begin{aligned} F_r &= m(\ddot{r} - r\dot{\theta}^2) \\ F_\theta &= m(r\ddot{\theta} + 2\dot{r}\dot{\theta}) \end{aligned}} \tag{4.7}$$

Polar coordinates are generally employed to advantage in those cases where the motion of the particle is on a curve and where r is given as a function of the angle θ or, in the special case, where the particle is moving on a circle.

Normal and tangential components. Newton's second law, expressed in normal and tangential components, is

$$F_t\bar{e}_t + F_n\bar{e}_n = m\left(\frac{dv}{dt}\bar{e}_t - \frac{v^2}{\rho}\bar{e}_n\right) \tag{4.8}$$

which implies the two scalar equations

$$F_t = m\left(\frac{dv}{dt}\right) \qquad F_n = -\frac{mv^2}{\rho} \tag{4.9}$$

The normal and tangential components are used in those cases where the motion of the particle is given as being on a curve and where $y = f(x)$ or, in the special case of motion, on a circle.

General force equation. The equation of motion, in terms of the general acceleration equation, may be written as

$$\boldsymbol{F} = m[\boldsymbol{a}_O + \boldsymbol{\omega} \times (\boldsymbol{\omega} \times \boldsymbol{\rho}) + \dot{\boldsymbol{\omega}} \times \boldsymbol{\rho} + 2\boldsymbol{\omega} \times \boldsymbol{v}_r + \boldsymbol{a}_r] \tag{4.10}$$

We shall now consider examples that illustrate the use of the equations of motion listed above.

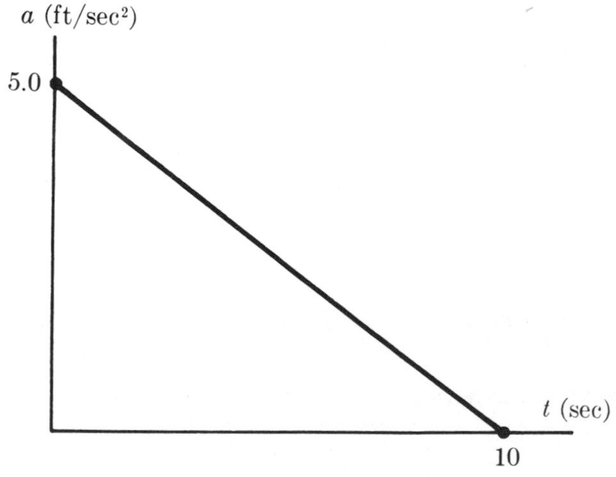

Figure 4-2

Example 4–1. The measured acceleration of a 3000-lb automobile is shown in Fig. 4–2. What motive force must be supplied to the automobile if the only significant resistive force is the force due to rolling friction? The motive force is the force of friction between the rear wheels and the road (assuming rear-wheel drive). The coefficient of rolling friction is 0.03.

Solution: Before the equation of motion can be written, a free-body diagram of the vehicle should be drawn as shown in Fig. 4–3. It is assumed that the vehicle

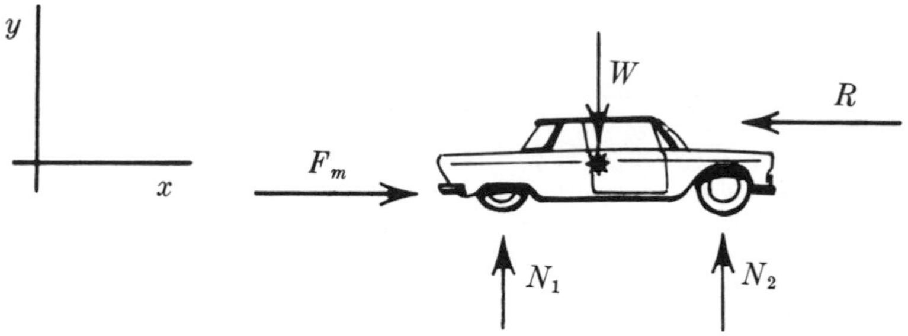

Figure 4-3

may be represented as a point mass. The force F_m is the motive force and the force R is the resistive force. The equation of motion may be written as

$$F_x = ma$$
$$F_m - R = ma$$

But, from Fig. 4–2, the acceleration is

$$a = 5 - \frac{t}{2}$$

The mass may be calculated as

$$m = \frac{W}{g} = \frac{3000}{32.2} = 93.2 \text{ slugs}$$

The rolling resistance is

$$\begin{aligned} R &= \mu_r W \\ &= 0.03(3000) \\ &= 90 \text{ lb} \end{aligned}$$

so that, finally, the motive force becomes

$$\begin{aligned} F &= 90 + 93.2\left(5 - \frac{t}{2}\right) \\ &= 556 - 46.6t \quad \text{lb} \end{aligned}$$

Example 4–2. A particle with a mass of 4.0 slugs is at point $(3, -2)$ and moving with a velocity of $\boldsymbol{v}_0 = (6\bar{\boldsymbol{i}} + 4\bar{\boldsymbol{j}})$ at $t = 0$. The force on the body is $\boldsymbol{F} = 2t\bar{\boldsymbol{i}} - 3t^2\bar{\boldsymbol{j}}$.

Determine (1) the velocity as a function of time, and (2) the displacement as a function of time.

Solution: First write the equation of motion as

$$\boldsymbol{F} = m\boldsymbol{a}$$
$$2t\boldsymbol{i} - 3t^2\boldsymbol{j} = 4\boldsymbol{a}$$

so that

$$\boldsymbol{a} = 0.5t\boldsymbol{i} - 0.75t^2\boldsymbol{j}$$

The velocity may be obtained by direct integration as

$$\boldsymbol{v} = \boldsymbol{v}_O + 0.25t^2\boldsymbol{i} - 0.25t^3\boldsymbol{j}$$

Substituting the initial conditions,

$$\boldsymbol{v} = (6 + 0.25t^2)\boldsymbol{i} + (4 - 0.25t^3)\boldsymbol{j}$$

The displacement as a function of time may be obtained by direct integration:

$$\boldsymbol{r} = \boldsymbol{r}_O + (6t + 0.083t^3)\boldsymbol{i} + (4t - 0.0625t^4)\boldsymbol{j}$$

and, substituting the initial conditions,

$$\boldsymbol{r} = (3 + 6t + 0.083t^3)\boldsymbol{i} + (-2 + 4t - 0.0625t^4)\boldsymbol{j}$$

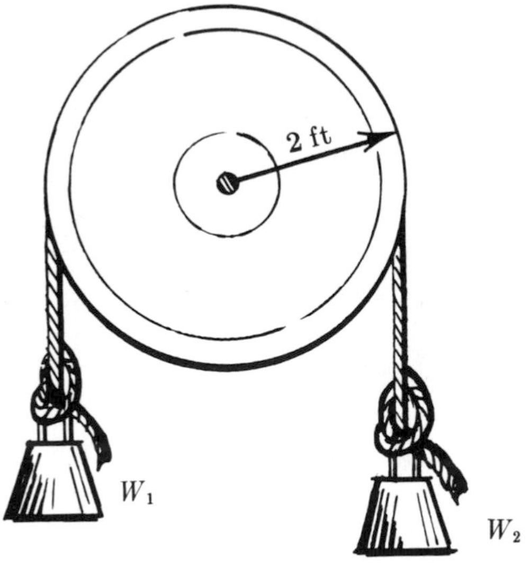

Figure 4-4

Example 4–3. Consider the pulley system shown in Fig. 4–4. If the system is released from rest, what will be the displacement as a function of time of each of the masses? W_1 is equal to 80 lb and W_2 is equal to 49 lb. It is assumed that the weight of the pulley is negligible.

Solution: Although this system may be construed as being a system of particles rather than a single particle (at this point we are not yet familiar with the analysis of a system of particles), the method of determining the motion of each individual particle is basically the same as used before, that is, draw the free-body diagram of the particle in question and impose upon this the equations of motion. The free-body diagram of each of the masses is shown in Fig. 4–5.

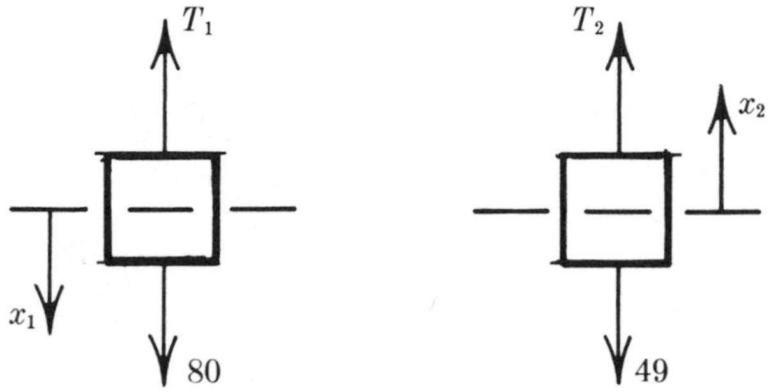

Figure 4-5

The coordinates for each of the masses were defined as being positive in the direction assumed to be that in which each mass would move. The only advantage in doing this is that it simplifies the calculations somewhat, since generally any arbitrary coordinate system may be employed.

Imposing the equations of motion on each of the particles, we get

$$F_1 = m_1 a_1 \qquad 80 - T_1 = \frac{80}{32.2} a_1$$

$$F_2 = m_2 a_2 \qquad T_2 - 49 = \frac{49}{32.2} a_2$$

At this point, we note that we may neither determine the acceleration of the first mass nor the acceleration of the second mass, since there is an additional unknown in each of the equations T_1 and T_2, respectively. We may now think of the equations of motion as forming two equations with four unknowns. The problem, then, is to find two more equations relating the same unknowns. One of the conditions that we may use is the fact that, since the weight of the pulley is negligible, the force in the rope will be constant (this assumes that the weight of the rope is also negligible). Thus,

$$T = T_1 = T_2$$

Also note that the motion of the first mass will be the same as the motion of the second mass because of the constraint, in this case the connecting rope:

$$a = a_1 = a_2$$

Now we have the required four equations with four unknowns. In terms of T and a,

$$80 - T = 2.47a$$
$$T - 49 = 1.51a$$

and, solving for the acceleration,

$$a = 7.80$$

so that the velocity and displacement of the first mass (and also the second) becomes, upon integration,

$$v = 7.80t$$
$$x = 3.90t^2$$

Example 4–4. A projectile is shot out of a cannon and is subjected to an aerodynamic drag force equal in magnitude to Cv^2. The muzzle velocity is v_O. Determine the velocity of the particle as a function of time, assuming that the projectile moves along a straight-line path.

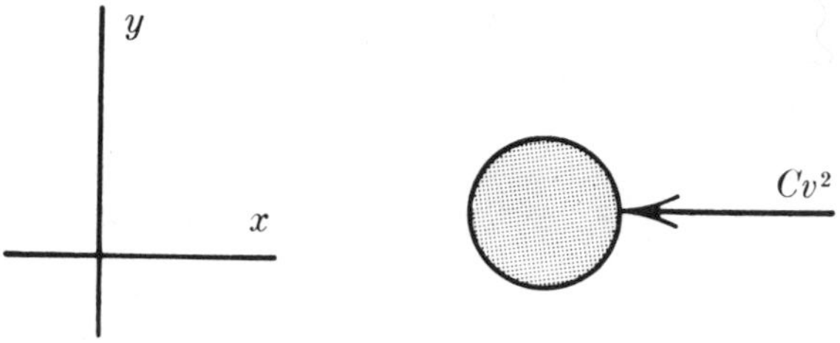

Figure 4-6

Solution: First draw a free-body diagram of the projectile as shown in Fig. 4–6. The net force acting on the body in the x direction is equal to $-Cv^2$. Thus, the equation of motion may be written as

$$F = ma$$
$$-Cv^2 = ma$$

If we let $K = C/m$ and follow the method of integrating when the acceleration is given as a function of the velocity, as outlined in Sec. 2–1, then

$$a = \frac{dv}{dt} = -Kv^2$$

$$\int_{v_O}^{v} \frac{dv}{v^2} = \int_0^t -K\,dt$$

Integrating:

$$\frac{-1}{v} - \frac{1}{v_O} = -Kt$$

Solving for v:

$$v = \frac{v_O}{Kv_Ot + 1}$$

Example 4–5. Shown in Fig. 4–7 is a man swinging a weight of 10 lb in a circular arc. The system makes 20 rpm. What is the force on the rope? (Assume that the system moves in a horizontal plane.)

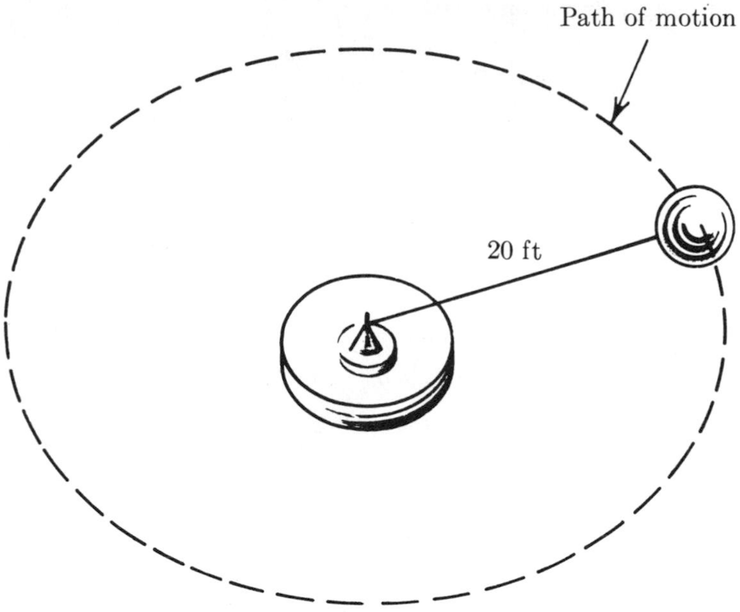

Figure 4-7

Solution: In order to write the equations of motion of the particle, we must first draw a free-body diagram (Fig. 4–8) in order to establish the forces acting

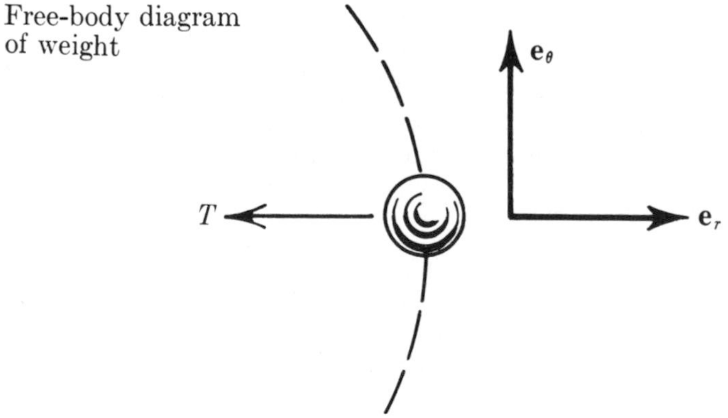

Figure 4-8

on the particle. Also shown in Fig. 4–8 are the unit vectors used for reference in writing the equations of motion. The equation of motion for motion in a radial direction is

$$F_r = m(\ddot{r} - r\dot{\theta}^2)$$

Tabulating each term in the equation:

$$F_r = -T$$
$$m = 10/32.2 = 0.31 \text{ slug}$$
$$\ddot{r} = 0$$
$$r = 20 \text{ ft}$$
$$\dot{\theta} = 20 \text{ rpm} = \frac{(2\pi)20}{60} = 2.09 \text{ radians/sec}$$

It should be noted that the force T, shown in the free-body diagram of Fig. 4–8, is assumed to be acting in a negative $\boldsymbol{e}_r$ direction. This is why the minus sign must be associated with the force.

By substituting into the equation of motion,

$$-T = -0.31(20)(2.09)^2$$

and, solving for the tension in the rope,

$$T = 27.2 \text{ lb}$$

The fact that T is positive proves the assumption that the force was directed inward toward the center of rotation to be correct. If T had been negative, the force would have been acting in a direction opposite to that assumed.

Example 4–6. A spring scale that measures the weight of a body does not register exactly the force of attraction exerted by the earth on the body (except when the body is being weighed at one of the two poles). The spin of the earth causes the body to move outward from the earth, the net result being that the weight of the body as measured by the scale will be less than the actual gravitational force. The problem now is to determine the effect of the spin of the earth on the weight of bodies when measured by a spring scale.

Solution: Since the effect of the spin of the earth would be greatest when the body is measured at the equator, we shall determine the apparent weight of the body at that point. A free-body diagram of the mass that is being weighed is shown in Fig. 4–9. The body moves along the path of motion because it is fixed to the moving earth. The force T in the spring is the measured weight of the body, and the force W is the actual weight (or gravitational attractive force) on the body. The unit vectors $\bar{\boldsymbol{e}}_r$, and $\bar{\boldsymbol{e}}_\theta$ are also defined in the figure. The equation of motion for the particle in the $\bar{\boldsymbol{e}}_r$ direction is

$$F_r = m(\ddot{r} - r\dot{\theta}^2)$$

The body is moving in a circular path; the radius of the circular path is the radius of the earth (4000 miles) and the constant angular velocity of the particle is the angular velocity of the earth (one revolution every 24 hr). Thus,

$$\ddot{r} = 0$$
$$r = 4000 \text{ miles} = 4000 \times 5280 = 2.11 \times 10^7 \text{ ft}$$
$$\dot{\theta} = \frac{1 \text{ rev}}{24 \text{ hr}} = \frac{2\pi}{24(3600)} = 7.27 \times 10^{-5} \text{ radian/sec}$$

From the free-body diagram of the mass, the force in the $\boldsymbol{e}_r$ direction is

$$F_r = T - W$$

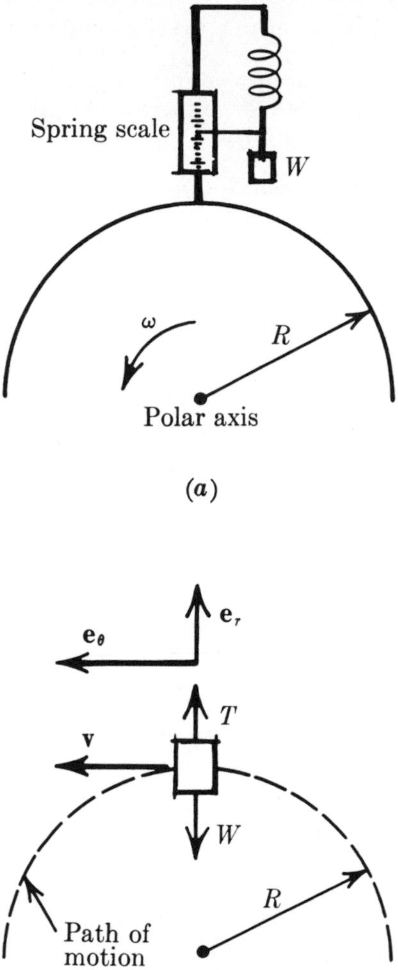

(b)

Figure 4-9

and since the mass of the body is

$$m = \frac{W}{g} = \frac{W}{32.2} \text{ slugs}$$

the equation of motion of the body is

$$T - W = \frac{W}{32.2}\{-(2.11 \times 10^{-7})(7.27 \times 10^{-5})^2\}$$

Solving for the force, in the spring T, we get

$$\begin{aligned} T &= W(1.0000 - 0.00357) \\ &= 0.996W \end{aligned}$$

Thus it is seen that, even at the equator, the effect of the spin of the earth has little effect on the measured weight of the body. If, for instance, the actual weight of the body were 1000 lb, the measured weight would be 996 lb. Again it should be pointed out that the effect of the spin on the weight of the body will be less at all other points on the surface of the earth.

Example 4–7. A 2800-lb automobile (Fig. 4–10) moves along a highway on a curve as $y = x^2/1000$. What is the total frictional force between the car and the road at the point (0,0) if the car travels through the curve at a constant 60 mph?

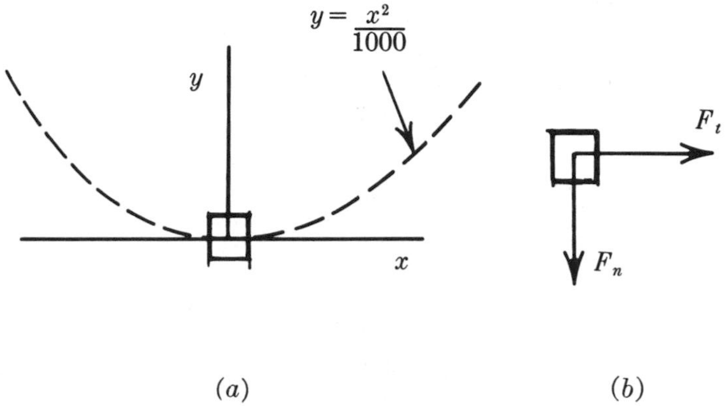

Figure 4-10

Solution: The total force on the car may be thought of as being a combination of a component along the path F_t and another normal to the path F_n.

The magnitude of the total frictional force is

$$F = \sqrt{F_t^2 + F_n^2}$$

and the equations of motion are

$$F_t = m\left(\frac{dv}{dt}\right)$$

$$F_n = \frac{-mv^2}{\rho}$$

Note that the acceleration of the car along the path dv/dt is equal to zero. The velocity is

$$v = 60 \text{ mph} = 88 \text{ fps}$$

The radius of curvature is

$$\rho = \frac{(1 + y'^2)^{3/2}}{y''}$$

and $y' = x/500$, and $y'' = 1/500$, so that

$$\rho = \frac{[1 + (x/500)^2]^{3/2}}{1/500}$$

At point (0,0), the radius of curvature is

$$\rho = 500 \text{ ft}$$

Since the tangential acceleration is zero, the tangential force is zero, and therefore the total force is identical to the normal force:

$$F = F_n$$

But the normal force is

$$F_n = \frac{-mv^2}{\rho} = \frac{(2800/32.2)(88)^2}{500}$$

and the total force becomes

$$F = 1350 \text{ lb}$$

Example 4–8. The motion of a ballistic missile moving in a plane may be described by two coordinates: v, the magnitude velocity of the missile, and ψ, the angle that the velocity vector makes with the vertical. The equations of motion of the missile in these coordinates are

$$m\frac{dv}{dt} = F - W\cos\psi \qquad (4.11)$$

$$mv\frac{d\psi}{dt} = W\sin\psi \qquad (4.12)$$

Derive these equatious from the equations of motion of the vehicle in normal and tangential form.

Solution: A free-body diagram of the missile is shown in Fig. 4–11, along with the unit vectors $\bar{e}_n$ and $\bar{e}_t$. The force $\boldsymbol{F}$ represents the sum of all the forces acting on the missile in the direction of the motion of the missile. This includes both the thrust force due to the engines and the aerodynamic drag force. The equations of motion of the missile in normal and tangential form are (letting $\dot{s}$ equal v)

$$F_n = \frac{-mv^2}{\rho} \qquad -W\sin\psi = \frac{-mv^2}{\rho} \qquad (4.13)$$

$$F_t = m\dot{v} \qquad F - W\cos\psi = m\frac{dv}{dt} \qquad (4.14)$$

It is seen immediately that Eq. 4.14 corresponds to Eq. 4.11. To verify the other relationship, consider Fig. 4–12.

The velocity v may be written as

$$v = \rho\dot{\theta}$$

but, since $\theta = \psi$, as seen in the figure, then

$$v = \rho\dot{\psi}$$

so that Eq. 4.13 may be written as

$$-W\sin\psi = -mv\frac{d\psi}{dt}$$

and this then corresponds to Eq. 4.12.

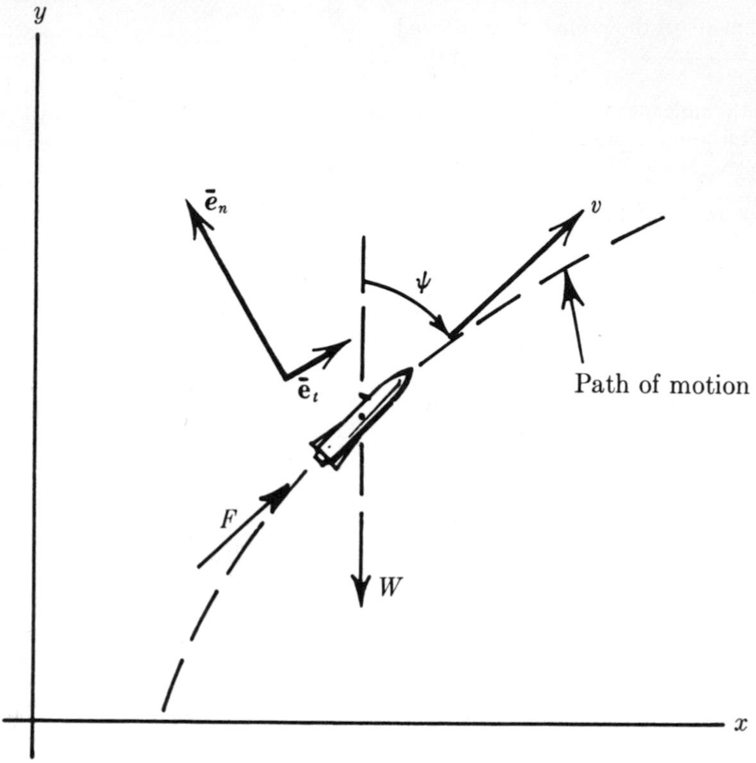

Figure 4-11

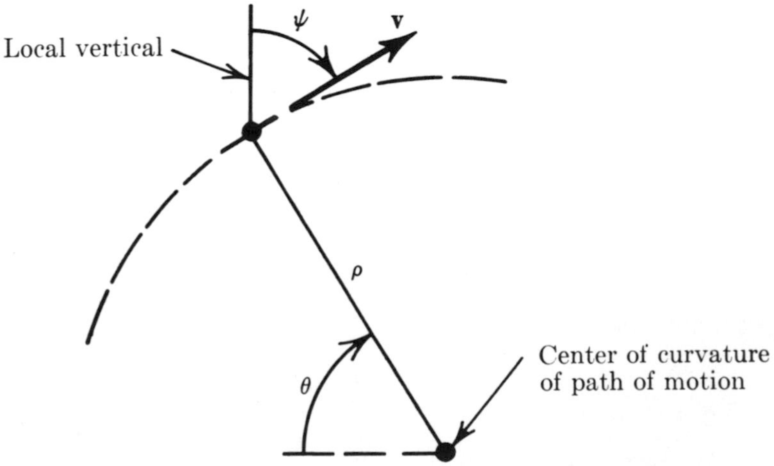

Figure 4-12

PROBLEMS

4-1. A 40-lb block on a horizontal plane is subjected to a constant horizontal force P of 20 lb. The coefficient of kinetic friction between the block and the plane is 0.20. If the block starts from rest, what will be the velocity of the block after it has traveled 20 ft?

4-2. Consider a 40-lb block (Fig. P.4–2) that is resting on a plane and is attached via a cord, which hangs over a frictionless pulley to a 20-lb block. If the system is

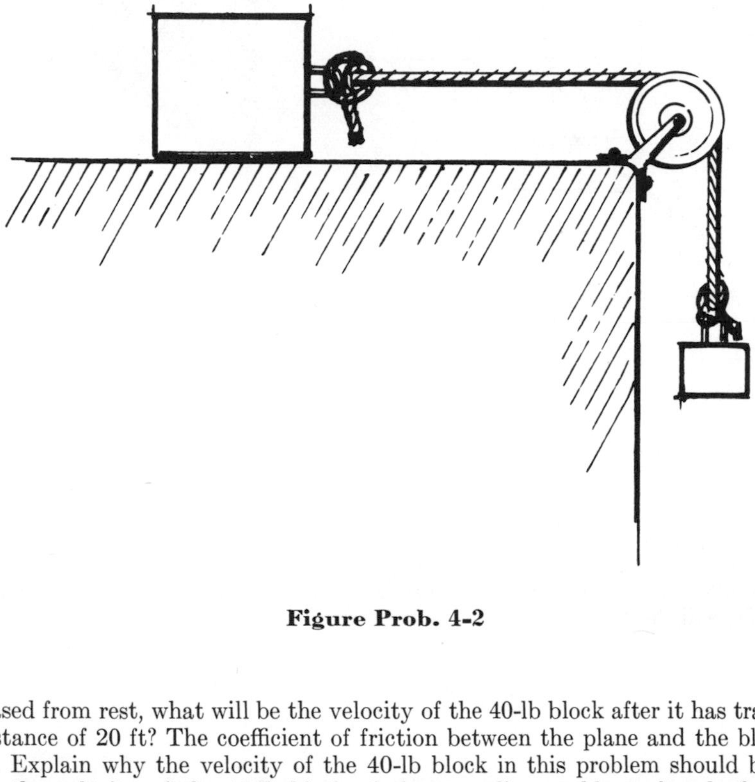

Figure Prob. 4-2

released from rest, what will be the velocity of the 40-lb block after it has traveled a distance of 20 ft? The coefficient of friction between the plane and the block is 0.20. Explain why the velocity of the 40-lb block in this problem should be less than the velocity of the 40-lb block of the preceding problem after both have traveled the same distance.

4-3. A 50-lb body is moving in a straight-line path in the positive y direction with a velocity of 5.0 fps. When it is at the point (3,4), a constant force of 8.0 lb is suddenly applied in the positive x direction. Determine the equation of the path of motion of the particle in the xy plane.

4-4. A 64.4-lb body is moving in two-dimensional space with a velocity of $\boldsymbol{v}_O = 2\bar{\imath} + 4\bar{\jmath}$ when, at the point (13,2) and at $t = 0$, a force is applied. The force is given as $\boldsymbol{F} = 6t\bar{\imath} - 2t^2\bar{\jmath}$. Determine the velocity of the particle at $t = 5$ sec.

4-5. At $t = 0$, a force of 28 lb is applied to a body weighing 96.6 lb. The force is acting in the direction defined in Fig. P.4–5. At $t = 0$, the body has an initial velocity of $\dot{x} = 2$, $\dot{y} = -3$, $\dot{z} = 1$. What is the position of the particle at $t = 3$ sec if

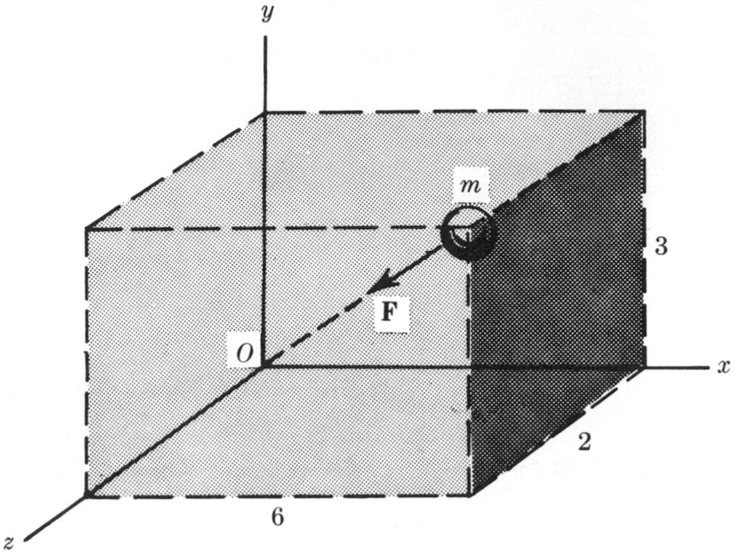

Figure Prob. 4-5

the force on the particle remains in the same direction? (Do not assume that any gravitational force is acting.)

4-6. Consider a 32.2-lb weight that is subjected to the force $\boldsymbol{F} = 3t\bar{i} + 4\bar{j} - 7t^2\bar{k}$. If the velocity of the mass at $t = 0$ is $\boldsymbol{v}_O = 3\bar{i} - 2\bar{j} - 2\bar{k}$, and the displacement of the particle at $t = 0$ is $\boldsymbol{r}_O = -\bar{i} + 4\bar{j} - 3\bar{k}$, determine the velocity and displacement of the particle as a function of time.

4-7. A 4000-lb automobile traveling with a velocity of 50 mph encounters a 3 percent grade. If the clutch is disengaged and the only force resisting the motion of the auto is the component of the gravitational force in the direction of the motion, how far will the car move up the grade before coming to a rest?

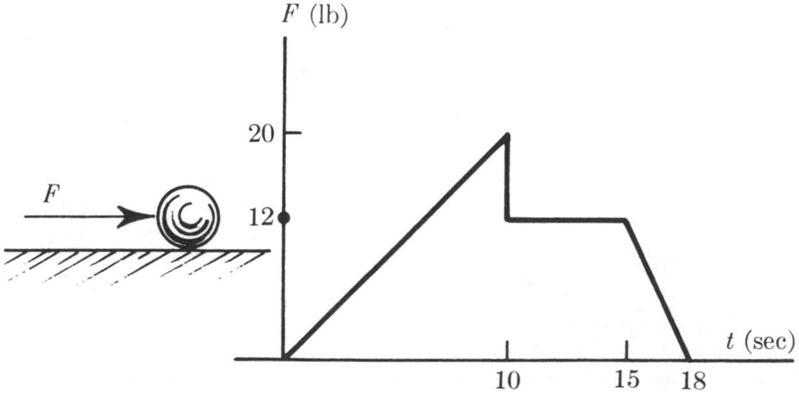

Figure Prob. 4-8

4-8. The force acting on the 40-lb weight, given as a function of time, is shown in Fig. P.4–8. Draw a sketch of the velocity of the body as a function of time. The body starts from rest.

4-9. An air-to-air missile is fired horizontally from an airplane traveling at 1200 fps. If the weight of the missile is 400 lb, what constant force must be applied to the missile so that it will have a velocity of 2000 fps in 3.0 sec after it has been fired? (Assume that the weight of the missile will be constant, even though some of its mass is lost as burned fuel. Also assume that the plane is high enough so that the drag force due to the air friction is small enough to be neglected.)

4-10. The drag force on a horizontally flying air-to-air missile is $C_D qA$, where A is the projection of the cross-sectional area of the missile and q is the dynamic pressure (equal to $\frac{1}{2}\rho v^2$, or $0.0012v^2$, at standard atmospheric conditions at sea level. V is given in feet per second). What thrust force is required for a missile if the missile is to fly at a constant velocity of 3000 fps? The weight of the missile is 600 lb, C_D is equal to 0.80, and the cross-sectional area is 120 in.^{2}.

4-11. The ball shown in Fig. P.4–11 strikes the wall with a velocity of 10 fps and rebounds with the same velocity. The force that the wall exerts on the ball is shown

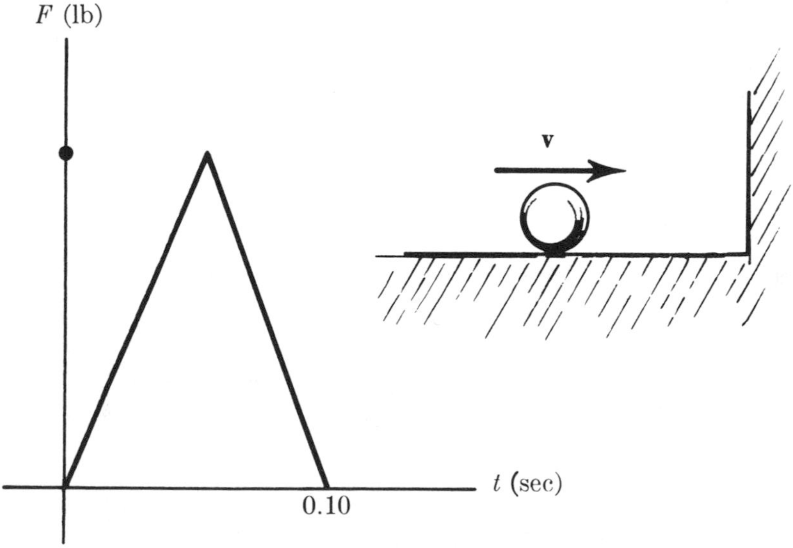

Figure Prob. 4-11

in the figure. If the mass of the ball is 0.70 slug, what is the maximum acceleration in g's that the ball will experience? (1 g is equal to 32.2 ft/sec^2.)

4-12. An automobile weighing 3600 lb accelerates along a level road from rest to 60 mph in 10 sec. The force causing the acceleration is the frictional force of the road on the rear wheels. Determine the motive force causing the motion, assuming that the acceleration of the car is constant.

4-13. Consider Problem 4–12. Suppose that the automobile is able to attain the same acceleration up a 3 percent grade. What would be the force of the road on the rear wheels in this case?

4-14. A 2500-lb automobile is traveling with a velocity of 30 mph. The automobile suddenly starts accelerating with a constant acceleration and attains a velocity of 50 mph in a mile. Determine the frictional force between the rear wheels and the road during this period.

4-15. The landing speed of a 70,000-lb airplane is 110 mph. If the plane relies on reverse thrust of the propellers to stop, how much thrust is needed if the plane is to come to a stop in 4000 ft, with a constant deceleration (and thus a constant thrust)?

4-16. In order to determine the motion of an elevator, a rather crude but simple experiment may be performed. A man weighing 160 lb places a spring scale on the floor of the elevator and stands on it. When the elevator is at rest, the scale registers 160 lb. As the elevator accelerates upward, the man observes that the scale registers a maximum value of 180 lb. What is the maximum acceleration of the elevator?

4-17. Consider Problem 4–16. How much will the scale register if the elevator has an acceleration downward of 1.0 ft/sec²? What will the scale register if the velocity of the elevator is a constant?

4-18. A plane flying horizontally fires a rocket weighing 620 lb. The rocket engine gives a thrust that is a function of time: $F(t) = 600t$ lb. What is the displacement and the velocity of the missile at $t = 5$ sec if the missile moves on a path that is horizontal to the surface of the earth?

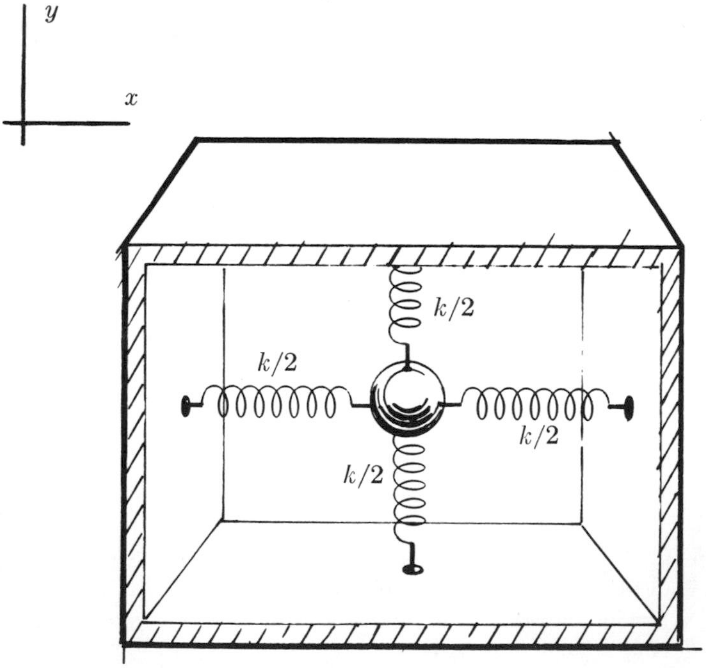

Figure Prob. 4-19

4-19. The equations of motion for a two-dimensional harmonic oscillator (Fig. P.4-19) are

$$m\ddot{x} = -kx$$
$$m\ddot{y} = -ky$$

for small oscillations. Shown that solutions to the equations for motion are

$$x(t) = A_1 \cos \omega t + A_2 \sin \omega t$$
$$y(t) = A_3 \cos \omega t + A_4 \sin \omega t$$

where $\omega^2 = k/m$. Also determine the conditions on the constant of integration, A_1, and so on, so that the path of motion of the mass is a circle. Also determine conditions for the constants for the case where the motion of the mass is an ellipse.

4-20. Consider the equation of motion $m\ddot{x} = kx^n$, where it is stipulated that n is not equal to -1. Determine the velocity as a function of the displacement. If $\dot{x}_O$ is equal to zero, what will be the displacement of the particle as a function of time (assuming now that n is not equal to 1)?

4-21. Consider the equation of motion $m\ddot{x} = k\dot{x}^n$. Determine the velocity as a function of displacement for the case when n is equal to 2, and then find the velocity as a function of the displacement for the case when n is not equal to 2.

4-22. Show that the equations of motion for a two-dimensional projectile (Fig. P.4-22) subjected to a drag force Cv^2, acting in a direction tangent to the path of motion of the projectile, are

$$m\ddot{x} = -C\dot{x}^2$$
$$m\ddot{y} = -C\dot{y}\dot{x} - mg$$

Assume in the derivation that the ratio $(\dot{y}/\dot{x})$ is small.

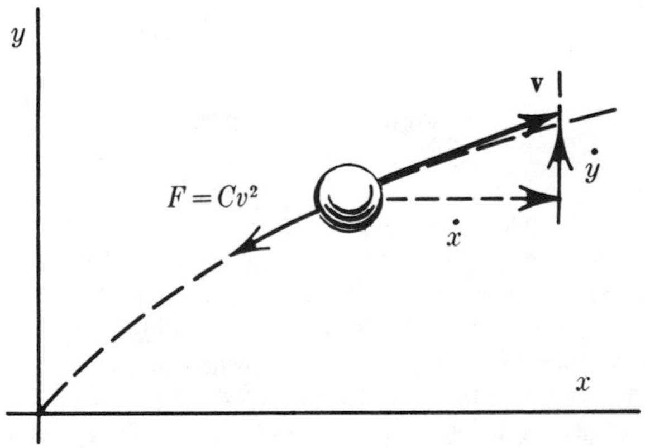

Figure Prob. 4-22

4-23. If the coefficient of friction of rubber tires on wet asphalt is 0.70, what is the maximum acceleration that a 3000-lb automobile can have (assuming that the wheels will slip before the maximum power of the engine has been exceeded)? The normal force of the rear wheels on the ground is $1500 + 0.2a$, where a is the acceleration of the auto.

4-24. The rolling resistance force of an automobile (the frictional force due to the flexibility of the tires) is equal to $\mu_r W$, where W is the weight of the automobile and μ_r is the coefficient of rolling resistance. An approximation to μ_r is $0.01\ (1 + v/120)$, where v is the velocity of the auto in feet per second. What is the velocity of the auto as a function of the displacement if the auto weighs 2500 lb and is initially traveling 40 mph on a level grade when the clutch is disengaged?

4-25. A projectile of mass m is shot out of a cannon and is subjected to a drag force that is directly proportional to its velocity squared. Determine the displacement of the projectile if the muzzle velocity is v_O. Assume that the projectile moves in a straight-line path.

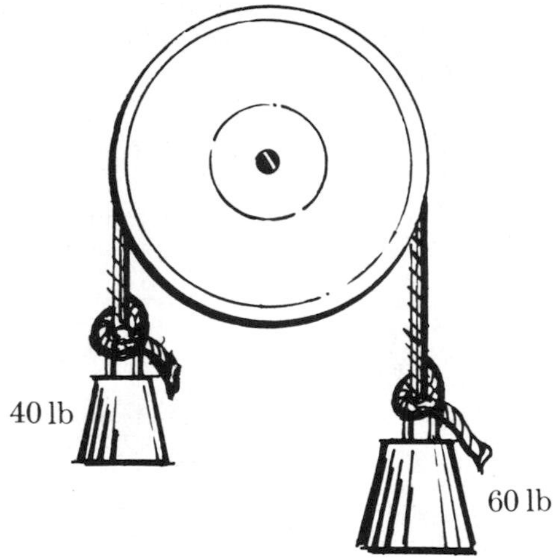

Figure Prob. 4-26

4-26. Determine the velocity of the 60-lb weight (Fig. P.4–26) 4 sec after the system has been released from rest. Assume that the weight of the pulley is negligible.

4-27. For the system shown in Fig. P.4–27, assume that the mass of the pulleys is negligible, and determine the acceleration of the 96.6-lb block.

4-28. For the system shown in Fig. P.4–28, assume that the mass of the pulleys is negligible, and determine the acceleration of the 50-lb weight.

4-29. A body of mass m is released from rest at the surface of a fluid and allowed to move downward in a straight-line path. The resistance of the fluid to the motion of the body (that is, the force of the fluid on the body) is proportional to the velocity of the body, $F_f = Kv$. Determine the displacement of the body below the surface of the fluid as a function of time.

4-30. The motion of a 16.1-lb weight is given in polar parametric form as $r(t) = 0.1t^4$ ft; $\theta(t) = t^2 - 4t + 0.2t^3$ radian. What is the magnitude of the total force on the mass at $t = 4$ sec?

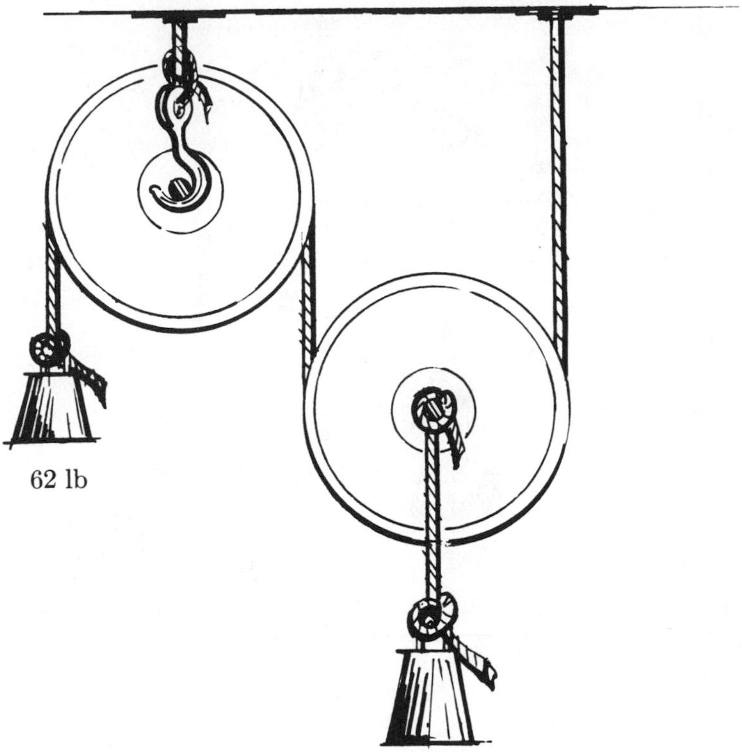

Figure Prob. 4-27

4-31. A particle of mass m is traveling on a path $r(\theta) = A \cos \theta$ ft; $\theta(t) = Bt$ radians. What is the magnitude of the force acting on the particle as a function of the angle θ?

4-32. A man weighing 161 lb walks outward along the radius of a turntable at a constant speed of 1.0 fps with respect to the turntable. If the turntable is rotating with a constant angular speed of 0.20 radian/sec, what is the force of the flywheel on the man at the point where the man is 5 ft from the center of rotation?

4-33. A block rests on a periphery of a spinning flywheel. The flywheel starts from rest and accelerates with a constant angular acceleration of 0.40 radian/sec^2. How long will it be before the block slides off the wheel, if the radius of the wheel is 10 ft, the weight of the block is 24 lb, and the coefficient of static friction between the block and the wheel is 0.50?

4-34. A box weighing 32.2 lb (Fig. P.4–34) is resting on the outer rim of a large flywheel, of 5-ft radius. The flywheel starts from rest and accelerates with an angular acceleration of 0.30 radian/sec^2. Show that the total frictional force between the box and the wheel, given as a function of time, is $1.5\sqrt{1 + (0.3t^2)^2}$, assuming that the box does not slide with respect to the wheel.

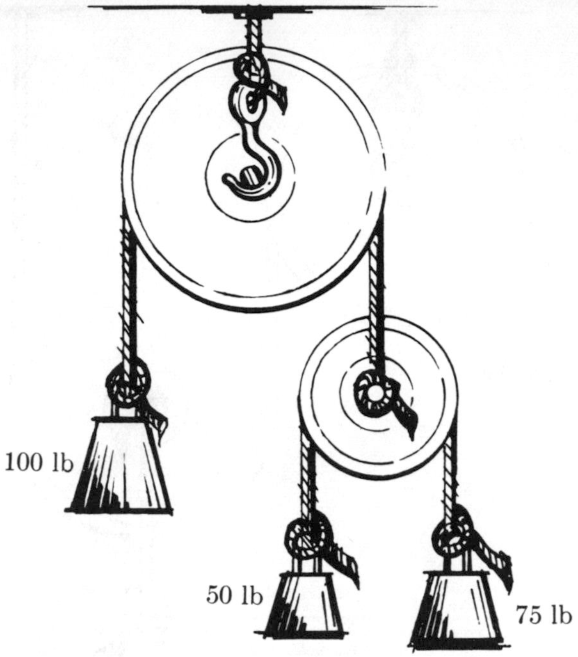

Figure Prob. 4-28

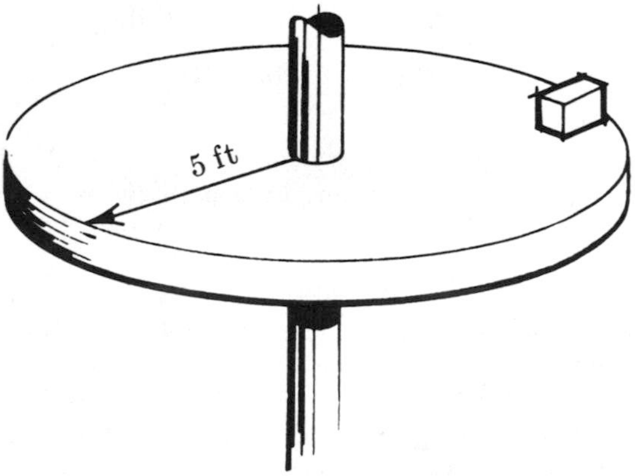

Figure Prob. 4-34

4-35. Consider Problem 4–34. If the coefficient of static friction between the box and the wheel is 0.60, what will be the angular velocity of the wheel when the block starts to slide?

4-36. The equations for a spiral in cylindrical coordinates in parametric form are

$$r(t) = 4.0 \qquad \text{(a constant)}$$
$$\theta(t) = 2t$$
$$z(t) = 3t^2$$

If a particle of mass m is moving on the spiral curve, what will be the force of the curve on the mass as a function of time?

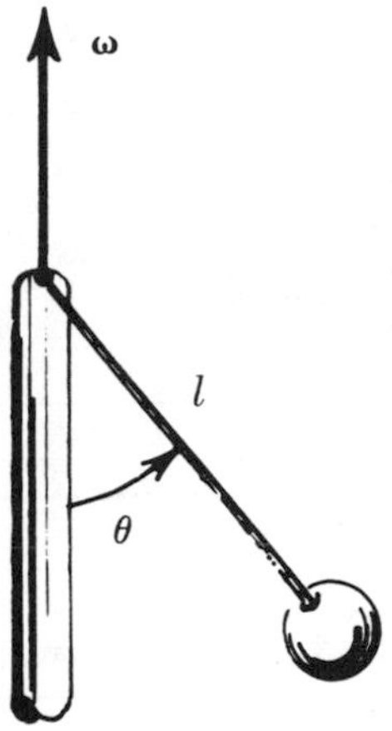

Figure Prob. 4-37

4-37. A particle weighing 28 lb (Fig. P.4–37) on the end of a rope is being swung in a circular arc. What is the relationship between the angular velocity ω and the angle θ. Note that θ should approach $\pi/2$ radians as ω gets large.

4-38. Shown in Fig. P.4–38 is a training apparatus for prospective pilots, to help them to become accustomed to large accelerations. The man in the chamber is rotated in a circular arc. If the man can withstand only 3-g acceleration (1 g equals 32.2 ft/sec²), what would be the maximum rotary speed of the chamber in rpm's? Also determine the shearing force in the pin at A if the man and the chamber weigh a total of 400 lb.

4-39. The first and second masses (Fig. P.4–39) are 0.30 and 0.80 slug, respectively. If the angular velocity of the first mass is 0.40 rps, what must be the radius r_O if m_2 is to be stationary?

4-40. A car is traveling on a curve in a highway. The curve is approximated by the equation $y = x^2/2000$. At the point where $x = 1000$ ft, the car is traveling 60 mph and is decelerating at a rate of 5 ft/sec². If the car weighs 3220 lb, what is the total force between the wheels and the road?

4-41. If the wire that constrains a model airplane to move in a circular path has an allowable strength of 20 lb, how fast could a 3-lb model airplane go in a circle of radius 25 ft?

4-42. An automobile weighing 3600 lb starts into a curve on a highway at 40 mph. The curve is a circular arc of radius 1600 ft. As soon as the car enters the curve,

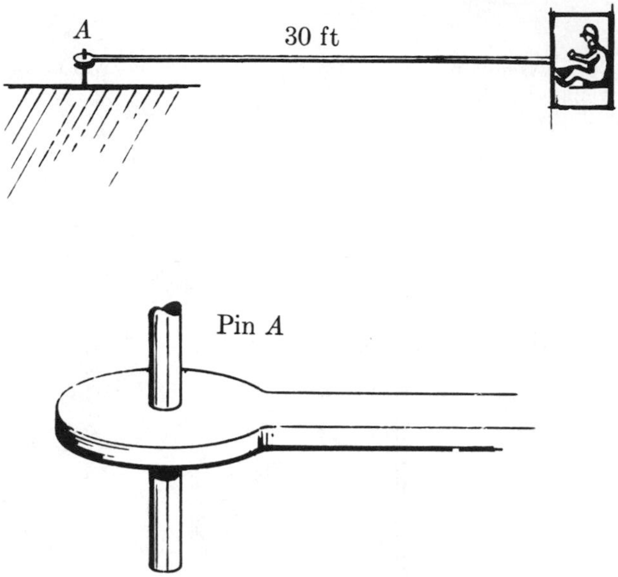

Figure Prob. 4-38

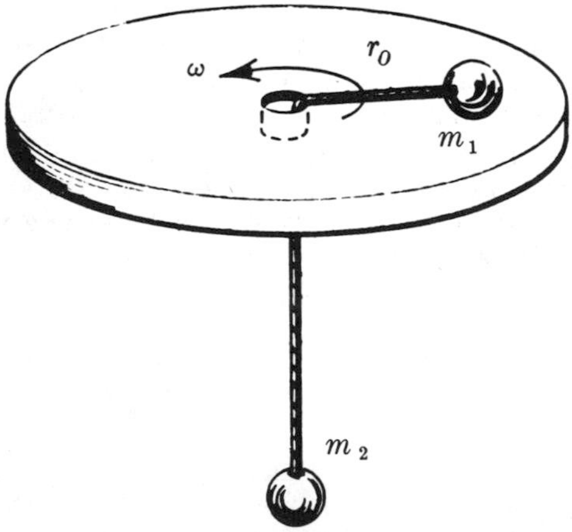

Figure Prob. 4-39

it starts accelerating at a constant rate, and 10 sec later it is moving 65 mph. Determine the frictional force between the wheels and the road 6 sec after the car starts accelerating.

4-43. An automobile weighing 3200 lb is traveling with a constant speed around a highway curve that is a circular arc having a radius of 2000 ft. If the coefficient of friction between the wheels and the road is 0.2, determine the maximum speed that the automobile may travel without sliding off the road.

4-44. It can be shown that the velocity of a particle as it moves down any path under the influence of a gravitational force is equal to $\sqrt{2gh}$, where h is the vertical distance that the particle has moved from rest. A particle is released from rest at the point (4,4) on the curve, $y = x^2/4$, and moves down the curve under the action of gravity. What is the normal force of the path on the particle when the particle is at point (0,0)? The weight of the particle is 8 lb.

4-45. Tests on a model airplane engine reveal that the thrust (lb) is equal to $0.004n$, where n is given in rpm. If this engine is to be mounted in a 2-lb model airplane, how fast must the engine be running if the airplane, which starts from rest, is to make one revolution in 8 sec on a 40-ft radius? Assume that the acceleration of the plane in the tangential direction (that is, along the path of motion) is constant.

4-46. For the preceding problem, determine the force in the wires that constrain the airplane to move in a circular path at one revolution.

4-47. For design purposes, suppose that the maximum acceleration that a pilot of a supersonic fighter can withstand is 3 g (1 g is equal to 32.2 ft/sec²). If the 50,000-lb plane is flying at 1500 fps, what would be the minimum radius of curvature that the plane could assume on a maneuver so as not to exceed the pilot's tolerance? What is the total aerodynamic lift on the plane at this point (that is, the force of the air on the bottom of the plane)? Assume that the pilot is pulling out of a dive and that the gravitational force is parallel to the aerodynamic lift force.

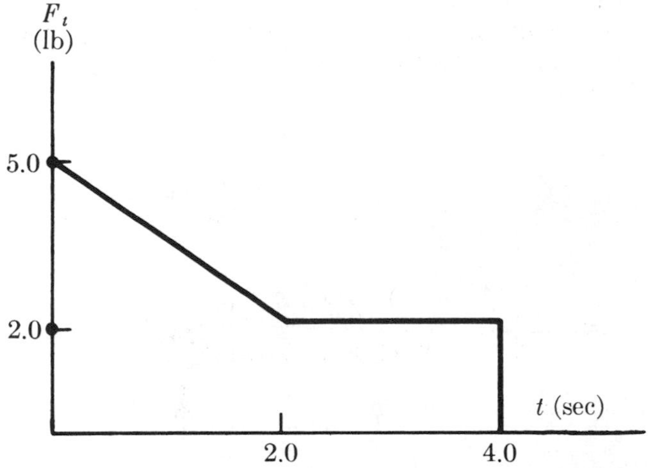

Figure Prob. 4-48

4-48. If a 40-lb body is moving on the curve $y = 4 + 2x + x^2$ in the horizontal plane, and if the force on the body tangential to the path of motion is as shown in Fig. P.4-48, determine (a) the velocity of the particle at $t = 4$ sec, if the particle starts from rest, and (b) the normal force of the curve on the particle if at $t = 4$ sec the particle is at point (2,12).

4-4. D'ALEMBERT'S PRINCIPLE

Consider Newton's second law:

$$\boldsymbol{F} = m\boldsymbol{a} \tag{4.15}$$

The term on the right-hand side of Eq. 4.15 may be transposed so that the equation reads

$$\boldsymbol{F} - m\boldsymbol{a} = 0 \tag{4.16}$$

Because the equation must be dimensionally homogeneous, the term $m\boldsymbol{a}$ obviously has to have units of force. Thus, $-m\boldsymbol{a}$ can be thought of as a force, commonly called an *inertia force*. Therefore, for a body in motion, we may say that the sum of the forces acting on the body must be equal to zero:

$$\sum_i \boldsymbol{F}_i = 0 \tag{4.17}$$

where it is understood that one of the external forces on the body is the force $-m\boldsymbol{a}$.

This is the simple interpretation of d'Alembert's principle. The question now is: Why should one prefer to use d'Alembert's viewpoint in approaching a dynamics problem rather than a direct application of Newton's second law? One advantage is that it appears that one might make a dynamics problem look very much like a statics problem. But is this really an advantage? It is rather obvious that no matter how the equation of motion is written, the same differential equation of motion will be obtained.

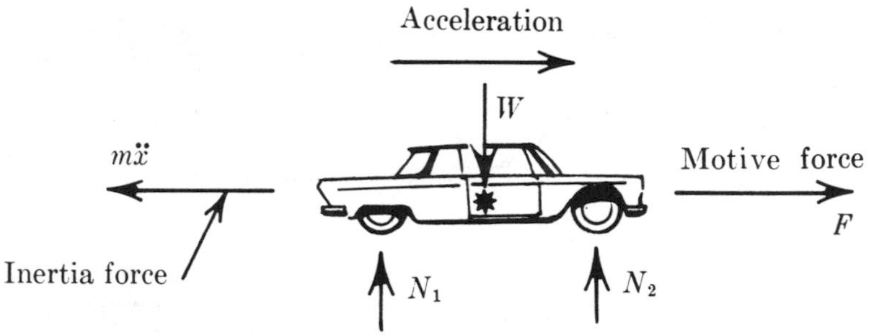

Figure 4-13

In the case of a body accelerating on a straight-line path, say, in the positive x direction, the inertia force, which is equal to $-m\ddot{x}$ may be drawn on the free-body diagram as shown in Fig. 4-13. The force $\boldsymbol{F}$ is the motive force that causes the particle to accelerate in the positive x direction.

It is often convenient to use d'Alembert's viewpoint in dealing with kinetics problems of bodies moving on circular paths. We note, for instance, that when we are riding in an automobile on a curve in a highway, there is a tendency for us to be thrown outward from the center of curvature. We experience a pseudoforce acting outward; this pseudoforce is nothing more than an inertia force. The acceleration of a particle moving on a curved path with a constant velocity v is

$$\boldsymbol{a} = -\frac{v^2}{\rho}\bar{\boldsymbol{e}}_n \tag{4.18}$$

so that the inertia force acting on the particle is

$$-m\boldsymbol{a} = \frac{mv^2}{\rho}\bar{\boldsymbol{e}}_n \tag{4.19}$$

and this force, drawn on a free-body diagram, would appear as in Fig. 4–14. In order that the sum of the forces (including the inertia force) on

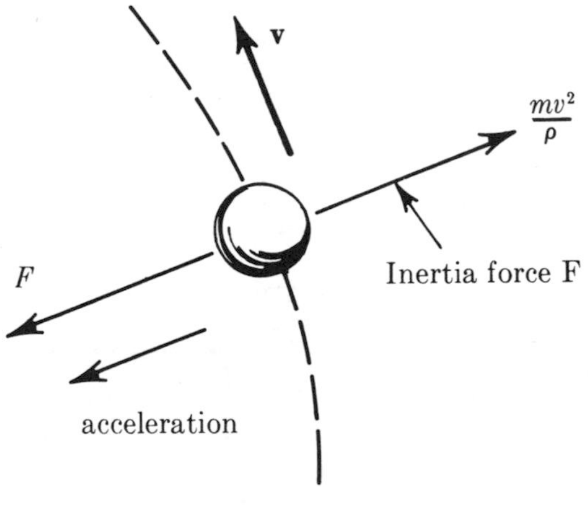

Figure 4-14

the body be equal to zero, there must be a force on the body as shown in the figure, which is equal in magnitude and opposite in direction to the inertia force. In the case of an automobile moving on a curve in the highway, the force $\boldsymbol{F}$ is the lateral frictional force of the road on the tires. This inertia force is referred to as a *centrifugal force;* it should be again noted that this centrifugal force is nothing more than a fictitious inertia force.

In using d'Alembert's principle, it is important to note that when the free-body diagram is constructed, the inertia force must appear just as if it were one of the external contact forces.

Example 4–9. An automobile weighing 3400 lb is driven by a man weighing 150 lb. It is moving on a circular curve in a highway; the curve has a radius of 2000 ft. If the automobile is moving with a velocity of 60 mph, how much centrifugal force does the man experience? Use d'Alembert's principle to find the frictional force between the wheels and the road.

Solution: The centrifugal force acting on the driver is nothing more than the inertia force on the man in the normal direction. As demonstrated in the preceding discussion, the centrifugal force on the driver will be equal to mv^2/ρ. In this case,

$$\text{Centrifugal force} = \frac{(150/32.2)(88)^2}{2000}$$

$$= 18.1 \text{ lb}$$

The force of the road on the wheels may be determined by drawing a free-body diagram of the car (Fig. 4–15). Recall that in order to employ d'Alembert's principle, the inertia forces must be included on all free-body diagrams (f is the frictional force of the road acting on the wheels). Imposing the condition that all the sum of the forces acting on the body must be equal to zero,

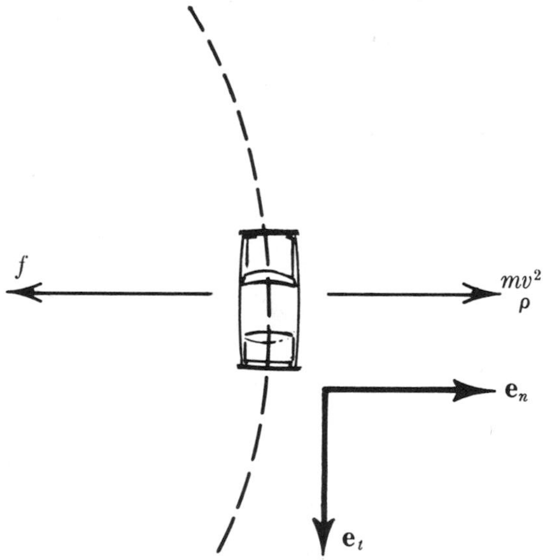

Figure 4-15

$$F_n = -f + \frac{mv^2}{\rho}$$
$$= 0$$

so that the force of the road on the wheels becomes

$$f = \frac{\left(\frac{3400 + 150}{32.2}\right)(88)^2}{2000}$$

$$= 426 \text{ lb}$$

PROBLEMS

4-49. A simple pendulum consists of a concentrated mass of 20 lb and an essentially weightless string. If the support to which the string is attached is given an acceleration to the right of 2.0 ft/sec^2, the pendulum will deflect through an angle of θ with the vertical. Use d'Alembert's principle to determine the angle θ. The angle will be constant as long as the acceleration is constant.

4-50. A weight of 50 lb is mounted in a frame (Fig. P.4–50) and attached to the frame by means of a spring with a spring constant of 100 lb/ft. If the frame is

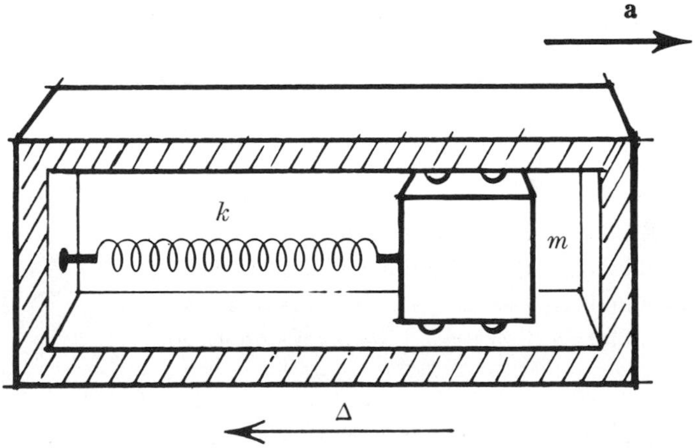

Figure Prob. 4-50

accelerating to the right, use d'Alembert's principle to determine the deflection of the spring as a function of the acceleration. Draw a sketch of the deflection in inches versus the acceleration in feet per square second.

4-51. A rocket sled with a man aboard is shot out along a straight track. A chart of the velocity of the sled as a function of time is shown in Fig. P.4–51. As the sled is accelerating, the man experiences a force on his back that is exerted by the sled. Use d'Alembert's principle to determine this force when $t = 10$ sec. The weight of the man is 160 lb.

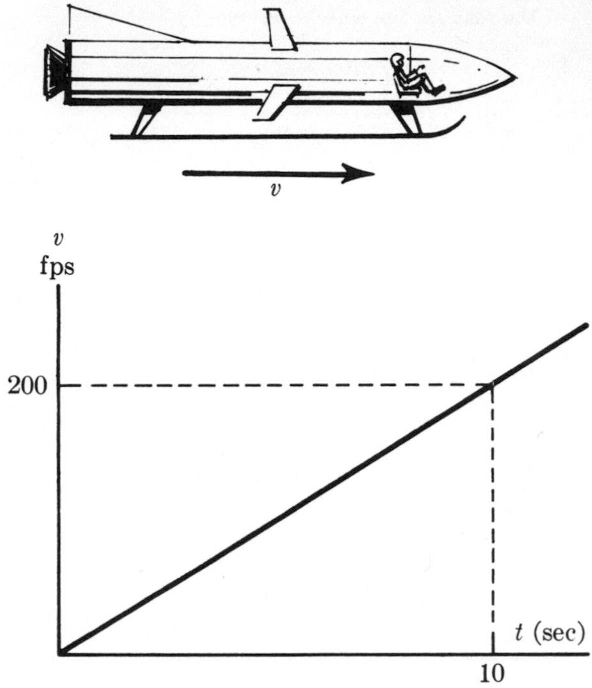

Figure Prob. 4-51

4-52. Solve Problem 4–16 using d'Alembert's principle.

4-53. Solve Problem 4–37 using d'Alembert's principle.

4-54. Solve Problem 4–38 using d'Alembert's principle.

4-55. Solve Problem 4–41 using d'Alembert's principle.

5

The Impulse-Momentum and Work-Energy Equations

In this chapter we shall consider a general integration of the equation of motion, first with respect to time, to obtain the impulse-momentum equation, and then with respect to displacement, to obtain the work-energy equation. We shall see that these equations are nothing more than restatements of Newton's second law and reveal nothing that Newton's second law does not reveal. However, we shall show that in certain dynamical situations, the impulse-momentum or the work-energy equation may be employed to obtain information concerning the motion of a particle, an operation much faster than the direct application of the equation of motion.

5-1. THE IMPULSE-MOMENTUM EQUATION

The impulse-moment equation. Consider Newton's second law, the equation of motion:

$$\boldsymbol{F} = m\boldsymbol{a} \tag{5.1}$$

Integrate both sides of the equation with respect to time between any two arbitrary instances in time or points on the path of motion, A and B:

$$\int_A^B \boldsymbol{F}\,dt = \int_A^B m\boldsymbol{a}\,dt \tag{5.2}$$

But since

$$\boldsymbol{a} = \frac{d\boldsymbol{v}}{dt} \tag{5.3}$$

the integrated equation becomes

$$\int_A^B \boldsymbol{F}\,dt = \int_A^B m\,d\boldsymbol{v} \tag{5.4}$$

and, after a direct integration of the right-hand side of Eq. 5.4,

$$\boxed{\int_A^B \boldsymbol{F}\,dt = m\boldsymbol{v}_B - m\boldsymbol{v}_A} \tag{5.5}$$

This equation is known as the *impulse-momentum equation:*

$$\int_A^B \boldsymbol{F}\,dt \equiv \textit{impulse}$$

$$m\boldsymbol{v} = \textit{momentum at a point (or instant in time)}$$

Thus, it is seen that the impulse due to the net force $\boldsymbol{F}$ on a particle during a certain amount of time is equal to the change in momentum of that particle during this time interval.

The impulse-momentum equation may be employed to advantage in those cases where the force on the particle is a known function of time and it is desired to determine the velocity of the particle or the change in velocity of the particle. Conversely, if the velocity or the change in velocity of the particle is known, then the impulse-momentum equation provides information concerning the force-time history of the net external force on the particle.

Conservation of momentum for a single particle. Consider now a particle on which there is no external force acting. Then Eq. 5.5 becomes

$$0 = m\boldsymbol{v}_B - m\boldsymbol{v}_A \tag{5.6}$$

which implies that

$$m\boldsymbol{v} = \text{constant}$$

It is possible to have momentum conserved in only one or two of the three directions. If, for instance, there is a net force on the particle in the x direction only, then momentum will be conserved in the y and z directions, but not in the x direction. The details of the proof of this are left for the student in Problem 5–1.

Units. The units of impulse are FT or, in the engineering units employed in this text, *pound-seconds*. Since the impulse-momentum equation must be dimensionally homogeneous, the units of momentum must also be pound-seconds.

Example 5–1. A ball weighing 8 lb (Fig. 5–1) is thrown against a solid wall. The ball strikes the barrier with a velocity of 30 fps and rebounds with the same velocity. If the time of contact between the ball and the wall is a quarter-second, determine the maximum force of the wall acting on the ball, assuming that the force-time curve is triangular.

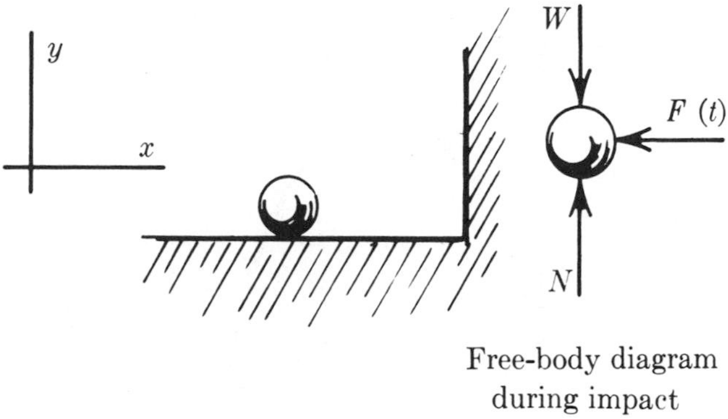

(a) (b)

Figure 5-1

Solution: Again the impulse-momentum equation may be employed, since the change in velocity of the particle is known and since it is desired to determine the force-time characteristics of the force of the wall acting on the ball during the impact:

$$\int_A^B \mathbf{F}\, dt = m\mathbf{v}_B - m\mathbf{v}_A$$

where A is the time immediately preceding impact and B is the time immediately after impact.

Since the velocity before and after impact is known, the impulse may be obtained by evaluating the change in momentum. First, the velocity before and after impact is

$$\mathbf{v}_A = 30\bar{\mathbf{i}} \text{ fps}$$
$$\mathbf{v}_B = -30\bar{\mathbf{i}} \text{ fps}$$

Then the impulse-momentum equation becomes (dropping the vector notation, since motion occurs in one dimension only)

$$\int_A^B F\, dt = \frac{8}{32.2}[(-30) - (+30)]$$
$$= -14.9 \text{ lb-sec}$$

The free-body diagram of the particle during impact is shown in Fig. 5–1(b). Since the net force in the y direction is equal to zero, momentum will be conserved in the y direction. In this case, the velocity is zero and will remain zero during the motion. The force $F(t)$ is the force that the wall exerts on the ball; thus it acts during contact only. Experiments have shown that the time distribution of that force during impact is roughly of the form shown in Fig. 5–2(a). In this case, it is assumed, for rather obvious analytical purposes, that the force-time distribution is triangular, as shown in Fig. 5–2(b).

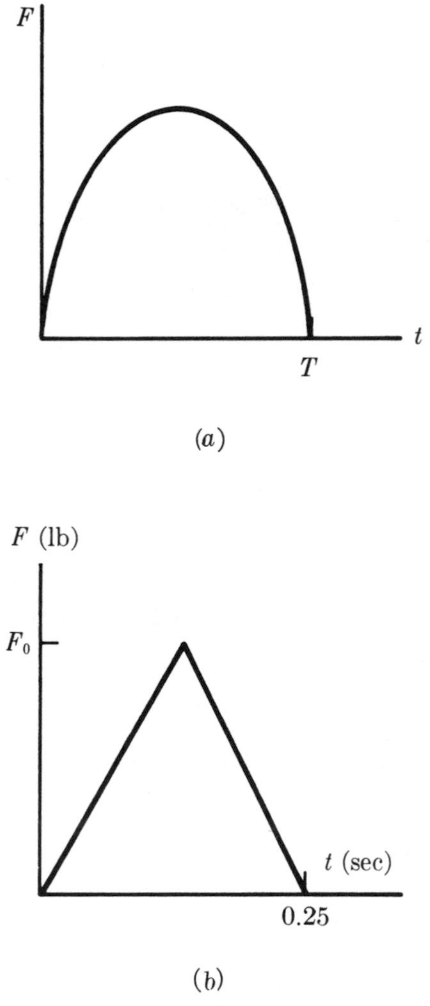

Figure 5-2

But the impulse is just the area under the force-time curve, so that

$$\begin{aligned}\text{Impulse} &= -\tfrac{1}{2}(0.25)(F_O)\\ &= -0.125F_O\end{aligned}$$

The minus sign must be chosen because $F(t)$ acts in the negative x direction. But we already know what the impulse must be for the ball to rebound as it does. Thus,

$$-0.125F_O = -14.9$$

and, solving for F_O,

$$F_O = 119 \text{ lb}$$

Example 5–2. A space vehicle weighing 1000 lb is traveling with a velocity of 1200 fps (in the positive x direction relative to the reference system shown in Fig. 5–3. One of the control rockets on the vehicle ignites and creates a force $F_1(t)$, as shown in the graph of Fig. 5–3. The force F_1 acts in the positive y direction and

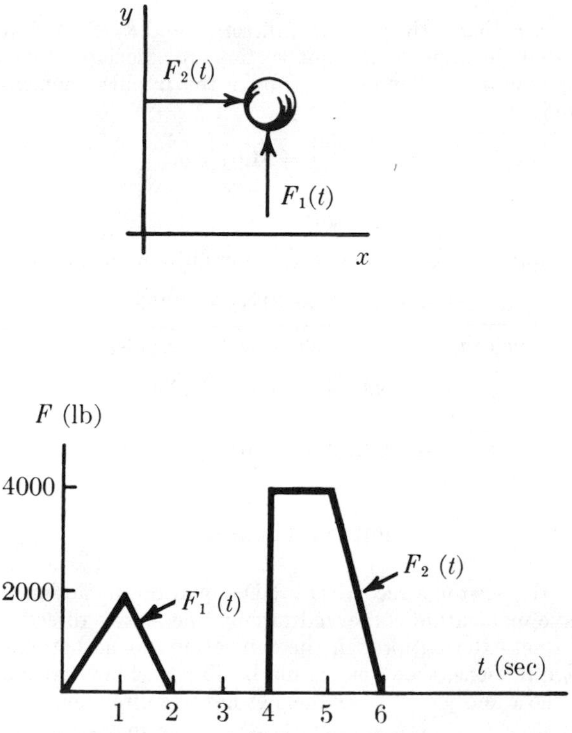

Figure 5-3

ignites at $t = 0$. At $t = 4$ sec, a second rocket ignites and creates a force $F_2(t)$, as shown; F_2 acts in a positive x direction. Determine the velocity of the vehicle after 8 sec have elapsed. Assume that the vehicle is far enough out into space that any gravitational or attractive force from any of the planets may be neglected.

Solution: Since the forces on the vehicle are given as functions of time, and since it is desired to determine the velocity of the vehicle, it appears that the impulse-momentum equation may be employed:

$$\int_0^8 \mathbf{F}\, dt = m\mathbf{v}_B - m\mathbf{v}_A$$

It is seen at a glance that the only unknown quantity in the preceding equation is the velocity of the vehicle after the impulse, $\boldsymbol{v}_B$. The impulse due to the force may be easily evaluated; it is equal in each direction to the area under the force-time curve. In this case, we have forces in two directions, and since the impulse-momentum equation is a vector equation, care must be taken to preserve the directions when writing the equation:

$$\int_0^8 \boldsymbol{F}\,dt = \int_0^8 F_1\bar{\jmath}\,dt + \int_0^8 F_2\bar{\imath}\,dt$$

$$= [\tfrac{1}{2}(2000)(2)]\bar{\jmath} + [(3000)(1) + \tfrac{1}{2}(3000)(1)]\bar{\imath}$$

$$= 4500\bar{\imath} + 2000\bar{\jmath} \quad \text{lb}$$

Note that F_1 is acting in the positive y direction and F_2 is acting in the positive x direction and that the appropriate unit vectors are associated with each impulse in the preceding equations. The other terms in the impulse-momentum equation may be evaluated:

$$m = \frac{1000}{32.2} = 31.0 \text{ slugs}$$

$$\boldsymbol{v}_A = 1200\bar{\imath} \quad \text{fps}$$

Making the appropriate substitutions into the impulse-momentum equation,

$$4500\bar{\imath} + 2000\bar{\jmath} = 31[\boldsymbol{v}_B - 1200\bar{\imath}]$$

and solving for the velocity of the vehicle after the impulse,

$$\boldsymbol{v}_B = 4500\bar{\imath} + 2000\bar{\jmath} + 37{,}200\bar{\imath}$$

we have

$$\boldsymbol{v}_B = 41{,}700\bar{\imath} + 2000\bar{\jmath} \quad \text{fps}$$

PROBLEMS

5-1. Starting with Newton's second law (the equation of motion), show that it is possible to have momentum conserved in only one or two directions. If, for instance, there is a net external force in the z direction but no net external force in either the x or y directions, then you should be able to show that momentum will be conserved in the x and y directions but not in the z direction.

5-2. A ball weighing 4 lb is thrown with a velocity of 50 fps against a brick wall. There is little loss in energy due to the impact, and the ball rebounds with the same velocity with which it is thrown. If the time of contact between the ball and the wall is 1/20 sec, what is the maximum force of the wall acting on the ball, assuming a triangular force-time distribution?

5-3. Consider Problem 5–2. Determine the average force of the wall acting on the ball.

5-4. An automobile traveling 90 fps is slowed to 40 fps in 10 sec under the action of the wind drag force. If the auto weighs 2400 lb, what is the average wind force acting on the car during the 10 sec, if it is assumed that the car is slowed by the wind drag force only?

5-5. A 16,000-lb plane is traveling horizontally with a velocity of 600 mph. An explosion occurs beneath the plane, and the effect of the explosion on the plane is given as an impulse, as shown in Fig. P.5–5. If it can be assumed that the aerodynamic lift force on the plane is equal in magnitude to the weight of the plane and the thrust of the engines is equal to the aerodynamic drag on the plane both before and after the explosion, determine the velocity of the plane 2 sec after the explosion hits it.

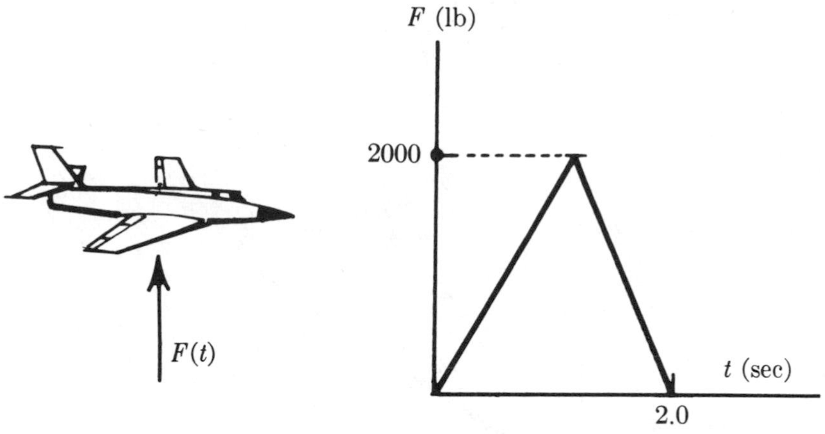

Figure Prob. 5-5

5-6. Using the impulse-momentum equation, determine the constant force required to increase the speed of a 6000-lb rocket traveling in a direction vertical to the surface of the earth from a speed of 1000 fps to a speed of 2000 fps in 5 sec.

5-7. A 64.4-lb body is moving with a velocity of $\boldsymbol{v}_1 = 2\bar{i} - 3\bar{j} + 4\bar{k}$ when it is subjected to an external force that imparts an impulse to the body, thus changing the velocity of the body. If the force can be assumed to be constant and the velocity of the body 3 sec after the force is applied is $\boldsymbol{v}_2 = 6\bar{i} + 3\bar{j} - \bar{k}$, what is the force?

5-8. A ball weighing 10 lb is dropped from a distance of 15 ft onto a floor. An elastic collision occurs (the rebound velocity is the same as the encounter velocity), and the maximum force of contact between the floor and the ball is measured as 1000 lb. Assuming a triangular force-time distribution, determine the duration of contact between the ball and the floor during the impact.

5-9. A jet aircraft weighing 60,000 lb is flying on a horizontal path with a velocity of 400 mph. The pilot desires to accelerate to a speed of 600 mph in the shortest time possible, but the maximum thrust available is only 10,000 lb. Use the impulse-momentum equation to determine the time that it would take the plane at maximum thrust (assumed to be constant) to attain a velocity of 600 mph.

5-10. An earth satellite in circular orbit at a height of 8000 miles has a velocity of 16,500 mph. The escape velocity of the satellite from the earth's gravitational force at this height is 23,400 mph. If the vehicle weighs 400 lb, what impulse would be required to put the orbiting vehicle into an escape trajectory? If the orbit control engines are capable of producing 500 lb of thrust, how long would they have to operate to attain the escape speed?

5-11. A body weighing 56 lb has an absolute velocity of $\boldsymbol{v}_O = 6\bar{i} - 2\bar{j} - 3\bar{k}$ when,

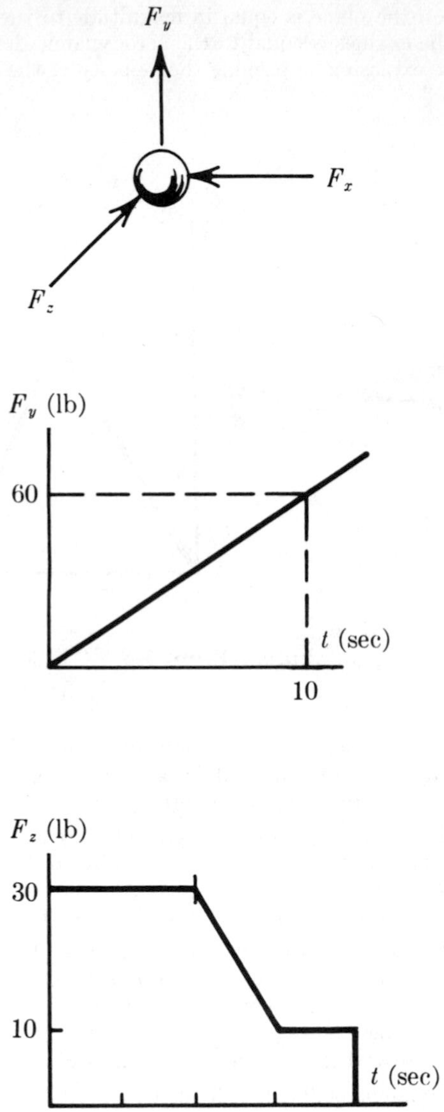

Figure Prob. 5-11

at $t = 0$, three rockets are ignited, which subsequently exert forces on the body in directions as shown in the free-body diagram of Fig. P.5–11. The force in the x direction is $F_x(t) = 0.20t^3$, and the forces in the y and z directions are as shown in the figure. What is the velocity of the body at $t = 4$ sec?

5-12. A body weighing 20 lb is released from rest at the surface of a fluid. The body falls through the fluid under the action of gravity, and 10 sec later it is observed to have a velocity of 0.50 fps. Determine the average force of the fluid acting on the body, that is, the drag force.

5-13. A block weighing 16 lb is moving downward on a plane that is tilted at an angle of 30 deg with the horizontal. The coefficient of friction between the plane and the block is 0.20. If, at $t = 0$, the block is moving down the plane with a velocity of 4.0 fps, determine (by using the impulse-momentum equation) the velocity of the block 6 sec later.

5-14. In experimental studies on impact, a block equipped with strain gages and mounted in frictionless wheels is shot against a solid boundary. If in one of the tests a 10-lb block is observed to rebound with a velocity of 5.0 fps, what was the velocity of the body before impact if the recorded force-time curve is as shown in Fig. P.5–14?

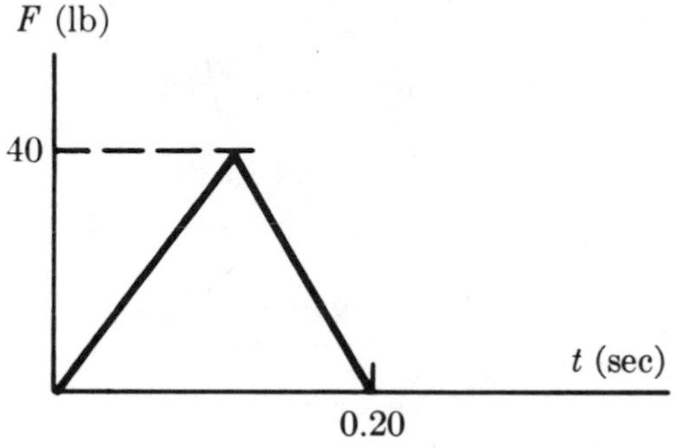

Figure Prob. 5-14

5-15. The 64.4-lb mass shown in Fig. P.5–15 is at rest when an impulse of 5.0 lb sec in the negative x direction is applied by an impact of a sledge hammer. What is the displacement of the mass as a function of time, if the general equation for the motion of the system is $x(t) = A \cos 3t + B \sin 3t$. *Hint:* Determine A and B.

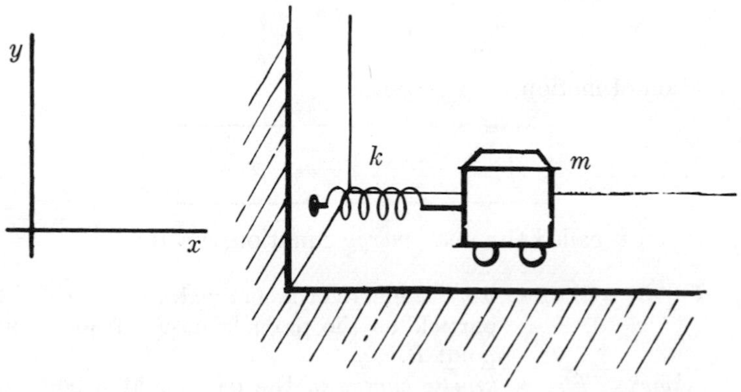

Figure Prob. 5-15

5-2. THE WORK-ENERGY EQUATION

The equation. The work-energy equation is obtained by integrating the equation of motion with respect to displacement. So, first consider the equation of motion of a particle:

$$\boldsymbol{F} = m\boldsymbol{a} \tag{5.7}$$

Then take the dot product of both sides of the equation with an increment of displacement, $d\boldsymbol{r}$:

$$\boldsymbol{F} \cdot d\boldsymbol{r} = m\boldsymbol{a} \cdot d\boldsymbol{r} \tag{5.8}$$

Consider now the right-hand side of Eq. 5.8. Multiply and divide by dt; then

$$m\boldsymbol{a} \cdot d\boldsymbol{r} = m\boldsymbol{a} \cdot \frac{d\boldsymbol{r}}{dt}\, dt$$

$$= m\boldsymbol{a} \cdot \boldsymbol{v}\, dt \tag{5.9}$$

But note that

$$\boldsymbol{a} \cdot \boldsymbol{v} = \frac{1}{2}\frac{d}{dt}(\boldsymbol{v} \cdot \boldsymbol{v}) \tag{5.10}$$

But,

$$\boldsymbol{v} \cdot \boldsymbol{v} = v^2 \tag{5.11}$$

where v is the magnitude of the velocity. Finally,

$$m\boldsymbol{a} \cdot d\boldsymbol{r} = \frac{1}{2} m \frac{d}{dt}(v^2)\, dt \tag{5.12}$$

Then Eq. 5.8 becomes

$$\boldsymbol{F} \cdot d\boldsymbol{r} = \tfrac{1}{2} m d(v^2) \tag{5.13}$$

Equation 5.13 is now integrated between any two points A and B on the path of motion of the particle:

$$\int_A^B \boldsymbol{F} \cdot d\boldsymbol{r} = \int_A^B \tfrac{1}{2} m d(v^2) \tag{5.14}$$

The equation of motion then becomes

$$\boxed{\int_A^B \boldsymbol{F} \cdot d\boldsymbol{r} = \tfrac{1}{2} m v_B^2 - \tfrac{1}{2} m v_A^2} \tag{5.15}$$

This equation is called the *work-energy* equation, where:

$\int_A^B \boldsymbol{F} \cdot d\boldsymbol{r} \equiv W_{AB} \equiv$ *work* done by the net external force $\boldsymbol{F}$ on the particle as the particle moves from point A to point B.

$\tfrac{1}{2} m v^2 \equiv T \quad \equiv$ *kinetic energy* of the particle at a point in time or space.

Thus the work-energy equation may be written in simpler form as

$$W_{AB} = T_B - T_A \tag{5.16}$$

which says that the work done by the net external force on a particle as the particle moves from point A to point B is equal to the change in kinetic energy of the body as it moves from one point to another.

It should be emphasized that the work-energy equation is nothing more than a restatement of Newton's second law and does not reveal anything that Newton's second law does not reveal.

It is important to note that, unlike the impulse-momentum equation, the work-energy equation is a scalar equation. To evaluate the kinetic energy, for instance, all one has to know is the speed of the particle.

Units. It is seen that the units of work are FL or, in the engineering units, *foot-pounds*. For the work-energy equation to be dimensionally homogeneous, the kinetic energy must have the same units as work; therefore kinetic energy also has units of foot-pounds.

Various expressions of work. It is usually more convenient to express the work done by a force in a form different from that of the integral definition given above. Here we shall consider different forms of work.

1. By the definition of the dot product, $\boldsymbol{F} \cdot \boldsymbol{dr}$ may be written as $F(\cos\theta)\,dr$, where θ is the angle between the force and incremental displacement. Thus,

$$W_{AB} = \int_A^B F(\cos\theta)\,dr \tag{5.17}$$

Because it is difficult in general to express F and θ in terms of r, this form is not often useful.

2. Using Cartesian coordinates,

$$\boldsymbol{F} = F_x\bar{\boldsymbol{i}} + F_y\bar{\boldsymbol{j}} + F_z\bar{\boldsymbol{k}} \tag{5.18}$$

$$\boldsymbol{dr} = dx\,\bar{\boldsymbol{i}} + dy\bar{\boldsymbol{j}} + dz\bar{\boldsymbol{k}} \tag{5.19}$$

By taking the dot product of $\boldsymbol{F}$ with $\boldsymbol{dr}$, and substituting into the definition of the work,

$$W_{AB} = \int_{x_A}^{x_B} F_x\,dx + \int_{y_A}^{y_B} F_y\,dy + \int_{z_A}^{z_B} F_z\,dz \tag{5.20}$$

Assuming, of course, that F_x is a function of x only, etc., this form is very useful in evaluating work.

3. If the force is constant, it follows from Eq. 5.20 that the work done by that force is simply equal to the force times the distance that force moves. The force is factored out of the integral, and the resulting integral is just the displacement. Thus,

W_{AB} = (force) × (displacement in the direction of the force)
W_{AB} = (displacement) × (force in the direction of the displacement)

From these definitions, it should be clear that work is positive when the force has a component in the same direction as the displacement, and that work is negative when the force has a component in a direction opposite to the displacement. This may be seen by inspection of Eq. 5.17. If the angle between the force and the incremental displacement is greater than 90 deg, then $\cos \theta$ is negative, and the work is negative.

Work done by a moment. To determine the work done by a moment, consider that the pivoted beam shown in Fig. 5–4 is subjected

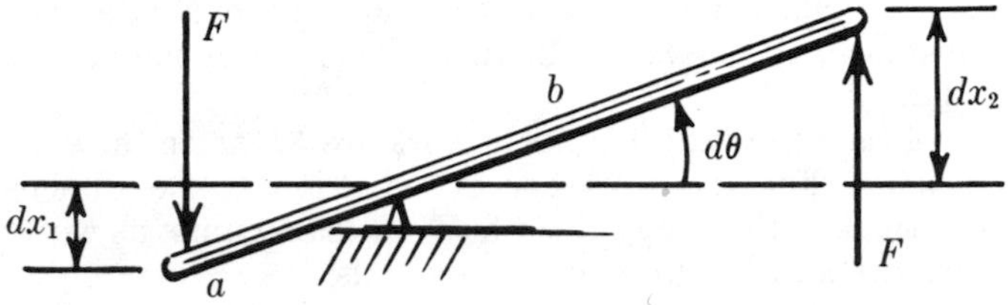

Figure 5-4

to two forces, which are equal in magnitude and oppositely directed. As the beam rotates through the angle $d\theta$, the amount of work done by each of the forces is nothing more than the force times the displacement. Thus,

$$dW = F\,dx_1 + F\,dx_2 \tag{5.21}$$

But for small displacements, the arc formula may be applied, so that

$$\begin{aligned} dx_1 &= a\,d\theta \\ dx_2 &= b\,d\theta \end{aligned} \tag{5.22}$$

and the work done by the forces becomes

$$dW = F(a + b)\,d\theta \tag{5.23}$$

But since $a + b$ is equal to d, and since Fd is equal to the moment of the couple, then

$$dW = M\,d\theta \tag{5.24}$$

Therefore, for a moment on a body that is acting about a fixed axis, the total work done by the moment as the body rotates from position A to position B is

$$W = \int_A^B M\,d\theta \tag{5.25}$$

For a body that is moving in space in some arbitrary manner, it may be easily seen that the work done by the moment may now be written as

$$W = \int_A^B \mathbf{M} \cdot d\boldsymbol{\theta} \tag{5.26}$$

where now $d\boldsymbol{\theta}$ is a vector representing a very small angular displacement.

Various forms of the kinetic energy function. The kinetic energy function T is defined as

$$T = \tfrac{1}{2}mv^2 \tag{5.27}$$

where v is the speed of the particle. It should be noted that the kinetic energy is a scalar quantity and therefore has no direction whatsoever associated with it. It should also be noted that the kinetic energy is always a positive quantity.

The kinetic energy may be expressed in terms of Cartesian coordinates. Since the velocity is given in Cartesian coordinates as

$$\boldsymbol{v} = \dot{x}\bar{\boldsymbol{i}} + \dot{y}\bar{\boldsymbol{j}} + \dot{z}\bar{\boldsymbol{k}} \tag{5.28}$$

the kinetic energy may be obtained by taking the dot product of the velocity with itself and by subsequent substitution of the quantity into Eq. 5.27:

$$T = \tfrac{1}{2}m(\dot{x}^2 + \dot{y}^2 + \dot{z}^2) \tag{5.29}$$

In terms of polar coordinates, the velocity is

$$\boldsymbol{v} = \dot{r}\bar{\boldsymbol{e}}_r + r\dot{\theta}\bar{\boldsymbol{e}}_\theta \tag{5.30}$$

so that the kinetic energy becomes

$$T = \tfrac{1}{2}m(\dot{r}^2 + r^2\dot{\theta}^2) \tag{5.31}$$

Finally, in terms of normal and tangential coordinates, the speed of the particle is simply equal to s, so that the kinetic energy can be written as

$$T = \tfrac{1}{2}m\dot{s}^2, \quad \text{or} \quad \tfrac{1}{2}m\left(\frac{dv}{dt}\right)^2 \tag{5.32}$$

Any one of these forms may be employed to determine the kinetic energy of a particle. The form to be used is usually dictated by the type or path of motion of the particle.

Example 5-3. Determine the work done by a force $\boldsymbol{F}$ (Fig. 5-5), which stretches a spring a total distance of Δ.

Solution: In this one-dimensional case, the work that the force does on the spring may be written as

$$W_{AB} = \int_A^B F_x\,dx$$

The force required to stretch the spring, assuming a linear spring, will be

$$F = kx$$

where x is measured from the unstretched position.

Therefore

$$W_{AB} = \int_A^B kx\,dx$$

$$= \frac{kx_B^2}{2} - \frac{kx_A^2}{2}$$

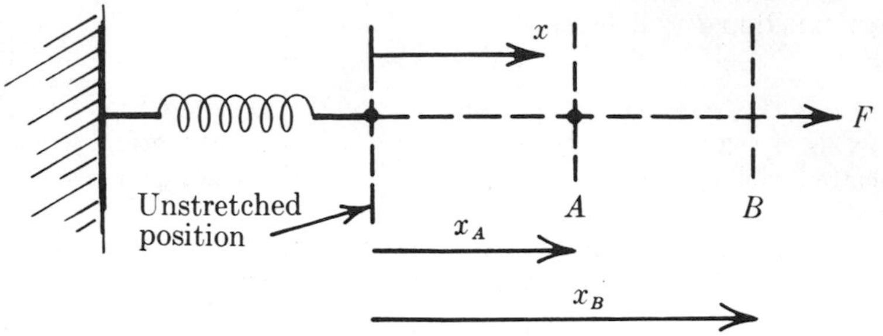

Figure 5-5

This result should not be confused with the work done *by* a spring. In this case, the spring force is in a direction opposite to the force exerted on the spring, and it follows that the work done *by* the spring force will be opposite in sign to that obtained here for the force *on* the spring.

It should also be noted that the work done by a spring force depends only upon the distance that the spring is stretched (or compressed). The results obtained here may be extended by letting the coordinate x equal the amount of stretch (or compression).

Example 5–4. A particle of mass m is released from rest at point A (Fig. 5–6) and moves down a two-dimensional curve $y = f(x)$. Assuming that frictional forces are negligible, determine the velocity of the particle as it passes point B.

Solution: A free-body diagram of the particle as it moves on the path (neglecting friction) is shown in Fig. 5-6. Since it is desired to determine the velocity of the particle at point B, one might be tempted to try to solve the problem by using the work-energy equation because the work-energy equation contains velocity terms:

$$W_{AB} = T_B - T_A$$

where

$$T_A = \tfrac{1}{2}mv_A^2 = 0 \qquad (v_A = 0)$$
$$T_B = \tfrac{1}{2}mv_B^2$$

and the work done by all external forces on the body as it moves from A to B is simply

$$W_{AB} = mgh$$

This was obtained by noting that the normal force N does no work because it is at all times perpendicular to the direction of motion of the body. The work done by the force mg is simply equal to the force times displacement in the direction of the force. The displacement in the direction of the force in this case is simply the distance $y_1 - y_2$, or the distance h. Thus, the work-energy equation becomes

$$mgh = \tfrac{1}{2}mv_B^2$$

and, solving for v_B,

$$v_B = \sqrt{2gh}$$

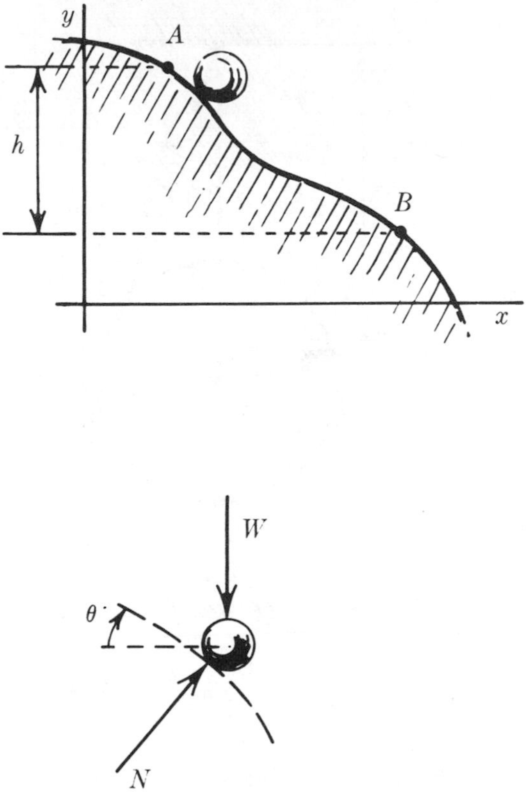

Figure 5-6

It is interesting to note that this velocity is the same velocity as one obtains by dropping a weight and allowing it to move in a straight-line path downward. The only difference is, of course, the direction of the velocity; the direction of the velocity is always along the path of motion.

Example 5-5. The circle shown in Fig. 5-7 is a track on which the small mass m is allowed to move. Assume that the track is well lubricated so that there is no frictional force between the mass and the track. The weight of the mass is 15 lb. The spring connecting the mass and the fixed point O has a stiffness of 10.0 lb/in. and is pivoted at point O. The unstretched length of the spring is 12 in. If the mass has a velocity of 20 in./sec to the right at point A, what will be the velocity of the mass at point B?

Solution: First a free-body diagram of the mass will be drawn in order to tabulate all forces (Fig. 5-8). Since the normal force of the track acting on the mass will do no work as the body moves on the track, and since the work done by the spring and gravitational forces may be easily evaluated, it appears that the best route for determining the velocity of the mass would be the work-energy equation:

$$W_{AB} = T_B - T_A$$

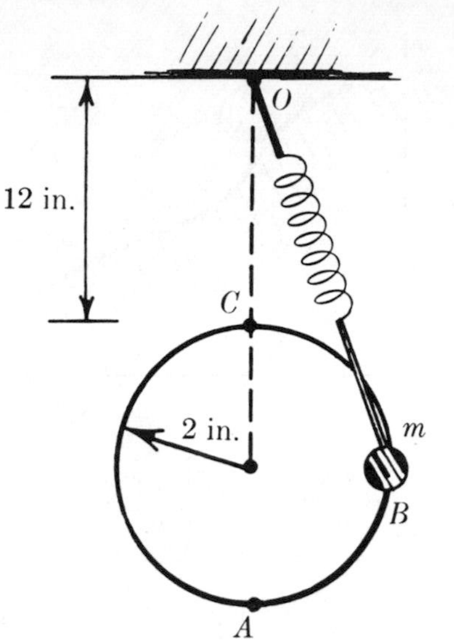

Figure 5-7

The next thing to do is to evaluate the work done by the forces. The work done by the gravitational force as the particle moves from A to B is

$$W_{AB} = -15(2) = -30 \text{ in.-lb}$$

The minus sign indicates that the force is in a direction opposite to the motion of the mass. The work done by the spring force may be determined by evaluating the amount that the spring has been stretched:

$$W_{AB} = \tfrac{1}{2}ks_A^2 - \tfrac{1}{2}ks_B^2$$

where s is the coordinate representing the distance from the point of the unstretched condition of the spring to the point at which it has been stretched. In this case, the spring has been stretched 4 in. when the mass is at point A. To determine the amount of stretch in the spring at point B, consider Fig. 5–8, showing the configuration of the spring when the mass is at point B. Then the amount that the spring has been stretched when the mass is at point B will be

$$\begin{aligned} s_B &= \sqrt{14^2 + 2^2} - 12 \\ &= 2.14 \text{ in.} \end{aligned}$$

Therefore the total work done by the spring force as the particle moves from A to B is

$$\begin{aligned} W_{AB} &= \tfrac{1}{2}(10)(4)^2 - \tfrac{1}{2}(10)(2.14)^2 \\ &= 57.1 \text{ in.-lb} \end{aligned}$$

The kinetic energy of the particle at point A is (noting that g must be taken as 386 in./sec², since we are using units of inches in this problem)

$$T_A = \frac{1}{2}\left(\frac{15}{386}\right)(20)^2 = 7.77 \text{ in.-lb}$$

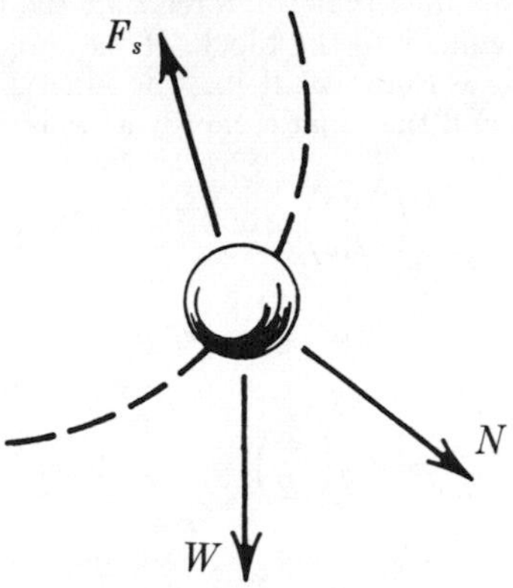

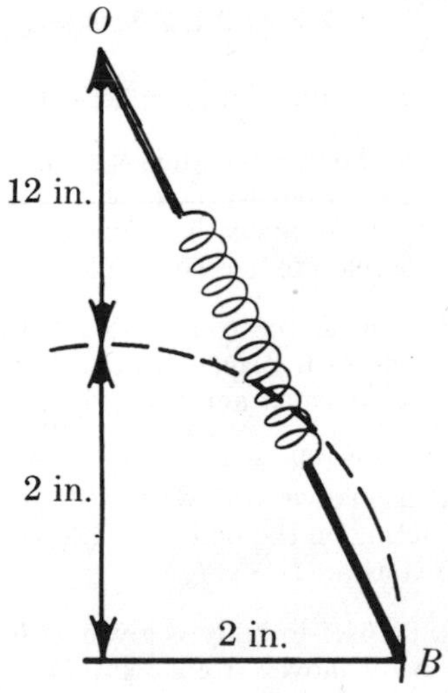

Figure 5-8

The work-energy equation then becomes

$$-30 + 57.1 = \frac{1}{2}\left(\frac{15}{386}\right) v_B^2 - 7.77$$

and, solving for the velocity of the mass at point B,

$$v_B = 31.6 \text{ in./sec}$$

Example 5-6. A bullet weighing 0.08 lb and having a muzzle velocity of 1000 fps is fired into a wooden block. If the bullet penetrates the block 2 in., what is the average force of the block acting on the bullet during the period that the bullet sinks into the block?

Solution: We have to assume that the force that the block exerts on the bullet is constant as the bullet sinks into the block. If the force is F_O, the work done by the block on the bullet is $-F_O(2/12)$ ft-lb. The kinetic energy at the end of the process, point B, is zero, and the kinetic energy at A is

$$T_A = \frac{1}{2}\left(\frac{0.08}{32.2}\right)(1000)^2 = 1250 \text{ ft/lb}$$

Thus,

$$W_{AB} = -T_A$$

and

$$-F_O\left(\frac{2}{12}\right) = -1250$$

$$F_O = 7500 \text{ lb}$$

PROBLEMS

5-16. Write the kinetic-energy function in spherical coordinates.

5-17. An airplane weighing 80,000 lb lands with a velocity of 150 mph. What would be the average force required to make the aircraft come to a rest after it had traveled a distance of 1 mile down the runway? To do this, assume that the force causing the plane to decelerate is a constant.

5-18. A large rock is thrown off the top of a 30-ft hill with a speed of 6.0 fps. What is the speed of the rock as it reaches the bottom of the hill, assuming that there is no frictional force whatsoever acting on the body?

5-19. A body weighing 30 lb is released in a viscous fluid. It is observed to have a velocity of 5.0 fps after it has traveled downward a distance of 10 ft. What is the average force of the fluid acting on the body if the force that the fluid exerts on the body can be considered a constant?

5-20. The force acting on a 64.4-lb body is given as $\boldsymbol{F} = 2\bar{\imath} + 3\bar{\jmath} - \bar{k}$. The force remains constant as the body moves from point $(4, -2,3)$ to point $(-2,0,-1)$. If the velocity of the body at point $(4,-2,3)$ is $\boldsymbol{v} = 4\bar{\imath} - 2\bar{\jmath} + 3\bar{k}$, what is the velocity of the body at point $(-2,0,-1)$? Note that only the magnitude of the velocity of the body at the second point may be determined from the work-energy equation. Other methods must be employed to determine the direction of the velocity.

5-21. A body weighing 20 lb has a velocity of $\boldsymbol{v} = 10\bar{\imath} + 6\bar{\jmath} - 12\bar{k}$ at the point $(-3,2,4)$. If the force on the particle is $\boldsymbol{F} = (2x)\bar{\imath} + (3y^2)\bar{\jmath} + (-6z + z^2)\bar{k}$, determine the velocity of the body at the point $(1,1,2)$.

5-22. The thrust of a 9500-lb rocket is given as a function of its height above the surface of the earth, as shown in Fig. P.5–22. Determine the velocity of the rocket at an altitude of 100,000 ft.

5-23. The spring shown in Fig. P.5–23 has a stiffness of 20 lb/ft and an unstretched length of 2.0 ft. If the system is released from the position shown, how far will the block fall?

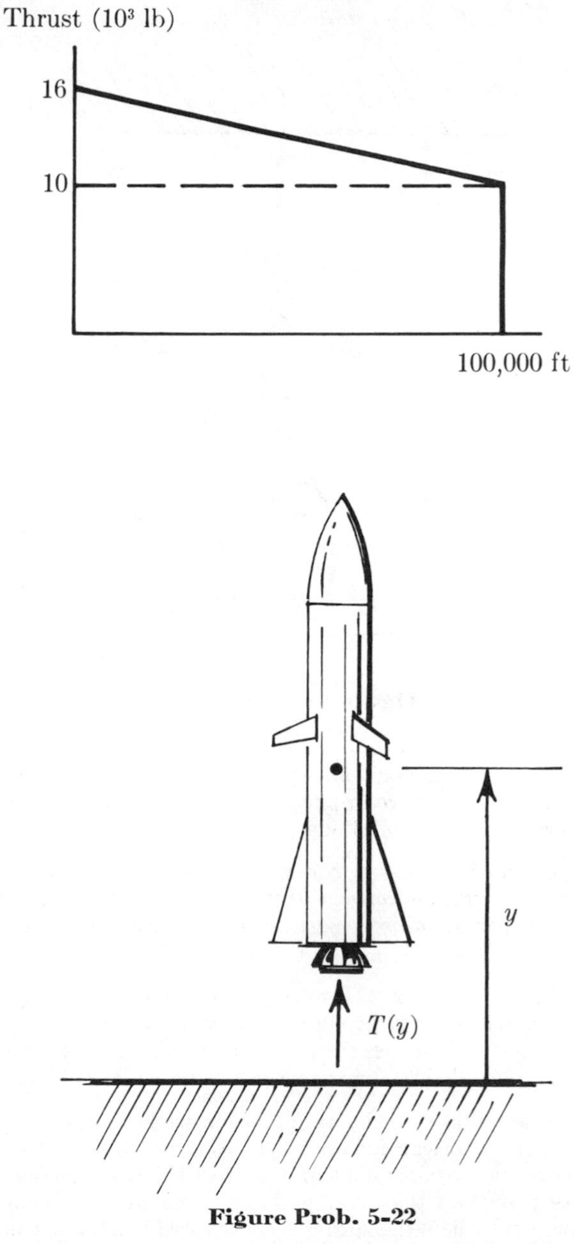

Figure Prob. 5-22

5-24. A body of mass m is dropped from a height h onto an assumed weightless platform, as shown in Fig. P.5–24. Upon impact, the mass sticks to the platform. Use the work-energy equation to determine the amount that the spring will deflect.

5-25. Experiments show that the coefficient of sliding friction between the wheels of an automobile and a certain type of road surface is 0.60. Draw a graph of the

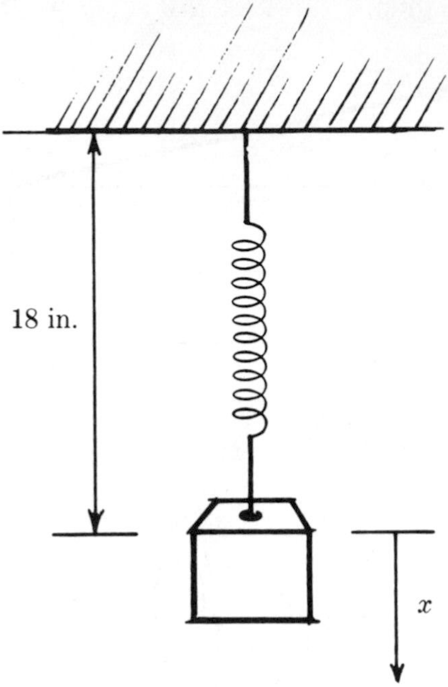

Figure Prob. 5-23

velocity of an automobile versus distance required to come to a complete stop if the brakes of the automobile were applied such that skidding occurred. Use the work-energy equation for the calculations.

5-26. A simple pendulum is released from position A, a position where the pendulum makes an angle of θ_o with the vertical. If the mass is m, what will be the velocity of the mass when the pendulum is in position B, a position where the mass is at its lowest point?

5-27. The unstretched length of the spring shown in Fig. P.5–27 is 14 in. The slider block has an initial velocity at point A of 10 in./sec downward. Determine the velocity of the block as it reaches the point where there is no force in the spring. The spring constant is 5.0 lb/in., and the weight of the block is 12 lb.

5-28. A spring-loaded gun is to fire pellets, each weighing $\frac{1}{4}$ lb with a muzzle velocity of 100 fps. In the design for the mechanism, it is desired to find a spring that has to compress only a maximum of 4 in. Use the work-energy equation to determine the spring constant that will fulfill this requirement. Also determine the spring force at the point where the spring is compressed a total of 4 in.

5-29. A 3500-lb automobile is traveling a highway with a constant velocity of 65 mph, and as the automobile encounters a 5 percent grade upward, the driver disengages the clutch. If no motive force is supplied by the motor, how far will the automobile move up the hill before it comes to a stop, assuming that there is no drag force on the auto?

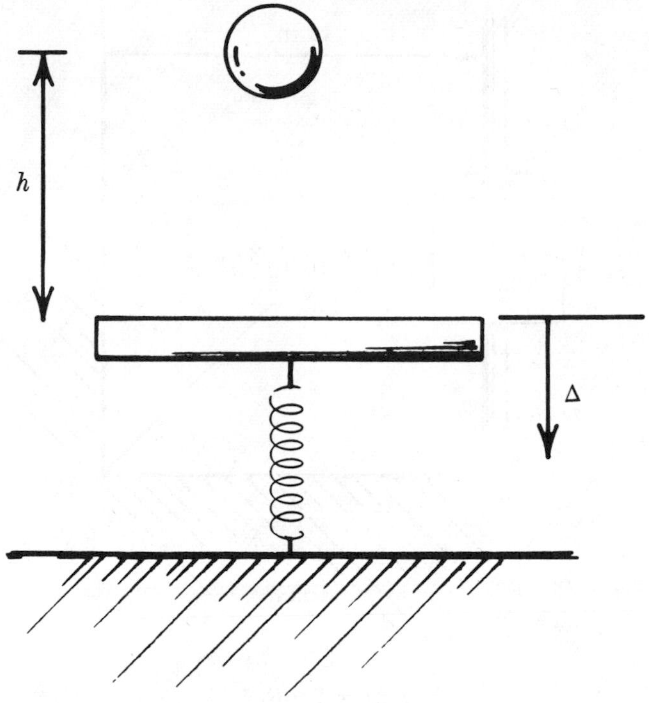

Figure Prob. 5-24

5-30. Determine the normal force of the surface of the path (Fig. P.5–30) acting on the particle at the point B. The particle, which weighs 4 lb, is released from rest at point A. In order to determine this reactive force, first use the work-energy equation to determine the velocity of the particle at B; then use the normal and tangential form of Newton's second law to determine the normal force.

5-31. A block weighing 120 lb is dropped from an airplane flying at an altitude of 1000 fps. The plane is flying at a speed of 200 mph with respect to the ground. If the block was observed to be traveling with a velocity of 110 mph when it strikes the ground, how much energy was absorbed by the atmosphere in the total trajectory of the body?

5-32. A roller coaster is moving with a velocity of 15 fps at point A (Fig. P.5–32). What is the velocity at point B and C if the occupants and the coaster weigh 4000 lb? Assume that there are no frictional forces acting.

5-3. THE POTENTIAL-ENERGY FUNCTION

Definition of the potential-energy function. In general, the work done by any force acting on a body as the body moves from

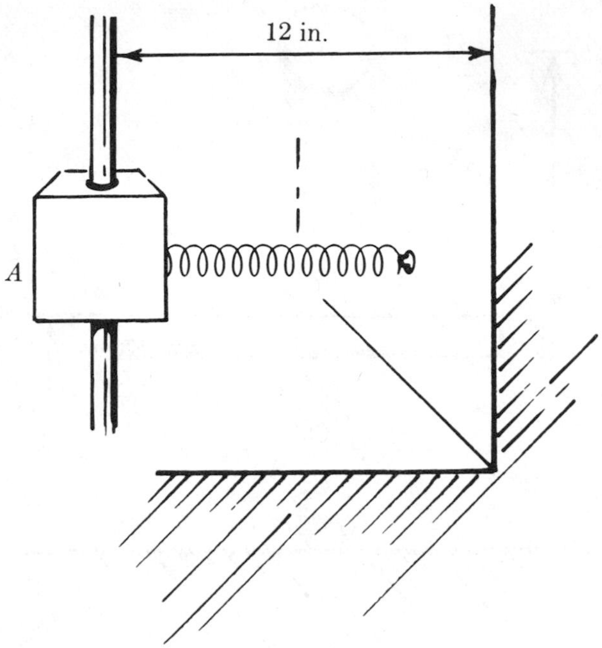

Figure Prob. 5-27

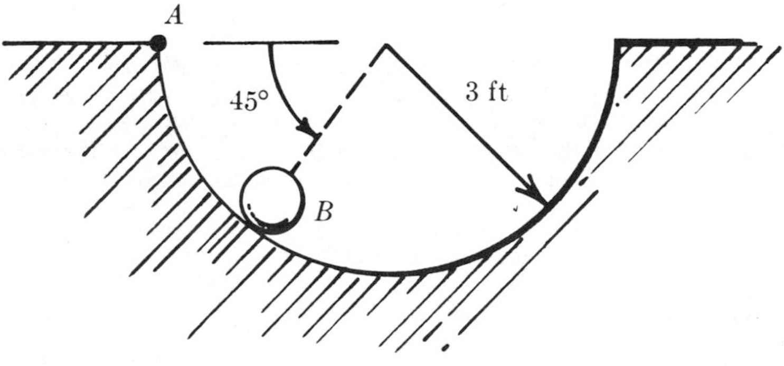

Figure Prob. 5-30

one point to another depends upon the path taken by the body. It is obvious that the work done by a frictional force, for instance, depends entirely upon what path is taken from one point to another. If the path is longer, the frictional force will do more work. The integral

$$\int_A^B \boldsymbol{F} \cdot d\boldsymbol{r}$$

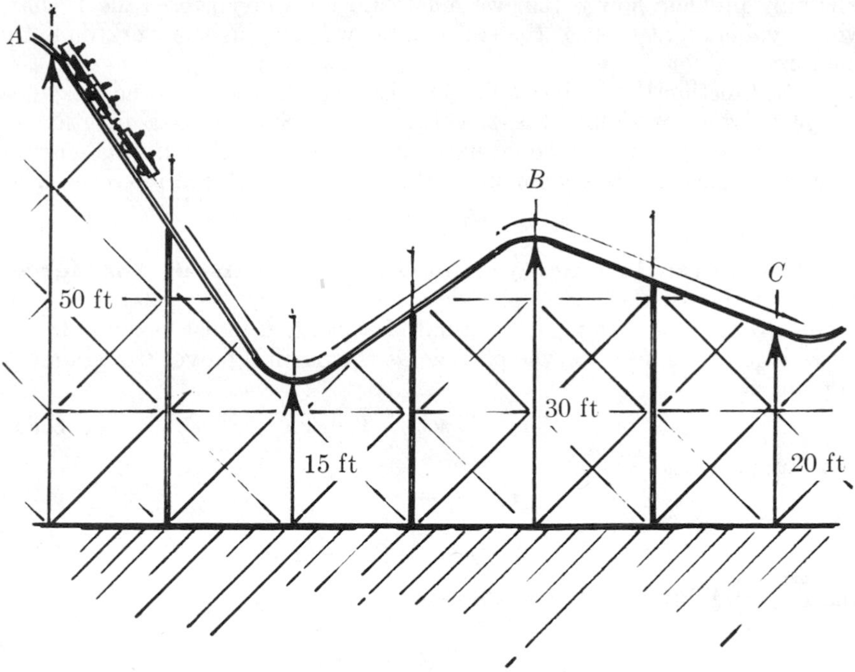

Figure Prob. 5-32

is said to be a function of the path taken, which means simply that the integral has a different value for each different path taken by the particle as it moves from A to B.

Suppose now that the work done by the force does not depend upon the path taken by the particle, so that the work done by the force as the particle moves from A to B is independent of the path taken. If this is the case, then the work done by the force depends only upon the positions of the points A and B in space. External forces on the particle that satisfy this condition are said to be *conservative forces*, and if only conservative forces are acting on a system, then the system is said to be a *conservative system*.

If the work done by a force on a particle depends only on the position of the end points of the path of motion, the existence of a function $V(x,y,z)$ is implied such that

$$\begin{aligned} W_{AB} &= \int_A^B \boldsymbol{F} \cdot d\boldsymbol{r} \\ &= V_A(x,y,z) - V_B(x,y,z) \end{aligned} \qquad (\mathbf{5.33})$$

If V were known for a given force acting on a particle, then all we should have to do to determine the work done by the force is evaluate V at the end points of the path of motion and perform the required subtraction.

The only problem now is that we must find for a given force the V that, when evaluated at each of the end points, will give us the work done by the force.

The function V, which is defined by Eq. 5.33, is known as the *potential-energy function* or simply the *potential energy*. Since it is a function in general of the Cartesian coordinates x, y, and z, the potential-energy function is entirely dependent upon the orientation of the reference axes we choose.

The potential-energy function in terms of the force. The definition of the potential-energy function from Eq. 5.33 is that V evaluated at point A, minus V evaluated at point B, must be equal to the work done by the force on the particle as the particle moves from point A to point B:

$$V_A - V_B = \int_A^B \mathbf{F} \cdot d\mathbf{r} \tag{5.34}$$

This implies that

$$\mathbf{F} \cdot d\mathbf{r} = -dV \tag{5.35}$$

Since

$$\mathbf{F} \cdot d\mathbf{r} = F_x\,dx + F_y d_y + F_z d_z \tag{5.36}$$

and the total differential of $V(x,y,z)$ is

$$-dV(x,y,z) = -\frac{\partial V}{\partial x}\,dx - \frac{\partial V}{\partial y}\,dy - \frac{\partial V}{\partial z}\,dz \tag{5.37}$$

it is seen from the comparison of Eq. 5.36 and Eq. 5.37 that

$$F_x = -\frac{\partial V}{\partial x} \qquad F_y = -\frac{\partial V}{\partial y} \qquad F_z = -\frac{\partial V}{\partial z} \tag{5.38}$$

This, then, is a condition that the potential-energy function associated with a given force must satisfy.

Determination of the potential-energy function. If a given force is known to be conservative, how do we determine the corresponding potential-energy function? This may be done in the following manner:

1. Choose a point in space where you want the potential energy to be zero. This is possible to do because the potential-energy function is dependent upon the orientation of the reference axes.
2. Then associate A with the reference point where the potential energy is to be zero, and associate B with any point (x,y,z) in

space where it is desired to determine the potential energy. Equation 5.34 may be written as

$$V(x,y,z) = -\int_{\text{Ref.}}^{(x,y,z)} \boldsymbol{F} \cdot d\boldsymbol{r} \tag{5.39}$$

Example 5–7. The gravitational force is a conservative force. Therefore there will be a potential-energy function associated with the force. For the reference system shown in Fig. 5–9, what is the potential energy?

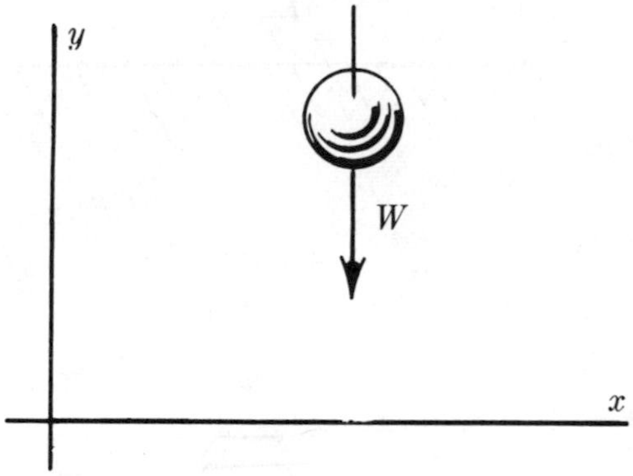

Figure 5-9

Solution: In this case, we choose arbitrarily the point (0,0) as the point where we want the potential-energy function to be zero. Then the potential-energy function may be determined by

$$V = -\int_{(0,0)}^{(x,y)} \boldsymbol{F} \cdot d\boldsymbol{r}$$

Since the only force on the particle is a force W in the negative y direction, the integral may be written

$$V = -\int_0^y (-W)\, dy$$

so that the potential-energy function then becomes

$$V = Wy$$

Since the force acts only in the y direction, we note that the potential energy will be zero at any point along the x axis. We may then say that the reference, or the point where the potential energy of the body is zero, is the x axis.

Example 5–8. The force that the linear spring exerts on the particle is a conservative force and thus may have a potential-energy function associated with it. If the potential energy is to be zero at the point where there is no force in the spring, what is the potential-energy function of the spring?

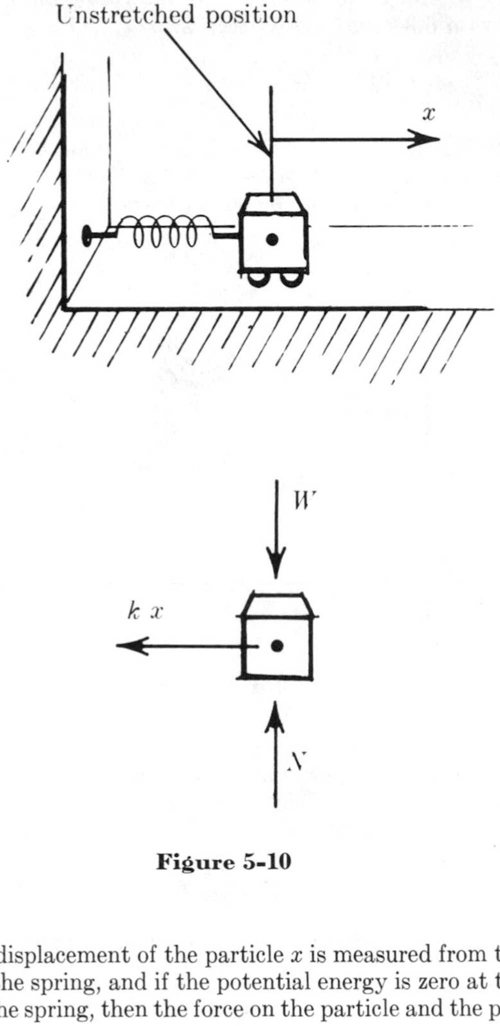

Figure 5-10

Solution: If the displacement of the particle x is measured from the point where there is no force in the spring, and if the potential energy is zero at the point where there is no force in the spring, then the force on the particle and the potential energy are, respectively,

$$F_x = -kx$$

$$V = -\int_0^x F_x \, dx$$

The potential energy may be evaluated by substituting the force into the potential-energy integral:

$$V = -\int_0^x (-kx) \, dx$$

and

$$V = \frac{kx^2}{2}$$

Conservation of energy. The work done by a force in moving a particle from point A to point B may be expressed in terms of the potential-energy function associated with that force:

$$W_{AB} = V_A - V_B \tag{5.40}$$

This is the way that the potential-energy function was originally defined, but there is no reason why the potential energy could not have been defined as $V_B - V_A$. The work in terms of the kinetic energy is

$$W_{AB} = T_B - T_A \tag{5.41}$$

By equating 5.40 to 5.41, it is seen that

$$T_B - T_A = V_A - V_B \tag{5.42}$$

or

$$T_A + V_A = T_B + V_B \tag{5.43}$$

This implies that the quantity $T + V$ must be a constant at all points on the path of motion of a particle. The sum of the potential and kinetic energies are defined as the total energy of the system E:

$$\boxed{E = T + V} \tag{5.44}$$

This equation is referred to as the *conservation of energy* equation, and applies only to those particles that have only conservative forces acting on them.

It is interesting to note that V was defined such that the work done by the force is equal to $V_A - V_B$ instead of $V_B - V_A$. This was done so that the total energy could be written as $T + V$ rather than $T - V$.

Example 5–9. The spring shown in Fig. 5–11 has a stiffness of 100 lb/ft and an unstretched length of 15 in. If the system is released from rest in the position shown, how far will the weight deflect? The weight is equal to 20 lb.

Solution: Using the coordinate system shown in Fig. 5–11, the potential-energy function for the gravitational force will be $-Wy$, and the potential-energy function for the spring will be $ky^2/2$. Thus the potential-energy function for the net force on the body is

$$V = \tfrac{1}{2}ky^2 - Wy$$

Since the kinetic energy of the body may be written as $m\dot{y}^2/2$, the total energy of the system becomes

$$\begin{aligned} E &= T + V \\ &= \tfrac{1}{2}m\dot{y}^2 + \tfrac{1}{2}ky^2 - Wy \end{aligned}$$

If the system is released from rest at point A, the velocity of the body at point A will be zero. The position of the mass at A is -8.0 in., or -0.67 ft. Thus the total energy at A becomes

$$\begin{aligned} E_A &= \tfrac{1}{2}(100)(-0.67)^2 - (20)(-0.67) \\ &= 35.9 \text{ ft-lb} \end{aligned}$$

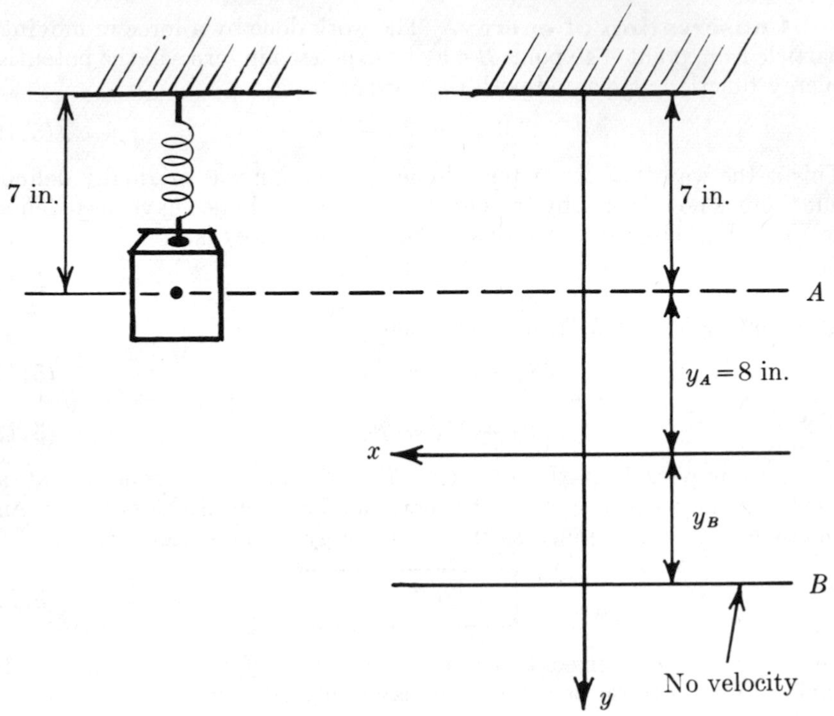

Figure 5-11

At point B the velocity of the body will be zero, and the position of the body at that point is the desired unknown y_B. Thus the total energy at B is

$$E_B = \tfrac{1}{2}(100)y_B^2 - 20y_B$$

and since energy must be conserved in the system, $E_A = E_B$ and

$$35.9 = 50y_B^2 - 20y_B$$

By solving the quadratic for y_B,

$$y_B = \frac{+20 \pm \sqrt{400 + 4(50)(39.5)}}{100}$$

$$= 1.11 \text{ ft, or } 13.3 \text{ in.}$$

Thus the total deflection of the mass from the point where it was released will be about 20 in. The positive root was considered in the solution of the above quadratic because the negative in this case has no meaning.

PROBLEMS

5-33. The potential-energy function depends upon the orientation of the reference system. By using the reference system shown in Fig. P.5–33, determine the potential-energy function for the gravitational force on the mass shown. Let the potential energy be zero at point (0,0).

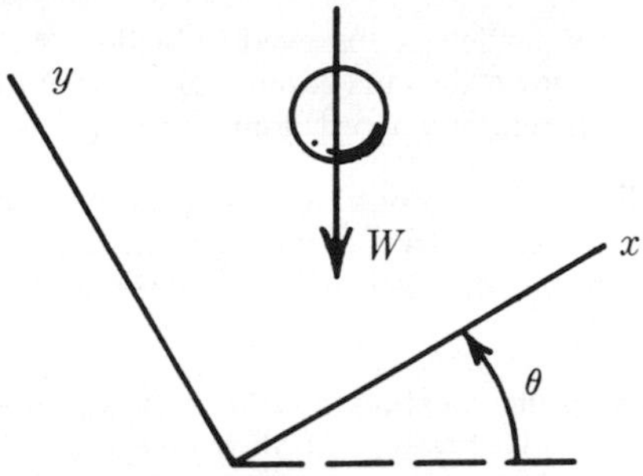

Figure Prob. 5-33

5-34. If the potential-energy function for a conservative force on a particle is $V(x,y,z) = 2x^2y - xz$, what is the work done by the force on the body as the body moves from $(3,-4,1)$ to $(2,3,-5)$?

5-35. Determine from the potential-energy function of Problem 5-34 the x, y, and z components of the force that are acting on the body.

5-36. Determine, using both the impulse-momentum equation and the conservation of energy equation, the minimum impulse that must be given to the mass m, shown in Fig. P.5–36, so that it will move in a circular vertical plane. In other words, how much velocity is required so that the pendulum will move through 180 deg? Assume that the link is a rigid link.

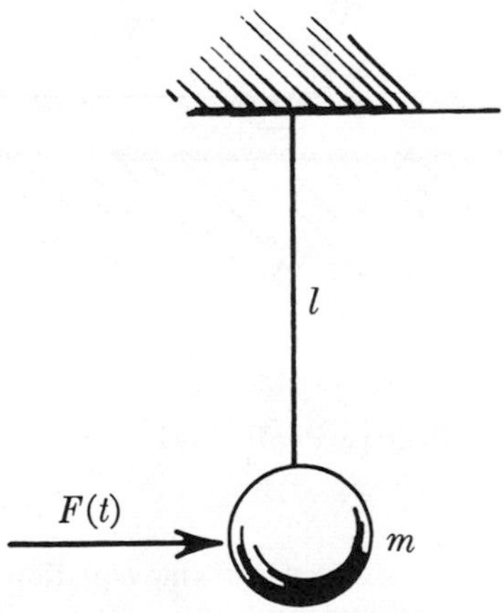

Figure Prob. 5-36

5-37. Consider Problem 5–36. Determine the minimum impulse that must be applied to the body so that it will move in a circular arc, assuming now that the link is a string that will not take a compressive force.

5-38. If the velocity of a particle is observed to be 30 fps at the point (0,0) of the curve $y = 3x^2$ as it slides down the curve under the action of a gravitational force, determine the point on the curve where the mass was released.

5-39. A mass of 30 lb is dropped onto a spring having a spring constant of 120 lb/ft. Since the system is conservative, determine (using the conservation of energy equation) how far the spring will deflect if the mass is dropped from a height of 10 ft.

5-40. A spring with a spring constant of 100 lb/ft is in an upright position with no force on it initially. A ball of weight 50 lb is placed on the spring and released. How far will the spring deflect?

5-41. If a system is conservative, then the total energy of the system will be constant, so that dE/dt must be equal to zero. Write the total energy of the system shown in Fig. P.5–41 in some arbitrary position, and show that by taking the time

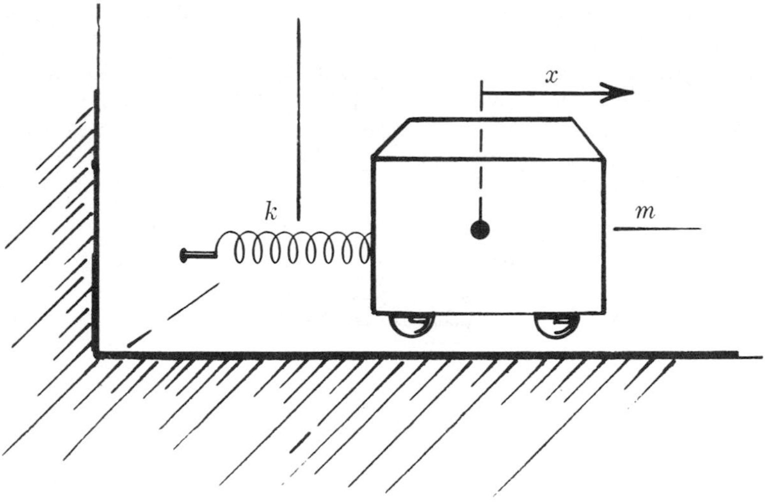

Figure Prob. 5-41

derivative of the total energy, you will get the same equation that you would have obtained by using Newton's second law.

5-42. Determine the potential-energy function of a spring force when the reference is taken at a point where the spring has been stretched a distance Δ. What is the potential-energy function for a spring force whose reference is taken at a point where the spring has been compressed a distance Δ?

5-4. POWER

Power due to a force. *Power* is defined as the time rate at which work is done by a force. Thus,

$$P = \frac{dW}{dt} \tag{5.45}$$

Then power is in general a function of time, and it represents the work done by a force per unit time at a certain instant of time. It is seen from Eq. 5.45 that power is a scalar quantity, which implies that there is no direction associated with power.

The power exerted by a force is the work done by the force per-unit time. For instance, a machine which exerts a force that can do twice as much work in the same amount of time as another machine is said to have twice the power. As it turns out, power is a convenient method for rating the capabilities of energy-producing devices. The rated power of a given motor is usually the maximum amount of work that the motor can do per given interval of time.

Now, since

$$dW = \boldsymbol{F} \cdot d\boldsymbol{r} \tag{5.46}$$

the power exerted by a force is

$$P = \boldsymbol{F} \cdot \frac{d\boldsymbol{r}}{dt} \tag{5.47}$$

or

$$P = \boldsymbol{F} \cdot \boldsymbol{v} \tag{5.48}$$

Consider the following special (but common) physical situation, where (1) the force $\boldsymbol{F}$ on the particle is a constant, and (2) the force is in the same direction as the motion of the particle. Then the equation for the power exerted by a force, for this one-dimensional case, becomes

$$\boxed{P = Fv} \tag{5.49}$$

Power in terms of the moment. The power exerted by a moment may be determined in the following manner: From Eq. 5.26 it is seen that

$$dW = \boldsymbol{M} \cdot d\boldsymbol{\theta} \tag{5.50}$$

But

$$P = \frac{dW}{dt}$$

$$= \boldsymbol{M} \cdot \frac{d\boldsymbol{\theta}}{dt} \tag{5.51}$$

so that

$$P = \boldsymbol{M} \cdot \boldsymbol{\omega} \tag{5.52}$$

For the special case of a constant moment acting about a fixed axis, the power exerted by the moment becomes

$$\boxed{P = M\omega} \tag{5.53}$$

Efficiency. In all real systems, when power is transmitted through a machine, the power output of the machine is always less than the power input to the machine. When 100 watts of electric power is supplied to a d-c motor, it may be observed that the maximum power output of the machine will be something less than 100 watts. The reason for this is that some fraction of the input power is absorbed internally in the machine and does not become available for useful work as power output. Power is absorbed internally in the machine by all bearings and moving parts where frictional forces are present. Since frictional forces may be thought of as energy-dissipating forces, some of the power supplied to the machine must be used to overcome the frictional forces.

The amount of internal-energy loss to a machine is usually measured in terms of a dimensionless ratio known as the *efficiency ratio.* Efficiency is defined as

$$\epsilon = \frac{\text{power output}}{\text{power input}} \tag{5.54}$$

Efficiency expressed as a percentage is obtained by multiplying Eq. 5.54 by 100.

From the previous discussion it is seen that the efficiency for a real system will always be a number less than 1. The perpetual-motion machine will have an efficiency of 1. The efficiency of a machine cannot be greater than 1, since from physical observations we know that the total energy of a complete physical system must be conserved.

Units. Since the units of work are FL, it must be that the units of power are FL/T, or in terms of the engineering units, *foot-pounds per second.* The use of the unit of *horsepower* is very common. Horsepower is defined as

$$1 \text{ hp} = 550 \text{ ft-lb/sec} \tag{5.55}$$

Power may also be measured in terms of the electrical units of *watts.* Watts are defined in terms of foot-pounds per second:

$$1 \text{ watt} = 0.738 \text{ ft-lb/sec} \tag{5.56}$$

Example 5–10. An electric motor (Fig. 5–12) is used to lift a 1600-lb block at a rate of 10 fpm. How much electric power (watts) must be supplied to the motor, if the motor lifting the block is 60 percent efficient? The weight W is 1600 lb.

Solution: The power requirement of the motor is the power exerted in lifting the block. The power exerted by the motor is the same as the power exerted by the force F in lifting the block. This is

$$P = Fv$$

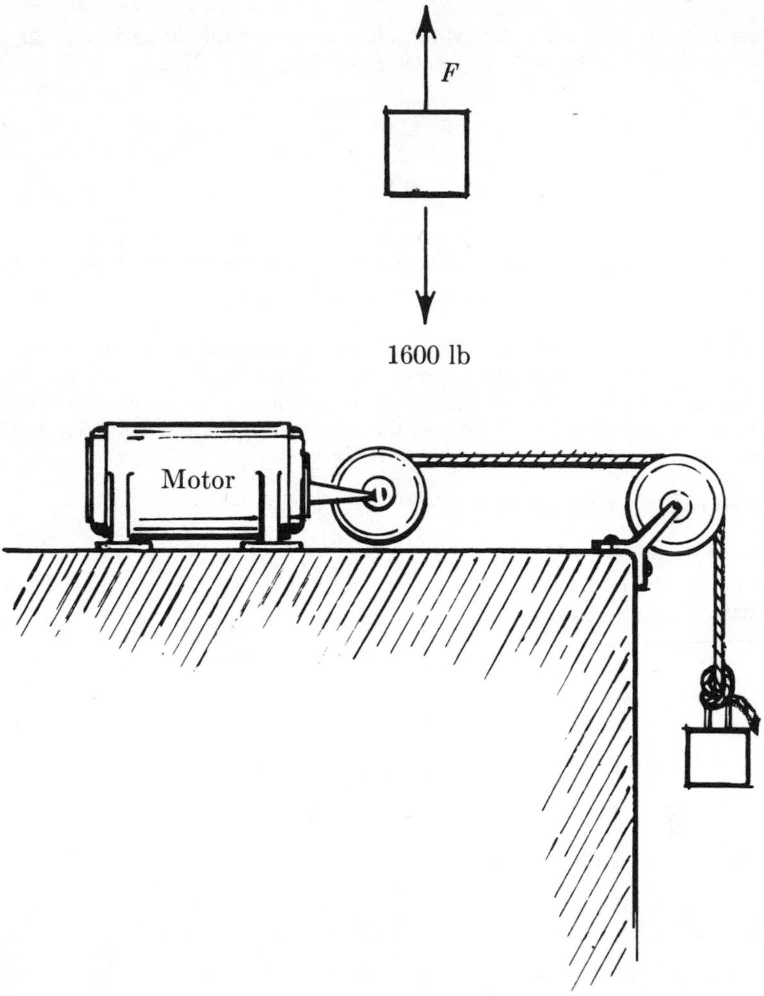

Figure 5-12

Since the block is moving at a constant velocity,

$$F = 1600 \text{ lb}$$

so that the power exerted by the motor is

$$P = Fv = (1600)\left(\frac{10}{60}\right) = 267 \text{ ft-lb/sec}$$

or, in terms of horsepower,

$$P = \frac{267}{550} = 0.485 \text{ hp}$$

This is the power required to lift the block at the velocity required, and this is the power that the motor has to produce. However, since the motor is only 60 percent efficient, the power input to the motor must be greater. Thus,

$$P_{\text{in}} = \frac{P_{\text{out}}}{\epsilon}$$

or

$$P_{\text{in}} = \frac{0.485}{0.60} = 0.81 \text{ hp}$$

and the power input in terms of the electric power supplied to the motor is

$$P_{\text{in}} = 0.81 \times 746 = 605 \text{ watts}$$

Example 5–11. A rather large motor is required to drill an oil well. In addition to the power required just to drill the rock, power is needed to overcome the frictional forces that act on the side of the drill stem. Suppose the motor that powers the drill stem is operating at 160 hp and the rotary speed of the drill stem is 80 rpm. Determine the total resistive torque of the system.

Solution: Since the power developed by a torque is

$$P = M\omega$$

in this case the power supplied is given, and it is desired to determine the torque, so that

$$M = \frac{P}{\omega}$$

The angular velocity is

$$\begin{aligned} \omega &= 80 \text{ rpm} \\ &= 2\pi \frac{80}{60} \text{ radians/sec} \\ &= 8.38 \text{ radians/sec} \end{aligned}$$

and the power supplied is

$$\begin{aligned} P &= 160 \text{ hp} \\ &= 160 \times 550 \\ &= 88{,}000 \text{ ft-lb/sec} \end{aligned}$$

Therefore the total resistive moment is

$$\begin{aligned} M &= \frac{P}{\omega} \\ &= \frac{88{,}000}{8.38} \\ &= 10{,}500 \text{ ft-lb} \end{aligned}$$

It should be noted that the total resistive torque is a combination of the torque on the bit (due to the force of the rock being drilled on the bit) and the frictional forces of the drilling fluid and the wall of the hole on the drilling stem.

PROBLEMS

5-43. How much horsepower would be required to move a 3200-lb automobile a distance of 2 miles along a 5 percent grade with a constant velocity of 60 mph?

5-44. For Problem 5–43, what is the horsepower output required of the engine if the mechanical efficiency of the transmission is only 40 percent?

5-45. A 4000-lb automobile is traveling at a constant speed of 60 mph on a level road. If the motor is producing 10 hp and the mechanical efficiency of the auto is 55 percent, what is the force of the wind on the car? Note that it is assumed that the force of the wind is the only external force on the car.

5-46. An electric motor rated at 200 watts is used to lift a block weighing 500 lb. How fast will the motor be able to lift the block if the efficiency of the motor is 90 percent?

5-47. Experiments show that a certain electric motor is 80 percent efficient. A wattmeter shows that the power input of the motor is 500 watts. If the motor is used as a lift, how large a weight may be lifted at a velocity of 2 fps?

5-48. Make a preliminary design for a motor for an elevator. The elevator weighs 2500 lb and it is to carry a maximum of ten passengers whose average weight is 160 lb. The maximum velocity of the elevator is to be 4 fps. Determine the power requirement of the motor (in terms of watts), and assume that the efficiency of the motor is 0.60.

5-49. The force required to maintain the velocity of a ship at 20 fps is 10,000 lb of thrust. What is the power requirement of the turbines driving the propellers, and what is the torque in the driveshaft of the propeller if it is spinning at 800 rpm?

5-50. What is the average power required to accelerate a 2-ton elevator, from rest, upward with a constant acceleration so that it will attain a velocity of 6 fps in 8 sec?

5-51. If the force on a particle is given as $\boldsymbol{F}(t) = 3t\bar{\boldsymbol{i}} - t^2\bar{\boldsymbol{j}} + 4\bar{\boldsymbol{k}}$ and the velocity of the particle is $\boldsymbol{v} = 6\bar{\boldsymbol{i}} - t^3\bar{\boldsymbol{j}} - (3 + t)\bar{\boldsymbol{k}}$, what is the power that the force exerts on the particle at $t = 2$ sec?

5-52. It is required to determine the amount of power or energy lost to friction in drilling an oil well. A recording device attached to the drilling bit showed that the torque on the bit as the drilling system rotated with an angular speed of 100 rpm was equal to 10,000 ft-lb. If the amount of power supplied to the drilling system was 250 hp, determine the frictional torque. How much of the supplied power was dissipated by the frictional force?

5-53. A 3600-lb automobile is traveling on a road with a 4 percent grade at a constant velocity of 30 mph. If the angular speed of the driveshaft is 1000 rpm, how much internal torque is there in the driveshaft? Assume no frictional losses.

6

Dynamics of Systems of Particles

In previous chapters, only dynamics of bodies (which can be assumed to be small particles) have been discussed. Nothing has been said about the dynamic analysis of mechanical systems that are comprised of several discrete particles which are mutually interacting.

In this chapter we shall attempt to develop methods of describing the motion of a system of discrete particles. The methods developed here will be subsequently applied to rigid bodies; a rigid body can be thought of as nothing more than a system of particles that are rigidly interconnected.

6-1. THE BASIC LAWS

The center of mass of a system of particles. It will be shown subsequently that the motion of the center of mass of a system of particles may be written as a function of the external forces that are acting on the system.

The center of mass of a system of n particles is defined in the following manner:

$$\boxed{\mathbf{r}_c = \frac{\sum_i m_i \mathbf{r}_i}{\sum_i m_i}} \qquad \textbf{(6.1)}$$

where the radius vector $\boldsymbol{r}_c$ is the displacement vector from the origin of any arbitrary, inertially fixed reference system to the center of mass of the system of particles. It was seen in statics that the center of mass of a system of particles defined the line of action of the resultant gravitational force on the system.

By expanding both sides of Eq. 6.1 into its three corresponding scalar equations, we obtain

$$x_c = \frac{\sum_i m_i x_i}{m}$$
$$y_c = \frac{\sum_i m_i y_i}{m} \tag{6.2}$$
$$z_c = \frac{\sum_i m_i z_i}{m}$$

The term m is just the total mass of the system and equal to $\sum_i m_i$, as seen in Eq. 6.1. These three scalar equations may be used to calculate the center of mass of a system of particles.

If we are able to choose our reference coordinate system in such a manner that the origin of our system coincides with the center of mass of the system, then the distance $\boldsymbol{r}_c$ to the center of mass will be zero, and it follows from Eq. 6.1 that

$$\sum_i m_i \boldsymbol{r}_i = 0 \tag{6.3}$$

This information will be used in the subsequent discussions.

If the system of particles is in motion, then the center of mass of the system will, in general, be moving with respect to inertial space, so that the vector $\boldsymbol{r}_c$ will be a function of time. The velocity and acceleration of the center of mass of the system may then be obtained by taking the first and second time derivatives of the displacement vector. Thus,

$$\boldsymbol{v}_c = \frac{d\boldsymbol{r}_c}{dt} = \frac{\sum_i m_i \boldsymbol{v}_i}{m} \tag{6.4a}$$

$$\boldsymbol{a}_c = \frac{d\boldsymbol{v}_c}{dt} = \frac{\sum_i m_i \boldsymbol{a}_i}{m} \tag{6.4b}$$

Newton's second law for a system of particles. Consider a system of n particles in space. In general, each particle has an external force applied to it. There is also an internal force applied to each particle. This internal force is the force due to the presence of the other particles. It may be a normal force of contact if the two particles lie next to each other, or it may be a force of mutual attraction, as in the case of gravitational attraction.

Shown in Fig. 6–1 is a set of the n particles in space (left) and a free-body diagram (right) of the ith particle. The force $\boldsymbol{F}_i$ represents the sum

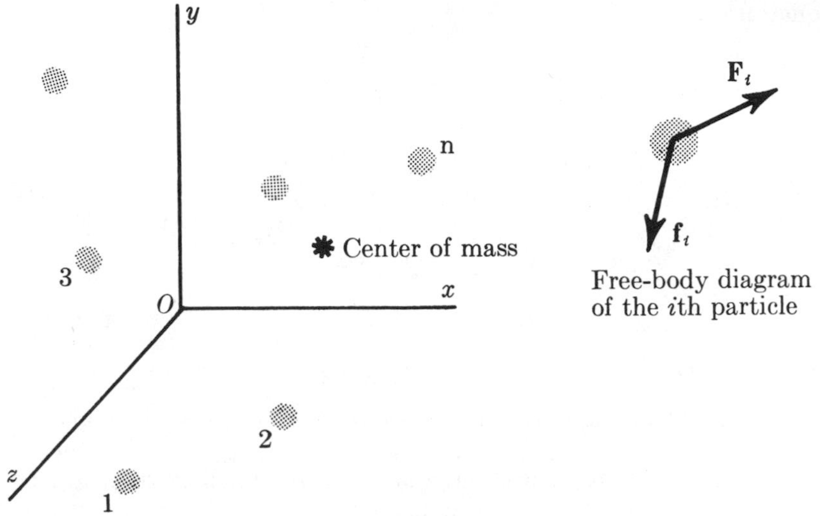

Figure 6-1

of the external forces acting on this particle, and the force $\boldsymbol{f}_i$ represents the sum of all internal forces acting on this particle. At this point, we should like to be able to describe the motion of this system of particles, but the only information we have is that we are able to write Newton's second law for a single particle. Therefore the approach we take is to write Newton's second law for each particle and then perform a summation over the system.

From the free-body diagram shown in Fig. 6–1, the equation of motion of the ith particle is

$$\boldsymbol{F}_i + \boldsymbol{f}_i = m_i\boldsymbol{a}_i \tag{6.5}$$

This equation of motion may be written for each particle of the system, and then the equations may be added to obtain

$$\sum_i \boldsymbol{F}_i + \sum_i \boldsymbol{f}_i = \sum_i m_i\boldsymbol{a}_i \tag{6.6}$$

At this point, we note that the sum of all internal forces is equal to zero. This is a consequence of Newton's third law, which states that action and reaction are equal and opposite.

In Fig. 6–2 we see two adjacent particles. Body 1 exerts a normal

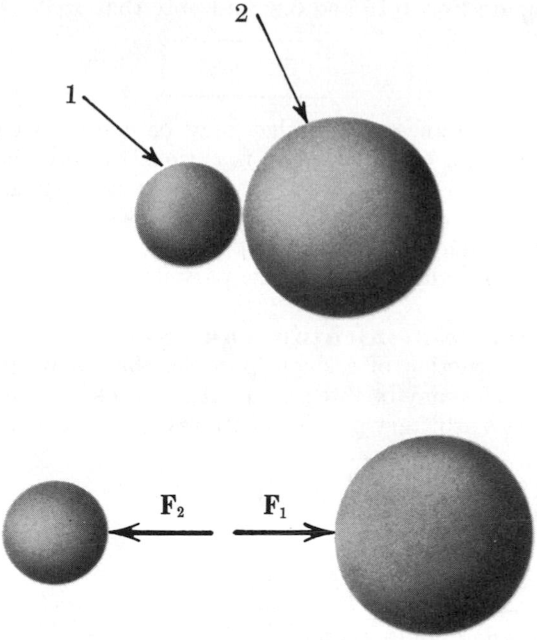

Figure 6-2

force on body 2, which is equal to $\boldsymbol{F}_1$ as shown. Body 2 will exert a normal force on body 1, which is equal to $\boldsymbol{F}_2$. By Newton's third law, $\boldsymbol{F}_1$ will be equal to a minus $\boldsymbol{F}_2$.

This implies, then, that in the system of n particles, all internal forces will occur in equal, opposite, and colinear pairs. Thus,

$$\sum_i \boldsymbol{f}_i = 0 \qquad \textbf{(6.7)}$$

and the equation of motion of the system becomes

$$\boldsymbol{F} = \sum_i m_i \boldsymbol{a}_i \qquad \textbf{(6.8)}$$

where

$$\boldsymbol{F} = \sum_i \boldsymbol{F}_i \qquad \textbf{(6.9)}$$

The force $\boldsymbol{F}$ is then interpreted as the sum of all external forces acting on the system.

Recall now the definition of the center of mass of a system of particles. From Eq. 6.4(b) it follows that

$$m\boldsymbol{a}_c = \sum_i m_i \boldsymbol{a}_i \qquad \textbf{(6.10)}$$

We compare Eqs. 6.10 and 6.8, and note that

$$\boxed{\boldsymbol{F} = m\boldsymbol{a}_c} \tag{6.11}$$

We now have an equation that may be considered the equation of motion of a system of particles. It is curious to note that the center of mass of the system of particles behaves in exactly the same way that a single particle will, of course assuming that this single particle has a mass equal to that of the system, and that the lines of action of the forces on the system all pass through the single particle.

The impulse-momentum equation. Just as in the case for the equation of motion of a single particle, the equation of motion of a system of particles may be integrated with respect to time. By integrating between any two arbitrary positions with respect to time, Eq. 6.11 becomes

$$\int_A^B \boldsymbol{F}\,dt = \int_A^B m\left(\frac{d\boldsymbol{v}_c}{dt}\right)dt \tag{6.12}$$

or

$$\int_A^B \boldsymbol{F}\,dt = m\boldsymbol{v}_{cB} - m\boldsymbol{v}_{cA} \tag{6.13}$$

This, then, is the impulse-momentum equation for a system of particles.

Consider now the case where there are no external forces acting on the system. Then the equation of motion becomes

$$0 = m\boldsymbol{a}_c$$

$$0 = \frac{d}{dt}(m\boldsymbol{v}_c) \tag{6.14}$$

Equation 6.14 implies, then, that if there are no external forces acting on a system of particles,

$$m\boldsymbol{v}_c = \text{constant} \tag{6.15}$$

This says that for the case in which no external forces are acting on a system, the total momentum of the system will be a constant.

This is known as the *conservation of momentum theorem.*

Expanded in terms of the three scalar Cartesian components, Eq. 6.15 becomes

$$\begin{aligned} m\dot{x}_c &= C_1 \\ m\dot{y}_c &= C_2 \\ m\dot{z}_c &= C_3 \end{aligned} \tag{6.16}$$

where C_1, C_2, and C_3 are the independent constants of integration.

It is quite possible to have momentum conserved in only one or two directions. If, for instance, there is an external force acting on a system, and that external force is acting in the x direction, then momentum will be conserved in the y and z directions, but momentum will not be conserved in the x direction.

Work. Consider again the ith particle of a system of n particles. Under the combined action of the external force and the internal force, the particle will move along some path in space. In Fig. 6–3 the total external force acting on the particle is given as $\boldsymbol{F}_i$, and the total internal

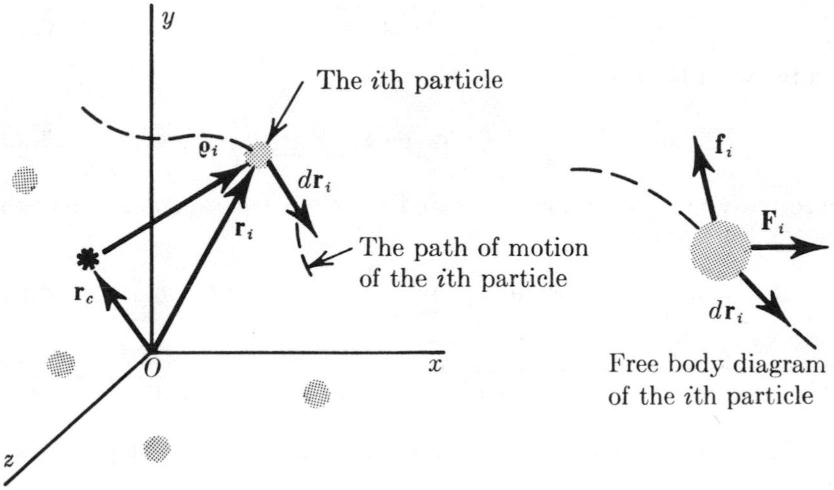

Figure 6-3

force on the particle is $\boldsymbol{f}_i$. As the particle moves through a small displacement, $d\boldsymbol{r}_i$, the work done by forces on the particle is

$$dW_i = (\boldsymbol{F}_i + \boldsymbol{f}_i) \cdot d\boldsymbol{r}_i \tag{6.17}$$

and the total work done by the forces as this particle moves from one point to another is obtained by a summation or integration:

$$\int_A^B dW_i = W_{AB_i} = \int_A^B (\boldsymbol{F}_i + \boldsymbol{f}_i) \cdot d\boldsymbol{r}_i \tag{6.18}$$

The work of all the forces on the whole system as the system moves from one configuration to another may be obtained by summing over the system. Thus,

$$\sum_i W_{AB_i} = W_{AB} = \sum_i \int_A^B (\boldsymbol{F}_i + \boldsymbol{f}_i) \cdot d\boldsymbol{r}_i \tag{6.19}$$

Equation 6.19 may be written as

$$W_{AB} = \sum_i \int_A^B \boldsymbol{F} \cdot d\boldsymbol{r}_i + \sum_i \int_A^B \boldsymbol{f}_i \cdot d\boldsymbol{r}_i \tag{6.20}$$

Therefore the total work done on a system of particles as the system moves from one configuration to another is equal to the work done by the external forces plus the work done by the internal forces.

The work done on a system of particles will now be expressed in terms of the work done by the external forces in moving the center of mass of a system. From Fig. 6–3 we note that

$$\boldsymbol{r}_i = \boldsymbol{r}_c + \boldsymbol{\rho}_i \tag{6.21}$$

so that

$$d\boldsymbol{r}_i = d\boldsymbol{r}_c + d\boldsymbol{\rho}_i \tag{6.22}$$

and the work becomes

$$W_{AB} = \sum_i \int_A^B \boldsymbol{F}_i \cdot (d\boldsymbol{r}_c + d\boldsymbol{\rho}_i) + \sum_i \int_A^B \boldsymbol{f}_i \cdot d\boldsymbol{r}_i \tag{6.23}$$

Since the vector $d\boldsymbol{r}_c$ is a constant and therefore is not summed over the system, the work may be written as

$$W_{AB} = \int_A^B \boldsymbol{F} \cdot d\boldsymbol{r}_c + \sum_i \int_A^B (\boldsymbol{F}_i \cdot d\boldsymbol{\rho}_i + \boldsymbol{f}_i \cdot d\boldsymbol{r}_i) \tag{6.24}$$

where the force $\boldsymbol{F}$ is again just the sum of the external forces on the system. This is just another form of work, and will be used in a later discussion.

Kinetic energy. The kinetic energy of a system of particles is just the sum of the kinetic energy of each of the particles:

$$\boxed{T = \sum_i \tfrac{1}{2} m_i v_i^2} \tag{6.25}$$

At this point, we shall examine another form of the kinetic energy; specifically we shall attempt to write the kinetic energy in terms of the velocity of the center of mass of the system. First we note that

$$v_i^2 = \boldsymbol{v}_i \cdot \boldsymbol{v}_i \tag{6.26}$$

The position vector $\boldsymbol{r}_i$ of the particle may be written in terms of the position vector of the center of mass of the system. This was done in Eq. 6.21. By differentiating Eq. 6.21 with respect to time,

$$\boldsymbol{v}_i = \boldsymbol{v}_c + \dot{\boldsymbol{\rho}}_i \tag{6.27}$$

By substituting Eq. 6.27 into Eq. 6.26, we get

$$v_i^2 = (\boldsymbol{v}_c + \dot{\boldsymbol{\rho}}_i) \cdot (\boldsymbol{v}_c + \dot{\boldsymbol{\rho}}_i) \tag{6.28}$$

Then

$$v_i^2 = v_c^2 + 2\boldsymbol{v}_c \cdot \dot{\boldsymbol{\rho}}_i + \dot{\rho}_i^2 \tag{6.29}$$

and

$$T = \sum_i \tfrac{1}{2} m_i v_c^2 + \sum_i m_i \boldsymbol{v}_c \cdot \dot{\boldsymbol{\rho}}_i + \sum_i \tfrac{1}{2} m_i \dot{\rho}_i^2 \tag{6.30}$$

Since the velocity of the center of mass of the system is not summed over the system, we note that

$$\sum_i m_i \boldsymbol{v}_c \cdot \dot{\boldsymbol{\rho}}_i = \boldsymbol{v}_c \cdot \sum_i m_i \dot{\boldsymbol{\rho}}_i \tag{6.31}$$

But

$$\sum_i m_i \dot{\boldsymbol{\rho}}_i = \frac{d}{dt} \sum_i m_i \boldsymbol{\rho}_i \tag{6.32}$$

and since $\boldsymbol{\rho}_i$ is measured from the center of mass of the system, then the expression on the right-hand side of Eq. 6.32 is equal to zero. (See Eq. 6.3 and accompanying discussion.)

Finally, the kinetic energy of the system may be written as

$$\boxed{T = \tfrac{1}{2} m v_c^2 + \sum_i \tfrac{1}{2} m_i \dot{\rho}_i^2} \tag{6.33}$$

This says that the kinetic energy of the system is the kinetic energy of the center of mass plus the kinetic energy of the system measured relative to the center of mass.

Potential energy. If all forces, both external and internal, on a system of particles are conservative, then there exists a potential-energy function for the whole system. As in the case of the single particle, the potential energy V may be defined in terms of the work done by all forces:

$$W_{AB} = V_A - V_B \tag{6.34}$$

where points A and B refer to any two configurations of the system of particles at two different instances in time. The potential-energy function for the whole system is the sum of the potential-energy functions for each of the forces.

The potential energy in terms of the forces on the particles may be expressed as in the case of the single particle. The forces in the x, y, and z directions on the ith particle of the system may be written as

$$\begin{aligned} \boldsymbol{F}_{x_i} &= -\frac{\partial V}{\partial x_i} \\ \boldsymbol{F}_{y_i} &= -\frac{\partial V}{\partial y_i} \\ \boldsymbol{F}_{z_i} &= -\frac{\partial V}{\partial z_i} \end{aligned} \tag{6.35}$$

In forming a potential-energy function for a system of particles, Eq. 6.35 may be employed as a check on the calculations.

The work-energy equation. The work-energy equation for the ith particle may be written as

$$W_{AB_i} = T_{B_i} - T_{A_i} \tag{6.36}$$

and the work-energy equation for the whole system may be constructed by adding the work-energy equation for each particle of the system together:

$$\sum_i W_{AB_i} = \sum_i (T_{B_i} - T_{A_i}) \tag{6.37}$$

Equation 6.37 may be written simply as

$$\boxed{W_{AB} = T_B - T_A} \tag{6.38}$$

This equation is identical to the work-energy equation for a single particle. It must be understood, however, that the work done on a system of particles includes not only the work done by all external forces on the particle but also the work done by the internal forces on the particles.

By expanding Eq. 6.38 by substituting Eqs. 6.24 and 6.33, we get

$$\int_A^B \boldsymbol{F} \cdot d\boldsymbol{r}_c = \sum_i \int_A^B (\boldsymbol{F}_i \cdot d\boldsymbol{\rho}_i + \boldsymbol{f}_i \cdot d\boldsymbol{r}_c)$$

$$= \tfrac{1}{2}mv_c^2 + \sum_i \tfrac{1}{2}m_i\dot{\rho}_i^2 \Big|_A^B \tag{6.39}$$

The equation of motion of a system of particles may be integrated with respect to displacement of the center of mass just as the equation of motion of a single particle was integrated to obtain the work-energy equation. Thus,

$$\int_A^B \boldsymbol{F} \cdot d\boldsymbol{r}_c = \tfrac{1}{2}mv_{cB}^2 - \tfrac{1}{2}mv_{cA}^2 \tag{6.40}$$

Using this result, Eq. 6.39 becomes

$$\sum_i \int_A^B (\boldsymbol{F}_i \cdot d\boldsymbol{\rho}_i + \boldsymbol{f}_i \cdot d\boldsymbol{r}_i) = \sum_i \tfrac{1}{2}m_i\dot{\rho}_i^2 \Big|_A^B \tag{6.41}$$

Equations 6.40 and 6.41 demonstrate, if nothing else, that the internal forces on the system have no effect upon the motion of the center of mass of the system. Equation 6.40 will be employed in the next chapter, which deals with the motion of rigid bodies.

Example 6–1. At $t = 0$, three particles are in a position as shown in Fig. 6–4. At this instant, particle 1 has a mass of 1 and a velocity of 3 upward. Particle 2 has a mass of 5 and a velocity of 2 in the positive x direction, and particle 3 has a mass of 4 and a velocity of 6 in the negative x direction. If there are no external forces on this system, determine (a) the subsequent motion of the center of mass, and (b) the total kinetic energy of the system of particles. The particles move in a horizontal plane.

Solution: Since there are no external forces acting on the system, momentum is conserved. Thus,

$$mv_c = \text{constant}$$

The first problem is to determine the constant. This is done by using the definition

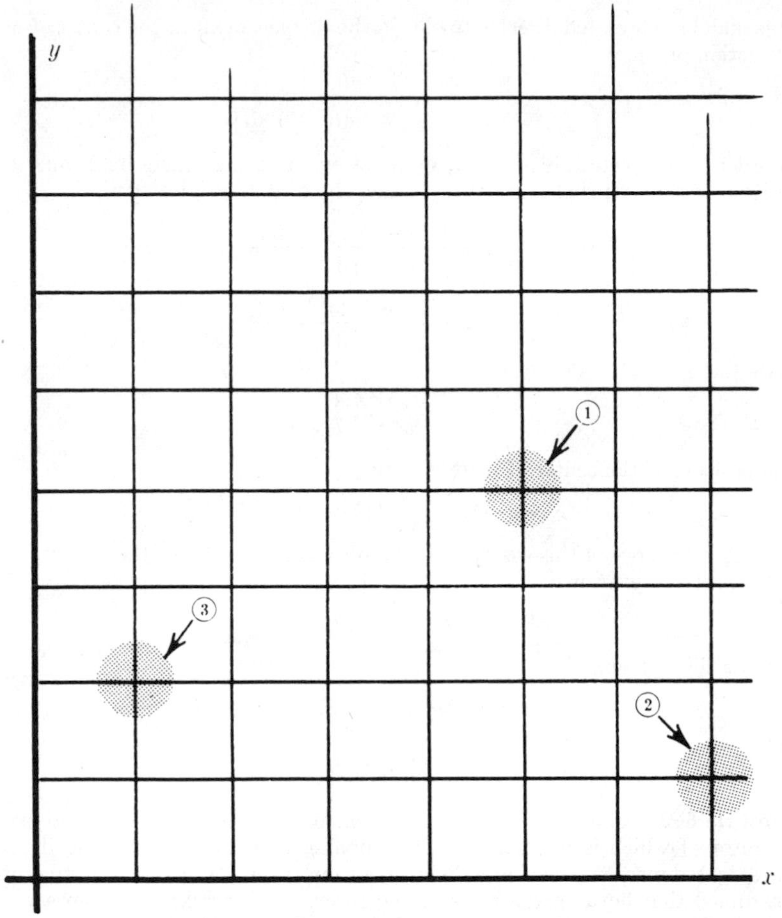

Figure 6-4

of the center of mass of the system and the fact that the velocity of each of the particles is known at $t = 0$.

$$\begin{aligned} m\boldsymbol{v}_c &= \sum_i m_i \boldsymbol{v}_i \\ &= (1)(3\bar{\boldsymbol{j}}) + (5)(2\bar{\boldsymbol{i}}) + (4)(-6\bar{\boldsymbol{i}}) \\ &= -14\bar{\boldsymbol{i}} + 3\bar{\boldsymbol{j}} \end{aligned}$$

The total mass m is

$$\begin{aligned} m &= m_1 + m_2 + m_3 \\ &= 1 + 5 + 4 \\ &= 10 \end{aligned}$$

Finally, the velocity of the center of mass is

$$\boldsymbol{v}_c = \frac{-14\bar{\boldsymbol{i}} + 3\bar{\boldsymbol{j}}}{10} = -1.4\bar{\boldsymbol{i}} + 0.3\bar{\boldsymbol{j}}$$

This may be integrated directly to obtain the displacement of the center of mass as a function of time:

$$\begin{aligned} \boldsymbol{r}_c &= \boldsymbol{r}_O + \int \boldsymbol{v}_c \, dt \\ &= \boldsymbol{r}_O + [-1.4t\bar{\boldsymbol{i}} + 0.3t\bar{\boldsymbol{j}}] \end{aligned}$$

In order to complete this problem, we must evaluate the constants x_O and y_O. The position of the center of mass at $t = 0$ may be evaluated directly:

$$x_c = \frac{1(5) + 5(7) + 4(1)}{10}$$

$$y_c = \frac{1(4) + 5(1) + 4(2)}{10}$$

so that

$$\begin{aligned} x_c &= 4.4 \\ y_c &= 1.7 \end{aligned}$$

The position of the center of mass is then

$$\boldsymbol{r}_c = [-1.4t + 4.4]\bar{\boldsymbol{i}} + [0.3t + 1.7]\bar{\boldsymbol{j}}$$

The kinetic energy of this system may be obtained directly, as the velocity of each of the particles is known:

$$T = \sum_i \tfrac{1}{2} m_i v_i^2$$

and, for this system,

$$T = \tfrac{1}{2}(1)(3)^2 + \tfrac{1}{2}(5)(2)^2 + \tfrac{1}{2}(4)(6)^2$$

and

$$T = 86.5$$

Example 6–2. Shown in Fig. 6–5 is a schematic diagram of an electrical machine, the rotor of which is unbalanced. The unbalance is shown schematically by the concentrated mass m placed at a distance e from the axis of rotation of the rotor. It is assumed that both m, the mass of the rotor, and e are known from a previous analysis. The mass of the remainder of the machine is M. The machine is placed on four mounts, shown as two in the figure. It is assumed that these mounts offer no resistance to the motion of the machine in the lateral direction for small oscillations. It is desired, then, to determine the motion of the machine in the lateral direction; the first thing to do is to establish a mathematical model. This is done in Fig. 6–5. The mass M moves on the rod shown with no friction between the mass and the rod. Determine the motion of the large mass, that is, the motion of the machine when the angular velocity of the rotor is ω.

Solution: Consider the system shown in Fig. 6–5. Since there are no external forces in the lateral direction, momentum of the system will be conserved in the lateral direction. This implies, then, that if the system starts from rest, the center of mass of the system will be at rest until such time that there is an external force on the system. It might also be noted that momentum is not conserved in the vertical, or y, direction because the bar shown in Fig. 6–5 must be exerting a force on M by virtue of the motion of m. If the lateral velocity of M is $\dot{x}_1$ and the lateral velocity of m is $\dot{x}_2$, then the statement that momentum of the system is conserved may be written as

$$m_T \dot{x}_c = M\dot{x}_1 + m\dot{x}_2 = 0$$

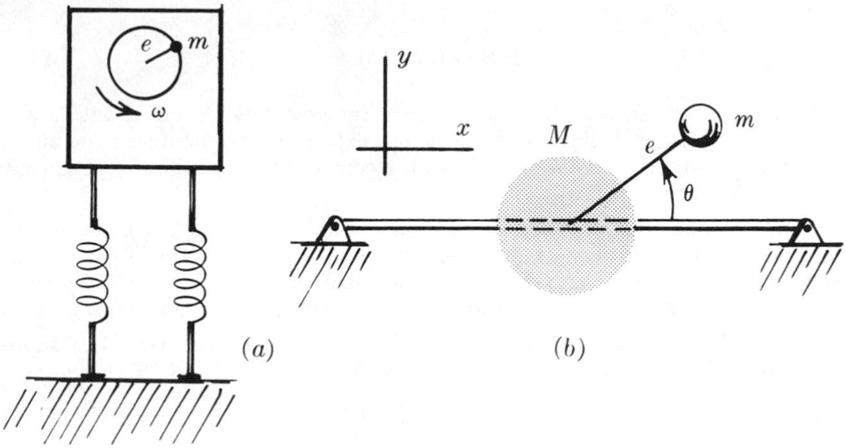

Figure 6-5

Now $\dot{x}_1$ may be expressed in terms of $\dot{x}_2$ by the relative velocity equation:

$$\boldsymbol{v}_2 = \boldsymbol{v}_1 + \boldsymbol{v}_{2/1}$$

or, for the x direction only, as

$$\dot{x}_2 = \dot{x}_1 + \dot{x}_{2/1}$$

The velocity of m with respect to M, $\dot{x}_{2/1}$, in the x direction may be evaluated by considering Fig. 6–5(b).

From Fig. 6–5, it is seen that

$$\dot{x}_{2/1} = -e\omega \sin \theta$$

so that

$$\dot{x}_2 = \dot{x}_1 - e\omega \sin \theta$$

and

$$M\dot{x}_1 + m(\dot{x}_1 - e\omega \sin \theta) = 0$$

Solving for the velocity of M,

$$\dot{x}_1 = \frac{me\omega \sin \theta}{M + m}$$

The displacement of the large mass M as a function of time may be determined by performing a time integration on the velocity, noting that $\theta = \omega t$:

$$x_1 = \frac{me}{M + m} \sin \omega t$$

This gives the lateral displacement of the machine due to the unbalance. It should be noted that the results obtained are quite conservative, owing to the fact that the mounts were assumed to give no lateral support, whereas the mounts are bound to give some lateral resistance. It should also be noted from the preceding equation that, under ordinary circumstances, the magnitude of the displacement of M should be relatively small, since both m and e are likely to be much smaller than M.

PROBLEMS

6-1. An explosive shell is traveling in space (no gravitational force) with a constant velocity. If the shell suddenly explodes, explain briefly (and showing any of the pertinent equations) what happens to the center of mass of the shell fragments after the explosion.

6-2. The calculated motion of a ballistic shell is a parabolic arc due to the earth's gravitational force. Owing to a malfunction of the system, the shell explodes at a point on its trajectory. What is the subsequent motion of the system of fragments? Explain what happens to the center of mass and show all pertinent equations.

6-3. The three particles occupy the positions and have the velocities shown (Fig. P.6-3) at $t = 0$. The speeds of the particles are tabulated. If there are no

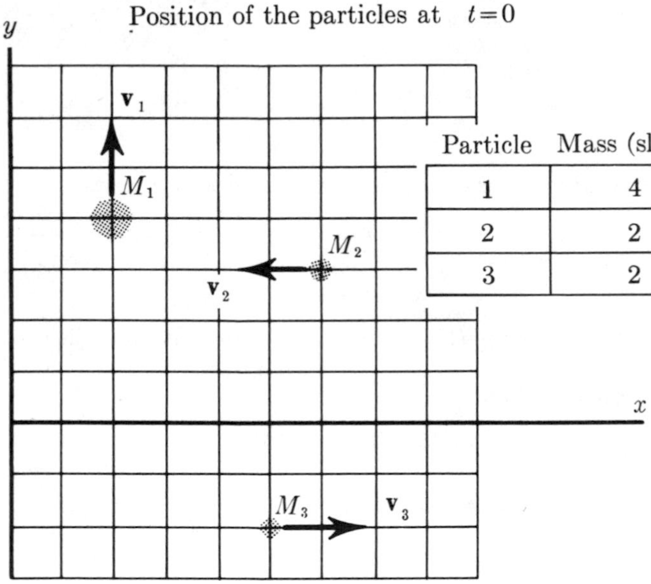

Particle	Mass (slugs)	$\mathbf{v}_O$ (fps)
1	4	3
2	2	2
3	2	8

Figure Prob. 6-3

external forces on the system, the particles will continue to move in the same directions with the same speeds. Determine the kinetic energy of the system for any time t.

6-4. For Problem 6-3, determine the subsequent motion of the center of mass of the system. Determine the radius-vector, describing the position of the center of mass as a function of time.

6-5. Consider Problem 6-3. Suppose now that forces act on the system. Specifically, the force on the first mass is $2\bar{i} + 6t\bar{j}$, and the force on the second mass is $2t\bar{i} + 4\bar{j}$. Integrate the equation of motion directly to obtain the position of the center of mass as a function of time.

6-6. A man is standing on the end of a long cart on frictionless rollers (Fig. P.6-6). If he were to walk to the opposite end of the cart, what would happen to the center of mass of the cart? The cart has a mass M and the man has a mass m.

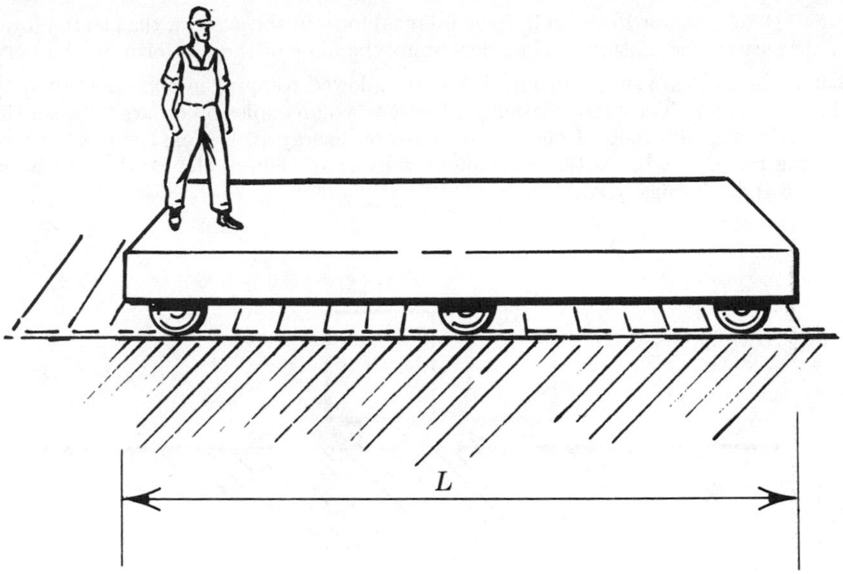

Figure Prob. 6-6

6-7. A 160-lb motorized cart is resting on a 3220-lb platform, which in turn is resting on frictionless rollers (Fig. P.6–7). The cart starts from rest and accelerates to the right. If the velocity as a function of time of the platform is observed to be equal to $0.20t$ ft/sec to the left, what is the velocity and acceleration of the cart?

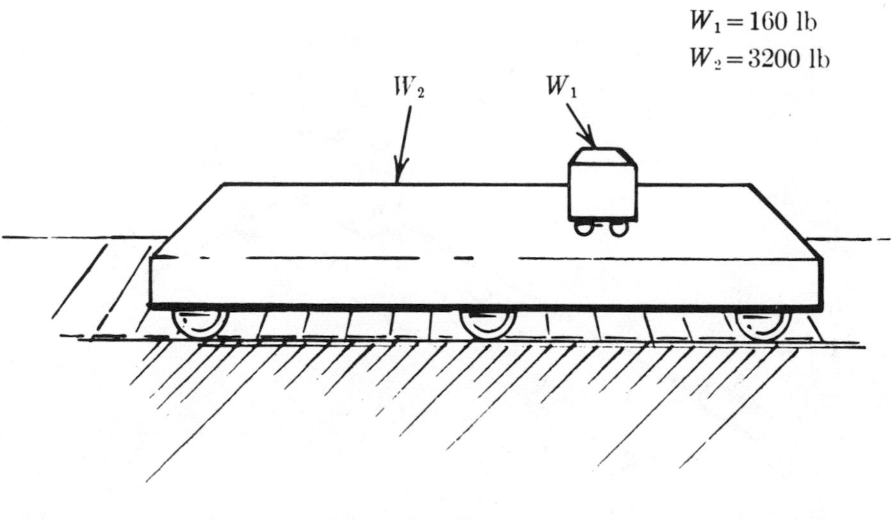

Figure Prob. 6-7

6-8. Determine for Problem 6–7 the internal force in the system, that is, the force of the cart on the platform. Then determine the force of the platform on the cart.

6-9. The two cars shown in Fig. P.6–9 are allowed to move in one direction only along the track. They are originally at rest when an explosion occurs between the two, releasing 400 ft-lb of energy. If the total energy of the explosion goes into moving the cars, what is the subsequent velocity of each of the cars? The masses are 0.5 and 1.5 slugs, respectively.

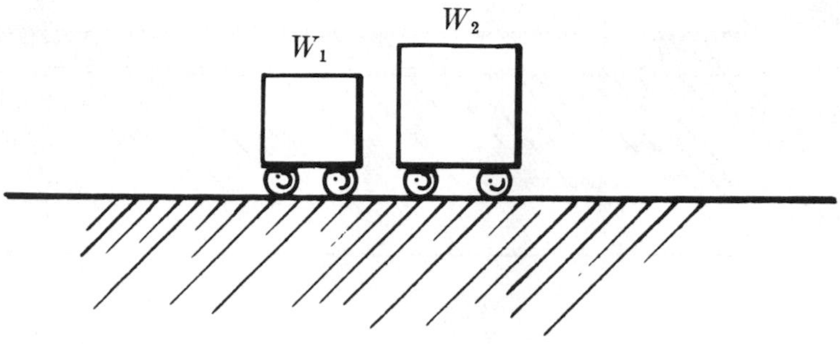

Figure Prob. 6-9

6-10. The system shown in Fig. P.6–10 is constrained to move in a horizontal plane. A small rocket is attached to the second mass so that its thrust is always in a direction perpendicular to the essentially weightless bar that connects the two

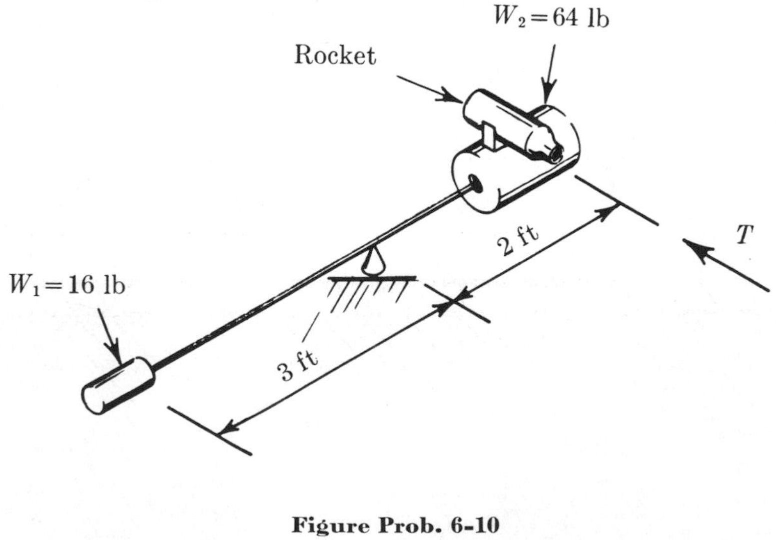

Figure Prob. 6-10

masses. The fuel burned by the rocket releases 40 ft-lb of energy. Determine the angular speed of the system after the fuel is burned, assuming that the system starts from rest and that 60 percent of the energy is available to move the system.

6-11. The two weights shown in Fig. P.6–11 are suspended at the center of mass and given an initial angular velocity of 2 radians/sec. The bar is then released and allowed to fall. What is the total kinetic energy of the system after the center of mass of the system is allowed to fall through a distance of 10 ft?

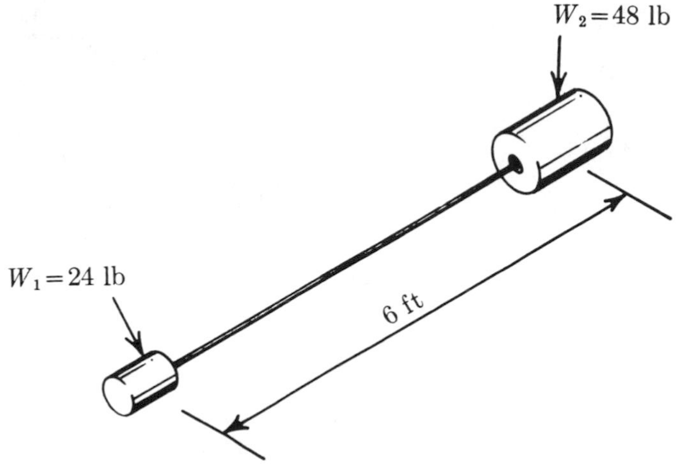

Figure Prob. 6-11

6-12. A projectile is traveling with a speed of 1000 fps and explodes into four fragments. Each fragment weighs 5 lb. If the velocity of each fragment is as tabulated in Fig. P.6–12, determine how much energy was released by the explosion.

6-13. The motor-driven eccentric in Fig. P.6–13 rotates with a constant angular velocity of 120 rpm. If the eccentric weight weighs 2 lb and is placed at a distance of 3 in. from its axis of rotation, and the weight of the block is 60 lb, determine (a) the velocity of the large block as a function of time, and (b) the internal force as a function of time, that is, the force of the eccentric acting on the block. Here, both eccentric and block may be treated as single particles. The system is initially at rest.

6-14. In their orbit about the sun, the earth and the moon revolve around each other about their center of mass. If the mean distance from the center of the earth to the center of the moon is 239,100 miles and if the earth weighs 83 times as much as the moon, determine the distance of the center of mass of the earth-moon system from the center of the earth, noting that the radius of the earth is 4000 miles.

6-15. Show that the equation of motion in the y direction of a machine, as discussed in Example 6–2, is $(M + m)\ddot{y}_1 + ky_1 = me\omega^2 \sin \omega t$. The coordinate y_1 is the displacement of the center of mass of the block upward from the equilibrium position.

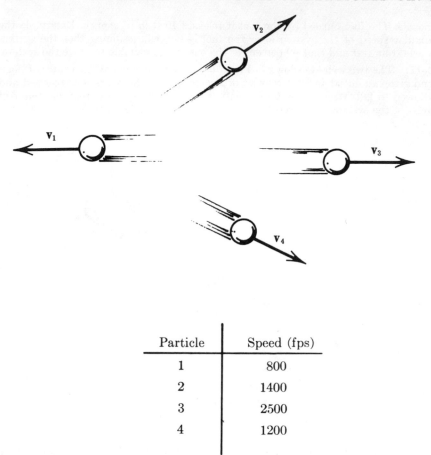

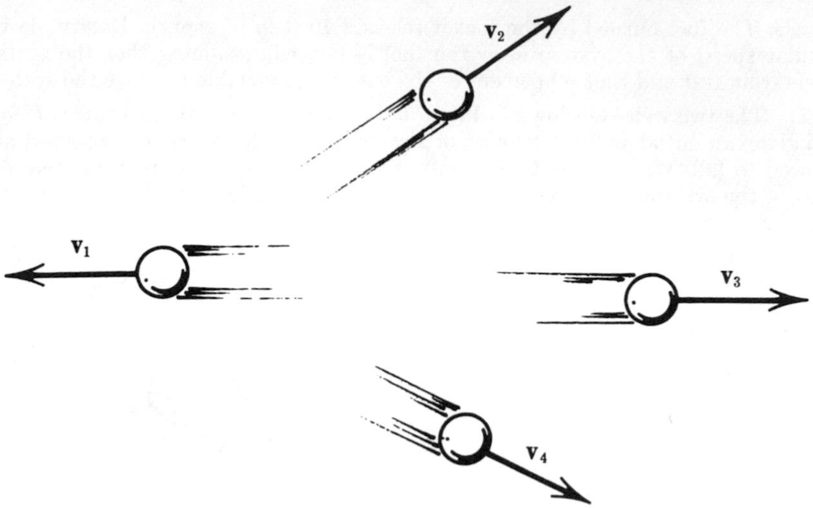

Particle	Speed (fps)
1	800
2	1400
3	2500
4	1200

Figure Prob. 6-12

6-2. THE MOMENT EQUATION

In this section we shall examine the relationship between the external moment on a system of particles, about some point in space, and the motion of that system. We are quite interested in this relationship in the case where the particles are physically connected to form one rigid body. As we shall see in Chapter 8 on rigid-body motion, the external moment may be related to the angular motion of that body.

The moment of the forces on a system of particles. Consider now a system of n particles with, in general, an external force applied to each particle along with a set of interacting internal forces. Shown in Fig. 6–6 is a free-body diagram of one of the particles of the set, say, the ith particle. The net external force acting on the body is shown

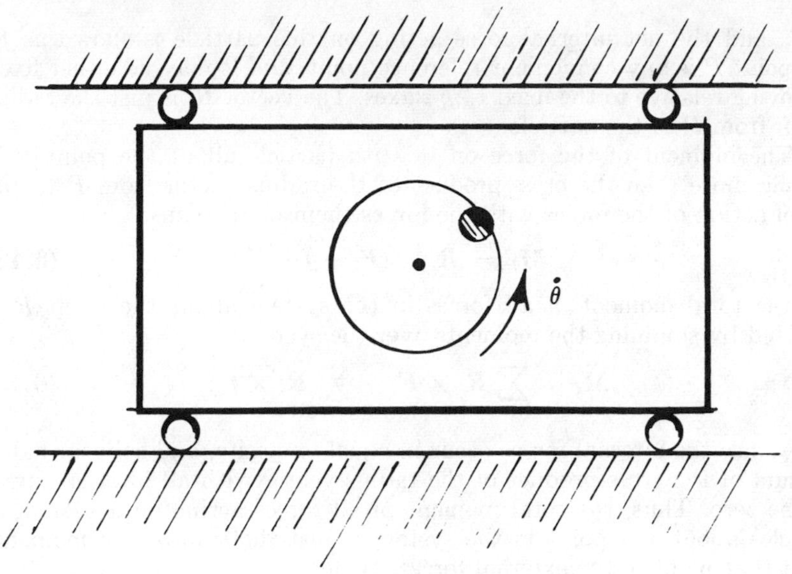

Figure Prob. 6-13

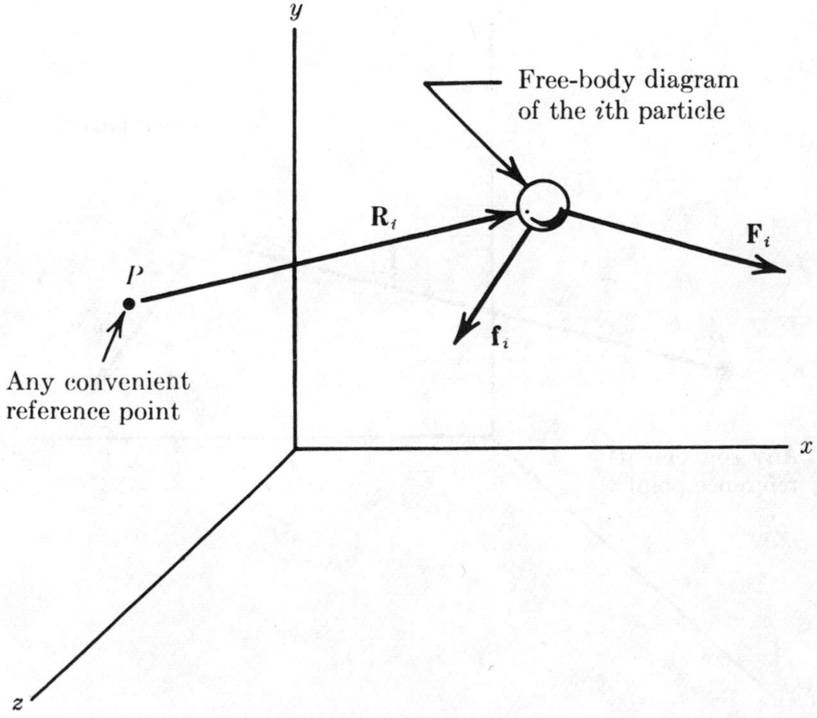

Figure 6-6

as $\boldsymbol{F}_i$, and the net internal force acting on this particle is shown as $\boldsymbol{f}_i$. The point P is any convenient reference point, and it may be either fixed or moving relative to the fixed x, y, z axes. The vector $\boldsymbol{R}_1$ is just the radius vector from P to the particle.

The moment of the force on this ith particle about the point P is nothing more than the cross-product of the radius vector from P to the line of action of the forces with the forces themselves. Thus,

$$\boldsymbol{M}_{P_i} = \boldsymbol{R}_i \times (\boldsymbol{F}_i + \boldsymbol{f}_i) \tag{6.42}$$

and the total moment of all forces in the system about the point P is obtained by summing the moments over the system:

$$\boldsymbol{M}_P = \sum_i \boldsymbol{R}_i \times \boldsymbol{F}_i + \sum_i \boldsymbol{R}_i \times \boldsymbol{f}_i \tag{6.43}$$

Now, since the internal forces occur in equal, opposite, and colinear pairs, the sum of the cross-product of the radius vector with all internal forces will be zero. Thus, the total moment of all forces acting on a system of particles about any point in the system is just the sum of the moments about that point of the external forces. Hence,

$$\boldsymbol{M}_P = \sum_i \boldsymbol{R}_i \times \boldsymbol{F}_i \tag{6.44}$$

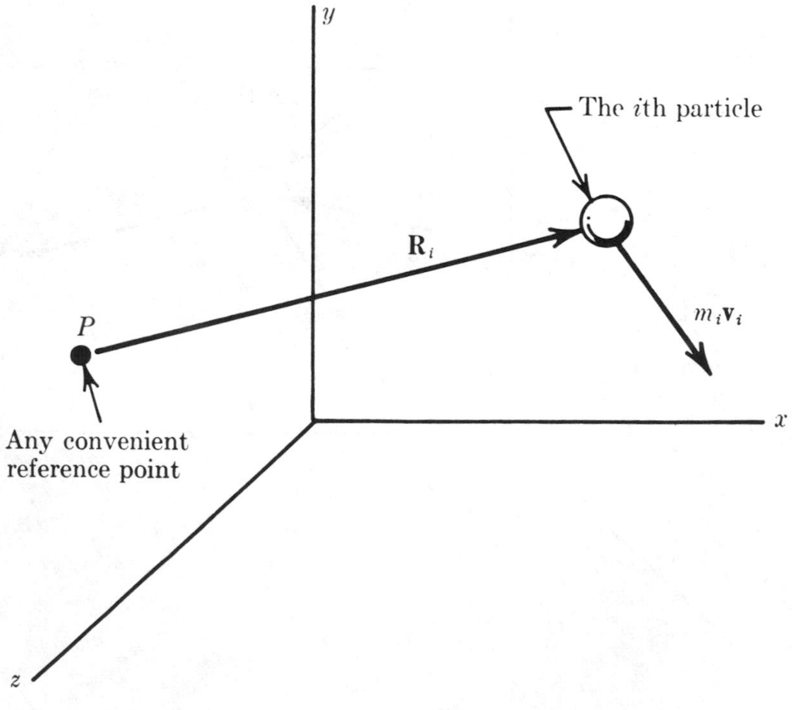

Figure 6-7

The moment of momentum about a point. Consider again the ith particle. Shown in Fig. 6–7 is the ith particle along with a vector representing the momentum of that particle at a particular instant of time. The *moment of momentum* of this particle about any reference point P may be defined as the magnitude of the momentum times the perpendicular distance from P to the momentum vector. It is seen that the moment of momentum is defined in exactly the same way that the moment of a force was defined. With this in mind, the moment of momentum of a particle may be defined also as a vector and written as

$$\boldsymbol{H}_{P_i} = \boldsymbol{R}_i \times m_i \boldsymbol{v}_i \tag{6.45}$$

The letter $\boldsymbol{H}$ is used to denote moment of momentum.

The total moment of momentum of the n particles of the system about the reference point P may be determined by taking the summation over the whole system. Thus,

$$\boxed{\boldsymbol{H}_P = \sum_i \boldsymbol{R}_i \times m_i \boldsymbol{v}_i} \tag{6.46}$$

Units. It may be seen from any of the above expressions for the moment of momentum that the units for the moment of momentum are $L(FT^2/L)L/T$, or FLT; or, in the engineering system, *foot-pound-second.*

The relationship between the moment and the moment of momentum for a system of particles. The moment of momentum of a system of particles about any convenient reference point P in the three-dimensional space may be related to the moment of the external forces on the system about that same point P. Consider again the ith particle of a system of n particles.

In Fig. 6–8, the point P is again any convenient reference point, either fixed in or moving relative to the x, y, z system. The position $\boldsymbol{r}_C$ of the moving center of mass of the system of particles is presumed to be known. A free-body diagram of the ith particle is shown, and again $\boldsymbol{F}_i$ is the net external force on the particle and $\boldsymbol{f}_i$ is the net internal force on the particle. The equation of motion of this ith particle is

$$\boldsymbol{F}_i + \boldsymbol{f}_i = m_i \boldsymbol{a}_i \tag{6.47}$$

Taking the cross-product of both sides of this equation with the radius vector from P to the ith particle,

$$\boldsymbol{R}_i \times (\boldsymbol{F}_i + \boldsymbol{f}_i) = \boldsymbol{R}_i \times m_i \boldsymbol{a}_i \tag{6.48}$$

and, summing over the system of n particles,

$$\sum_i \boldsymbol{R}_i \times (\boldsymbol{F}_i + \boldsymbol{f}_i) = \sum_i \boldsymbol{R}_i \times m_i \boldsymbol{a}_i \tag{6.49}$$

It is to be noted that, from a previous discussion, the sum of the moments of the internal forces, $\sum_i \boldsymbol{R}_i \times \boldsymbol{f}_i$, is equal to zero. The left-hand

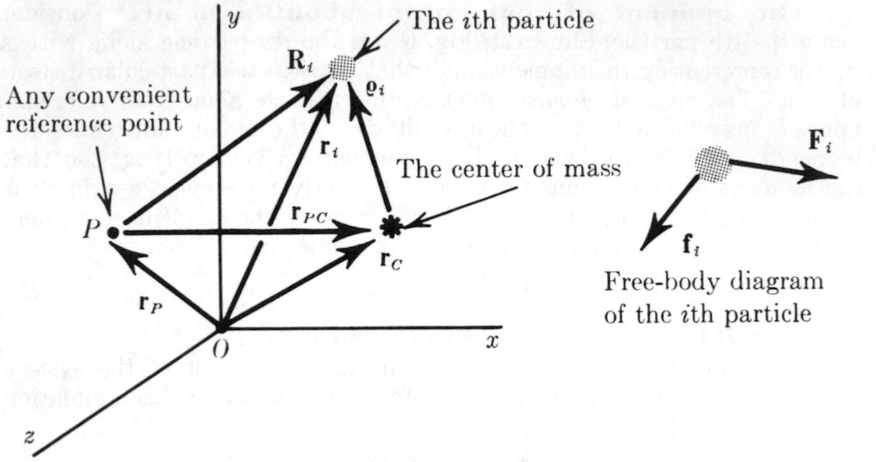

Figure 6-8

side of Eq. 6.49 is just the moment of the external forces about the point P. Thus,

$$\boldsymbol{M}_P = \sum_i \boldsymbol{R}_i \times m_i \boldsymbol{a}_i \tag{6.50}$$

Now consider the total moment of momentum of the system of particles about the point P as given by Eq. 6.46. Taking the first time derivative of this equation,

$$\dot{\boldsymbol{H}}_P = \sum_i \dot{\boldsymbol{R}}_i \times m_i \boldsymbol{v}_i + \sum_i \boldsymbol{R}_i \times m_i \boldsymbol{a}_i \tag{6.51}$$

and, since Eq. 6.51 has a term in common with Eq. 6.50, we may write

$$\boldsymbol{M}_P = \dot{\boldsymbol{H}}_P - \sum_i \dot{\boldsymbol{R}}_i \times m_i \boldsymbol{v}_i \tag{6.52}$$

At this point we shall attempt to rewrite the summation term in the right-hand side of Eq. 6.52. By referring to Fig. 6–8, we may obtain the following vector relationships:

$$\begin{aligned} \boldsymbol{r}_i &= \boldsymbol{R}_i + \boldsymbol{r}_P \\ \boldsymbol{R}_i &= \boldsymbol{r}_{PC} + \boldsymbol{\rho}_i \\ \boldsymbol{r}_c &= \boldsymbol{r}_{PC} + \boldsymbol{r}_P \end{aligned} \tag{6.53}$$

The first time derivatives of these equations are:

$$\begin{aligned} \boldsymbol{v}_i &= \boldsymbol{R}_i + \boldsymbol{v}_P \\ \dot{\boldsymbol{R}}_i &= \boldsymbol{v}_{PC} + \dot{\boldsymbol{\rho}}_i \\ \boldsymbol{v}_C &= \boldsymbol{v}_{PC} + \boldsymbol{v}_P \end{aligned} \tag{6.54}$$

By making the substitution for $\boldsymbol{v}_i$, the summation term of Eq. 6.52 becomes

$$\sum_i \dot{\boldsymbol{R}}_i \times m_i \boldsymbol{v}_i = \sum_i \dot{\boldsymbol{R}}_i \times m_i \dot{\boldsymbol{R}}_i - \boldsymbol{v}_P \times \sum_i m_i \dot{\boldsymbol{R}}_i \tag{6.55}$$

But it is seen immediately that the first term on the right-hand side of Eq. 6.55 is equal to zero by the definition of the cross-product. Making the substitution for $\dot{\boldsymbol{R}}_i$,

$$\sum_i \dot{\boldsymbol{R}}_i \times m_i \boldsymbol{v}_i = -\boldsymbol{v}_P \times \sum_i m_i \boldsymbol{v}_{PC} - \boldsymbol{v}_P \times \frac{d}{dt} \sum_i m_i \boldsymbol{\rho}_i \qquad (6.56)$$

Since the vector $\boldsymbol{\rho}_i$ is measured from the center of mass of the system, $\sum_i m_i \boldsymbol{\rho}_i$ is equal to zero (see Eq. 6.3). Making the substitution for $\boldsymbol{v}_{PC}$, the summation now becomes

$$\sum_i \dot{\boldsymbol{R}}_i \times m_i \boldsymbol{v}_i = -\boldsymbol{v}_P \times \boldsymbol{v}_C \sum_i m_i + \boldsymbol{v}_P \times \boldsymbol{v}_P \sum_i m_i \qquad (6.57)$$

$$= -m\boldsymbol{v}_P \times \boldsymbol{v}_C$$

Finally, the moment as a function of the moment of momentum becomes

$$\boxed{\boldsymbol{M}_P = \dot{\boldsymbol{H}}_P + m\boldsymbol{v}_P \times \boldsymbol{v}_C} \qquad (6.58)$$

At this point, recall that we have complete liberty over the choice of the reference point P. Equation 6.58 may be further simplified by choosing P so that $\boldsymbol{v}_P \times \boldsymbol{v}_C$ is equal to zero. This may be accomplished by choosing P in any one of the three following ways:

1. Choose P as a fixed point in the system so that $\boldsymbol{v}_P$ is equal to zero.
2. Choose the point P as the center of mass so that $\boldsymbol{v}_P$ is equal to $\boldsymbol{v}_C$.
3. Choose point P so that P is moving parallel to the center of mass at all times. If the velocity of the center of mass is parallel to the velocity of point P, then the cross-product of the two vectors will be zero.

It turns out that the third condition is rather impractical for the simple reason that, generally, it is so difficult to pick a reference point moving parallel to the center of mass of the system at all times. Ignoring condition 3, we may say in summary that

$$\boxed{\boldsymbol{M}_P = \dot{\boldsymbol{H}}_P} \qquad (6.59)$$

where it is understood that the *point P is either a point that is fixed in inertial space or a point that coincides with the moving center of mass.* If P satisfies neither of these two requirements, then the more complicated moment equation, Eq. 6.58, must be used. In the discussions in this text, however, we shall be careful to consider only reference points that are either fixed or moving with the center of mass.

Conservation of moment of momentum. Consider now the moment equation for a system of particles:

$$\boldsymbol{M}_P = \dot{\boldsymbol{H}}_P \qquad (6.60)$$

Suppose now that there is no moment on the system of particles. Then it follows that

$$\dot{\boldsymbol{H}}_P = 0 \tag{6.61}$$

which in turn implies that

$$\boldsymbol{H}_P = \text{constant} \tag{6.62}$$

Thus the moment of momentum of a system of particles about the point P will be a constant, provided there is no net external moment applied to the system about the point P.

Example 6–3. Two masses are rotating on a weightless rod in a horizontal plane, as shown in Fig. 6–9. Both are at a distance L from the axis of rotation. The smaller mass is given as m, and the larger mass is given as $2m$. The angular velocity of the system is a constant, and is equal to ω_1. If the two masses are released and allowed to move out to the end of the rod, what will happen to the angular velocity of the rod?

Solution: We choose, in this case, the reference point P at the point O, which is a fixed point. Since there are no external moments acting on the two particles about the point O, we may say that the moment of momentum of this system is conserved. This implies that the moment of momentum of the system about the point O before release, $\boldsymbol{H}_1$, will be equal to the moment of momentum of the system about the point O after release, $\boldsymbol{H}_2$. For before release:

$$\begin{aligned}\boldsymbol{H}_1 &= (2mv_1)L\overline{\boldsymbol{k}} + (mv_2)L\overline{\boldsymbol{k}}\\ &= (2mL\omega_1)L\overline{\boldsymbol{k}} + (mL\omega_1)L\overline{\boldsymbol{k}}\\ &= 3mL^2\omega_1\overline{\boldsymbol{k}}\end{aligned}$$

For after release:

$$\begin{aligned}\boldsymbol{H}_2 &= (2mV_1)(2L)\overline{\boldsymbol{k}} + (mV_2)(2L)\overline{\boldsymbol{k}}\\ &= (2m)(2L\omega_2)(2L)\overline{\boldsymbol{k}} + (m)(2L\omega_2)(2L)\overline{\boldsymbol{k}}\\ &= 12mL^2\omega_2\overline{\boldsymbol{k}}\end{aligned}$$

and since

$$\boldsymbol{H}_1 = \boldsymbol{H}_2$$

then

$$3mL^2\omega_1\overline{\boldsymbol{k}} = 12mL^2\omega_2\overline{\boldsymbol{k}}$$

Therefore, solving for ω_2,

$$\omega_2 = \frac{\omega_1}{4}$$

so that when the two masses move to the end of the rod, the angular velocity will decrease by a factor of 4. One might suspect that this problem could be solved by using the fact that the kinetic energy of the system before release is equal to the kinetic energy of the system after release. But if we use this, we find to our surprise that the angular velocity of the rod after release is different from the value as calculated above. It turns out that kinetic energy is not conserved for this system because the internal forces in the system must do work in decelerating the masses when they reach the end of the rod.

One might also be tempted to use the conservation of momentum theorem for a system of particles, but momentum is not conserved because there is an external force on the system, namely, the force that the reaction exerts on the bar. The

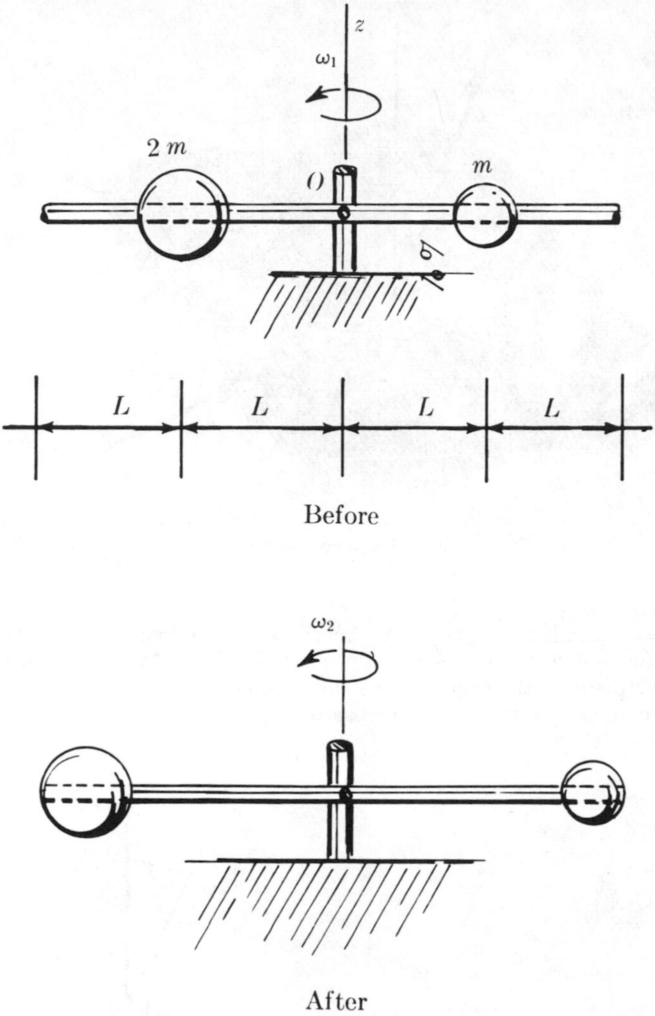

Figure 6-9

center of mass of the system is not at the point O, and therefore has an acceleration, since it is moving in a circular path about O. Therefore, since the center of mass has an acceleration, there must be a force causing that acceleration.

Example 6–4. Shown in Fig. 6–10 is the orbit of an artificial earth satellite. Because the earth is rotating on its polar axis, it appears to an observer on earth that the orbit plane is regressing. What is actually happening is that the orbit plane has a fixed orientation in space, and the earth is spinning relative to the orbit plane. Use the moment equation to show that this is what is actually happening physically. The line of action of the force of attraction that the earth exerts on the satellite passes through the center of the earth.

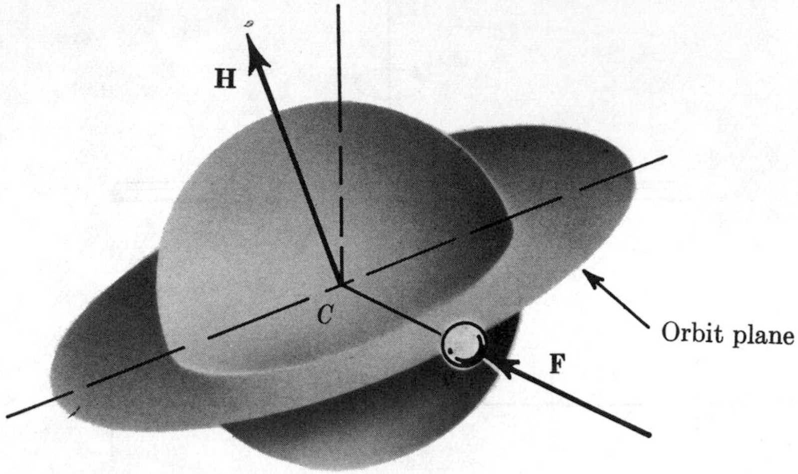

Figure 6-10

Solution: Consider the center of the earth, C, as being the reference point. Since the force of the earth acting on the satellite has a line of action that passes through the point C, the center of the earth, then the moment about the point C of the force on the particle is equal to zero:

$$\boldsymbol{M}_C = 0$$

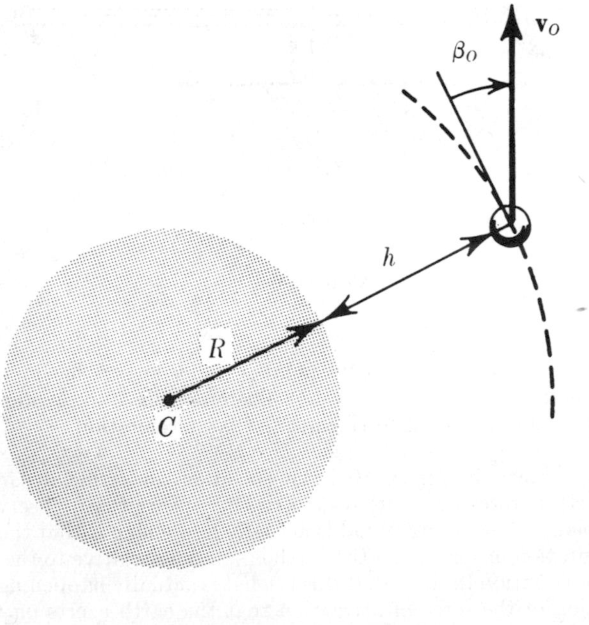

Figure Prob. 6-16

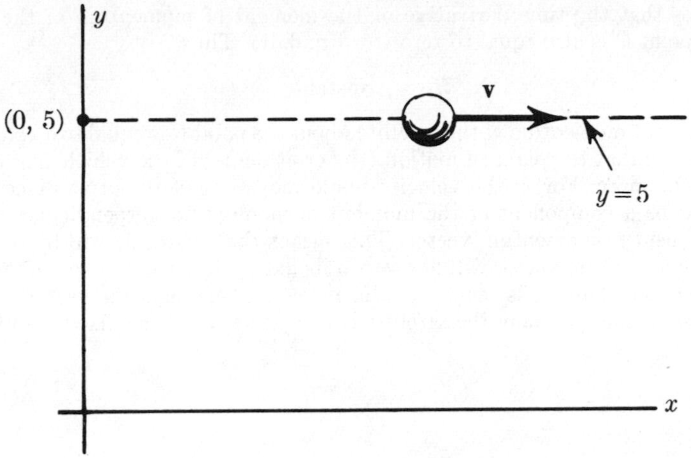

Figure Prob. 6-19

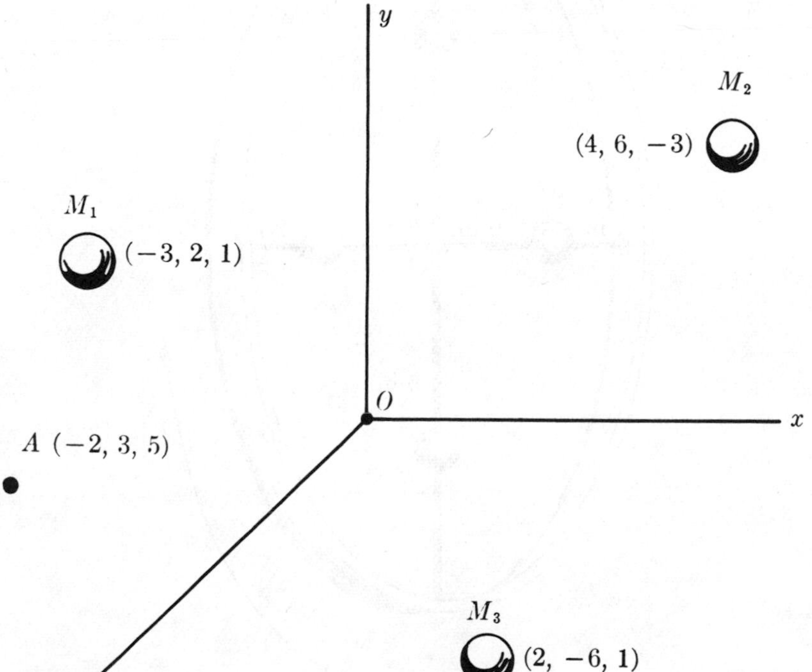

Figure Prob. 6-20

This implies that the time derivative of the moment of momentum of the body about the point C is also equal to zero (by Eq. 6.61). Thus,

$$\boldsymbol{H}_C = \text{constant}$$

If the moment of momentum of the satellite about the point C is equal to a constant, then it must be that the plane of motion (the orbit plane) of the vehicle has a fixed orientation in space. For, if the vehicle should move out of the orbit plane, then there would be a component of the moment of momentum perpendicular to the original moment-of-momentum vector. This means the net result will be that the moment-of-momentum vector will not retain its fixed orientation in space, but will change direction. Thus it is seen that the moment-of-momentum vector will be constant only if the motion of the satellite is in a plane that has a fixed orientation in space.

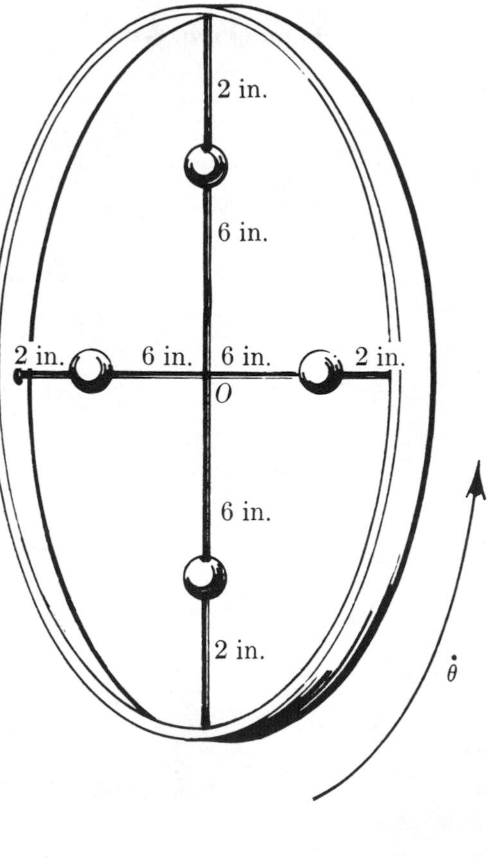

Figure Prob. 6-22

PROBLEMS

6-16. Shown in Fig. P.6–16 is the orbit plane of an earth satellite that is launched with a velocity of $\boldsymbol{v}_0$ at an altitude h. The moment of momentum about the center of the earth, C, of the satellite in orbit will be constant. What is the moment of momentum of the vehicle?

6-17. The moment of momentum of a system of particles about a fixed point O, given as a function of time, is $\boldsymbol{H}_O = 4t\bar{\boldsymbol{i}} - 3t^2\bar{\boldsymbol{j}} + t^4\bar{\boldsymbol{k}}$. Determine the moment of the force (as a function of time) acting on this system about the point O.

6-18. The moment of a set of forces acting on a system of particles about a fixed point O, given as a function of time, is $\boldsymbol{M}_O = 4t^3\bar{\boldsymbol{i}} - 3t^2\bar{\boldsymbol{j}} + 5\bar{\boldsymbol{k}}$. Determine the moment of momentum of the system about the point O, as a function of time, if the moment of momentum of the system at $t = 0$ was $\boldsymbol{H}_O = 2\bar{\boldsymbol{i}} - 3\bar{\boldsymbol{j}} + 2\bar{\boldsymbol{k}}$.

6-19. A 16-lb weight starts from the point (0,5) and travels in a straight-line path along the line $y = 5$ (Fig. P.6–19). Its displacement as a function of time is $\boldsymbol{r}(t) = 3t^4\bar{\boldsymbol{i}}$. Determine the moment of momentum of the particle about the point O as a function of time. Determine the moment of the force on the particle about the point O and from it determine the force that must be acting on the particle.

6-20. The masses of the particles shown in Fig. P.6–20 are three, six, and two, respectively (for masses one, two, and three). In the position shown, the velocity of the first mass is $3\bar{\boldsymbol{i}} - 2\bar{\boldsymbol{j}} - \bar{\boldsymbol{k}}$; the velocity of the second mass is $-4\bar{\boldsymbol{i}} - \bar{\boldsymbol{j}} + 2\bar{\boldsymbol{k}}$; and the velocity of the third mass is $2\bar{\boldsymbol{i}} + 4\bar{\boldsymbol{j}} + 3\bar{\boldsymbol{k}}$. What is the moment of momentum of the particles about the point O for the position shown?

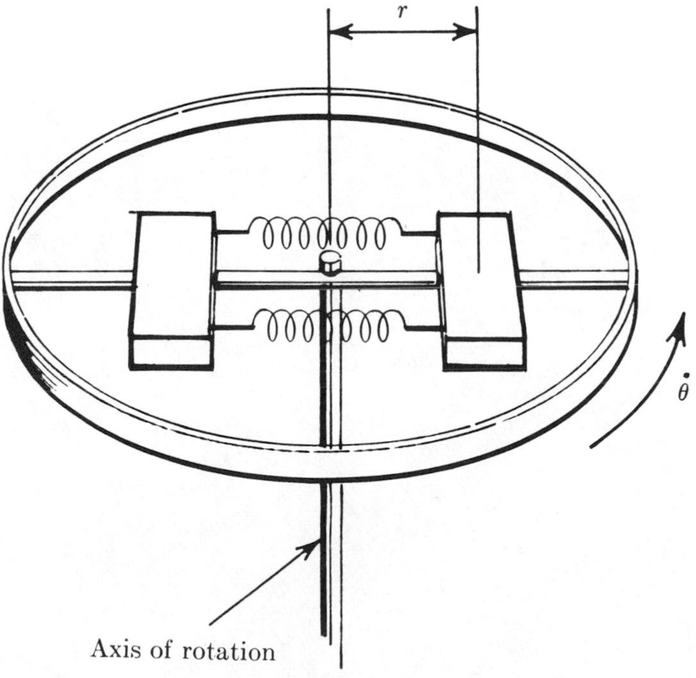

Figure Prob. 6-23

6-21. Consider Problem 6–20. Determine the moment of momentum of the system about the point A.

6-22. The wheel shown in Fig. P.6–22 is spinning with an angular velocity of 4 radians/sec. If all four of the masses are released and move 2 in. outward to the edge of the wheel, how will the angular velocity of the wheel be changed? Calculate the magnitude of the change. Each of the masses weighs 32.2 lb.

6-23. When the two masses shown in Fig. P.6–23 are not moving with respect to the rod, the angular velocity of the system is 2 radians/sec, and both springs are compressed. If the two masses are suddenly released, the ensuing motion of the masses is observed to be $r(t) = 6 + 4(\sin t)$ft, where r is the distance of each mass from the axis of rotation, O. What is the angular velocity of the system after the masses are released? Each mass weighs 48 lb, and the system rotates in a horizontal plane.

7

Special Topics in Particle Dynamics

7-1. IMPACT

In this section we shall examine the effect of collision on the motion of a body that collides with another body. The collision of two bodies is characterized by reactive forces, which have relatively large magnitudes and small time durations. If the time duration of impact is short enough to be considered instantaneous, it may then be stated that the collision of two bodies results in an instantaneous change in the velocities of the two bodies. In any case, we are not so much concerned with the forces of impact as we are with change in the motion, or the velocity, of the bodies due to the impact. Therefore we shall attempt to determine the change in velocity of a body due to its impact with another body.

We know from observation and experiment that forces of impact have relatively short time duration and a large magnitude. Fig. 7–1(a) shows the shape of the force-time curve for a typical collision. The force $F(t)$ may be thought of as either the force of the wall on the ball (or vice versa), since by Newton's third law, they are equal and opposite in direction and magnitude.

Consider the impulse-momentum equation for one dimension:

$$\int_A^B F_x \, dt = m\dot{x}_B - m\dot{x}_A \qquad \textbf{(7.1)}$$

The force F_x now refers to the force acting on the particle; in Fig. 7–1(b), point B is "after impact" and A is "before impact." For a body thrown against a wall, and which rebounds with the same velocity with which it is thrown, the impulse will be the same no matter how long the ball is in contact with the wall. When a very hard, elastic body strikes the wall, the

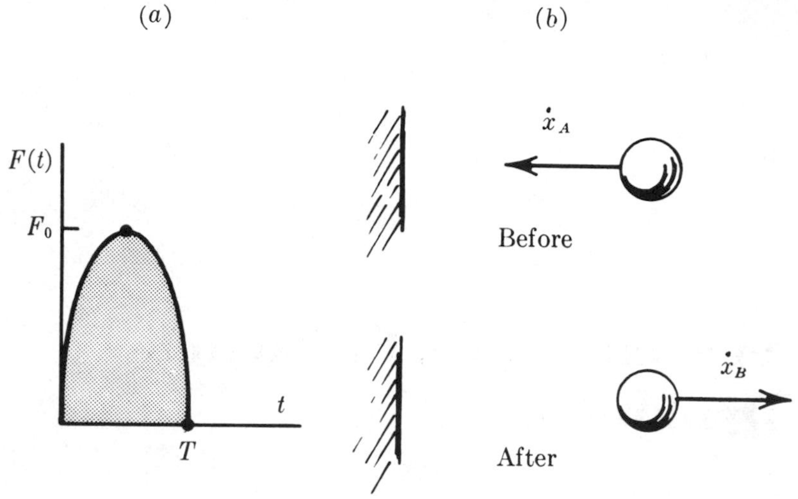

Figure 7-1

time of contact, T, is very small, so that the maximum force produced, F_0, is very large (the area under the force-time curve will be the same if the impulse is the same). Thus, for objects that are relatively hard, the maximum force of contact will be rather large. For this reason, very high stresses are induced at the point of contact when hard objects collide.

Since it is difficult to determine the forces acting between two bodies when they collide, two particles will be treated as a system of particles, and then the force of contact will be considered as an internal force of the system. Assuming that there are no other external forces on the system, momentum for the system of two particles will be conserved.

$$m\boldsymbol{v}_C = \sum_{i=1}^{2} m_i\boldsymbol{v}_i = \text{constant} \qquad \textbf{(7.2)}$$

Therefore, before the impact,

$$m_1\boldsymbol{v}_1 + m_2\boldsymbol{v}_2 = \text{constant} \qquad \textbf{(7.3)}$$

where $\boldsymbol{v}_1$ is the velocity of the first body before impact and $\boldsymbol{v}_2$ is the velocity of the second mass before impact.

After impact, the total momentum is equal to the same constant, since there are no external forces on the system.

$$m_1V_1 + m_2V_2 = \text{constant} \tag{7.4}$$

where V_1 is the velocity of the first body after impact and V_2 is the velocity of the second body after impact. Therefore,

$$m_1v_1 + m_2v_2 = m_1V_1 + m_2V_2 \tag{7.5}$$

The simple problems of interest to us here are those where the velocities of the bodies are known before the collision and the velocities of the bodies after the collision are the desired unknowns. Equation 7.5 represents a total of three scalar equations, but there are a total of six unknowns in these three scalar equations. In an attempt to reduce the complexity of this discussion, we shall at this point assume one-dimensional motion. Other contemporary texts (Housner-Hudson, *Applied Mechanics*, Van Nostrand; Shames, *Engineering Mechanics*, Prentice-Hall) discuss the oblique impact problem, which is the general two-dimensional impact problem, but since the application of the results is limited, no mention of this problem will be made here. Thus, Eq. 7.5 becomes

$$\boxed{m_1v_1 + m_2v_2 = m_1V_1 + m_2V_2} \tag{7.6}$$

and this is subsequently referred to as the *momentum equation.*

In Eq. 7.6, there are two unknowns: the two velocities V_1 and V_2. In order to determine these velocities, we must seek another equation in which these velocities will appear. An obvious choice would be the kinetic-energy equation. The kinetic energy of the two bodies before the impact is

$$T_1 = \tfrac{1}{2}m_1v_1^2 + \tfrac{1}{2}m_2v_2^2 \tag{7.7}$$

and the kinetic energy of the system after the impact is

$$T_2 = \tfrac{1}{2}m_1V_1^2 + \tfrac{1}{2}m_2V_2^2 \tag{7.8}$$

But for any real system, the energy of the bodies after the impact will be less than the energy of the bodies before the impact. The reason for this is that there is energy lost in the collision. Energy is lost to:

1. Noise.
2. Internal deformation and heat.
3. Internal vibrations of the body.

Thus,

$$T_1 > T_2 \tag{7.9}$$

Since we cannot say that T_1 is equal to T_2, the problem appears to be insoluble. However, the approach generally taken is to assume that energy is conserved, solve the energy equation simultaneously with the momentum equation, and then rewrite the resulting equation to conform with systems where energy is not conserved. If energy is conserved,

$$\tfrac{1}{2}m_1v_1^2 + \tfrac{1}{2}m_2v_2^2 = \tfrac{1}{2}m_1V_1^2 + \tfrac{1}{2}m_2V_2^2 \tag{7.10}$$

By eliminating m_1 and m_2 between this equation and the momentum equation,

$$V_1 - V_2 = -(v_1 - v_2) \tag{7.11}$$

Now, if there is a loss of energy due to the collision, the vector difference between the final velocities will be smaller than the vector difference between the original velocities. Thus, the right-hand side of Eq. 7.11 will be greater than the left-hand side. Since this is true, Eq. 7.11 may be written as

$$\boxed{V_1 - V_2 = -e(v_1 - v_2)} \tag{7.12}$$

where the coefficient e is defined as the coefficient of restitution. In the situation where there is no energy loss, the coefficient of restitution is seen to be equal to 1. A collision in which there is no energy loss is known as the *perfectly elastic collision.* (The student should realize that there is no such thing as an elastic collision, but it is possible to have an "almost" elastic collision. The collision of two billiard balls, for instance, is almost elastic.)

At the other extreme is the case where the two bodies collide and stick together. This type of collision is a *plastic collision,* and the coefficient of restitution must be equal to zero because both V_1 and V_2 are the same. In this case the right-hand side of Eq. 7.12 must be zero.

The coefficient of restitution varies between zero and 1. This coefficient must be determined experimentally by actually observing velocities of impact and rebound. As pointed out previously, the rebound velocity depends not only upon the physical properties of the material, but also upon the impact velocity. Therefore the coefficient e is not really a constant for the impact of two given bodies of a given material, but is a function of the velocity of impact. Again, this functional relationship must be determined experimentally. However, for the first approximation (in the examples below) the coefficient of restitution is not considered a function of the velocity of impact, but rather a constant.

Example 7–1. The first mass shown in Fig. 7–2 has a weight of 322 lb and a velocity to the right of 4 fps. The second mass has a weight of 257.6 lb and a

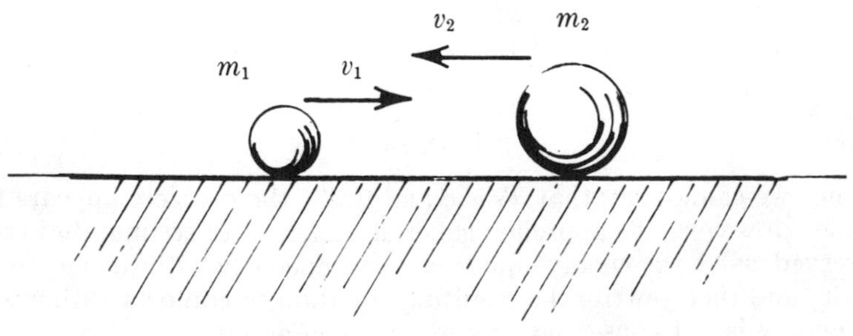

Figure 7-2

velocity to the left of 2 fps. The coefficient of restitution between the two bodies is 0.50. What will be the velocity of each mass after the collision?

Solution: Since there are two unknowns in this problem, it is necessary to obtain two independent equations. One equation available is the so-called energy equation:

$$V_1 - V_2 = -e(v_1 - v_2)$$

The other equation is the momentum equation:

$$m_1v_1 + m_2v_2 = m_1V_1 + m_2V_2$$

By direct substitution, the first equation becomes

$$\begin{aligned} V_1 - V_2 &= -0.50[(4) - (-2)] \\ &= 3 \text{ fps} \end{aligned}$$

The second equation becomes

$$\frac{322}{32.2}(4) + \frac{257.6}{32.2}(-2) = \frac{322}{32.2}V_1 + \frac{257.6}{32.2}V_2$$

$$10V_1 + 8V_2 = 24$$

By solving the two equations simultaneously,

$$\begin{aligned} V_1 &= 0 \\ V_2 &= 3 \text{ fps} \end{aligned}$$

The impact causes the first mass to come to rest; the second mass rebounds to the right with a velocity of 3 fps. This is just about what would be expected from an intuitive examination of the problem.

Example 7-2. Shown in Fig. 7-3 is a ballistic pendulum. A bullet of known mass is shot into the block, and the angle θ, or the distance h, that the block moves

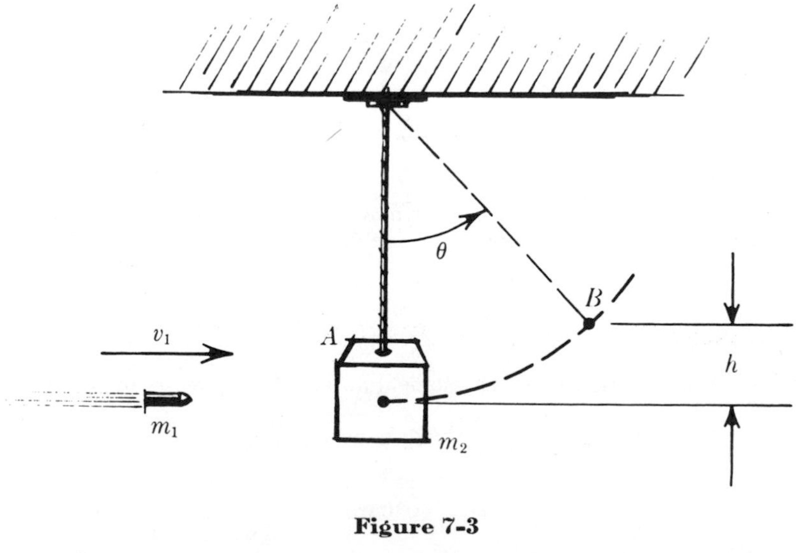

Figure 7-3

depends upon the velocity of the bullet. In this case, a plastic collision occurs because the two bodies stick together after the collision. The problem is solved; that is, the distance h is determined as a function of the velocity of the bullet by using a combination of the momentum equation and the work-energy equation for a single particle.

Suppose the bullet weighs 0.10 lb and the large block weighs 100 lb. The bullet, when shot into the block, causes the block to swing through such an angle that the block moves a vertical distance h upward of 1.00 ft. How fast was the bullet moving?

Solution: By using the momentum equation, the velocity of the large block immediately after the impact may be determined:

$$m_1v_1 + m_2v_2 = m_1V_1 + m_2V_2$$

and

$$0.10v_1 = (100 + 0.10)V$$

Note that v_2 is equal to zero because the large block is initially at rest. Also note that V_1 and V_2 are equal because the bullet sticks in the block.

The distance h that the block will rise depends upon the velocity of the block at point A. The work-energy equation may be employed to determine the distance h in terms of the velocity V. The work-energy equation is

$$W_{AB} = T_B - T_A$$

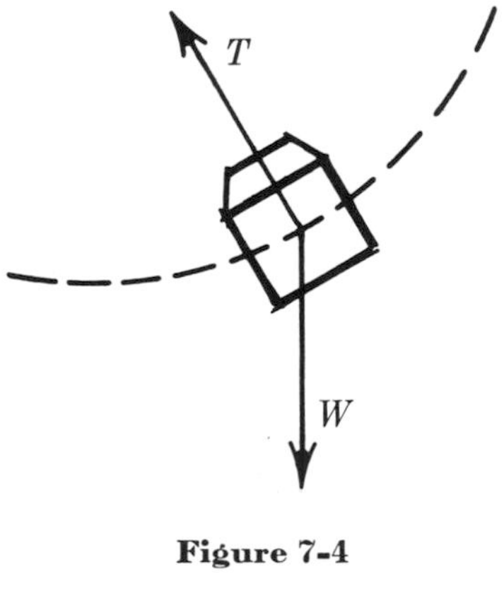

Figure 7-4

The free-body diagram of the block as it moves from A to B is given in Fig. 7–4.

By evaluating the work-energy equation directly,

$$-mgh = -\tfrac{1}{2}mV^2$$

or

$$V = \sqrt{2gh}$$

Combining this equation with the momentum equation gives v_1 in terms of h:

$$v_1 = \frac{(100 + 0.10)}{0.10}(2 \times 32.2 \times 1.00)^{1/2}$$

and

$$v_1 = 8030 \text{ fps}$$

PROBLEMS

7-1. A 96.6-lb ball is moving along a horizontal surface to the right with a velocity of 10 fps. It is overtaken and struck by another ball weighing 128.8 lb, which is moving also to the right with a velocity of 16 fps. What is the final velocity of each ball if the coefficient of restitution for the two bodies is 0.50?

7-2. In Fig. 7–2, the coefficient of restitution between the first mass and the second is 0.40, and the coefficient of restitution between the second mass and the third is 0.60. Initially, the first mass is moving to the right with a velocity of 4.0 fps; the second mass is moving to the left with a velocity of 5.0 fps; and the third mass is moving to the left also at a velocity of 3.0 fps. The first and second masses collide; the second mass rebounds and collides with the third mass. Determine, then, the final velocity of the third mass.

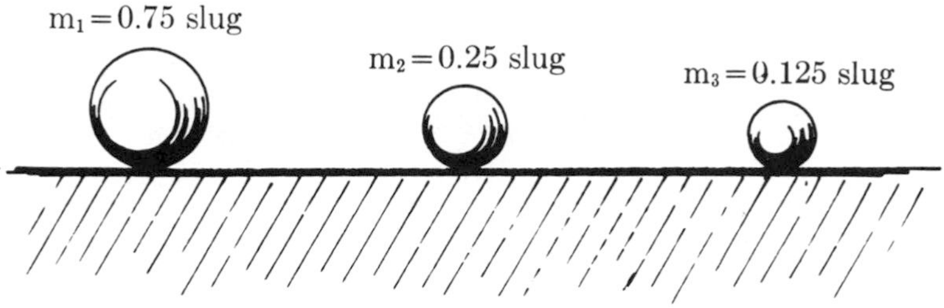

Figure Prob. 7-2

7-3. What must be the speed of a 1-lb golf club if the ball leaves the tee traveling 150 fps? The coefficient of restitution between the club and the ball is 0.65 and the weight of the ball is 0.20 lb. Assume that the velocity of the club after impact is $\frac{1}{2}$ of the velocity before impact.

7-4. A ballistic pendulum has a mass weighing 50 lb. Through what angle, θ, will the pendulum move if the 0.40-lb bullet strikes the mass with a velocity of 1000 fps? The length of the pendulum is 6.0 ft.

7-5. An automobile weighing 3000 lb is traveling east with a speed of 30 mph. It strikes another automobile weighing 2500 lb, which is traveling north with a speed of 40 mph. What is the velocity of the two cars after impact if they stick together? Neglect all frictional forces between the tires and the road after the impact.

7-6. In a head-on collision between a bus weighing 12,000 lb (traveling with a velocity of 40 mph) and an automobile weighing 3600 lb (traveling with a velocity of 50 mph), what will be the resulting velocity of the car and the bus after collision, assuming that they stick together?

7-7. In Fig. P.7–7, a railroad car rolls down an incline, starting from rest at point A, and rolls to the bottom, where it strikes another car at rest on the tracks. What is the velocity of the two cars if they stick and roll away together?

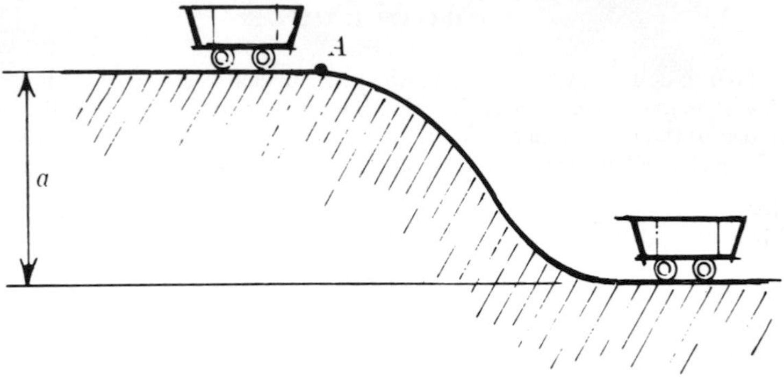

Figure Prob. 7-7

7-8. It is curious to note that in Problem 7–7, a certain amount of energy must be released by the collision. Calculate the energy loss of the collision and discuss the mode in which the energy is lost.

7-9. In Fig. P.7–9, the coefficient of restitution between the two masses is 0.60. The second mass is attached to a spring with a stiffness of 20 lb/ft and is originally at rest. If the first mass, which is originally traveling with a velocity of 3.0 fps, strikes the second mass, how far will the spring deflect? The first mass weighs 20 lb and the second mass weighs 40 lb.

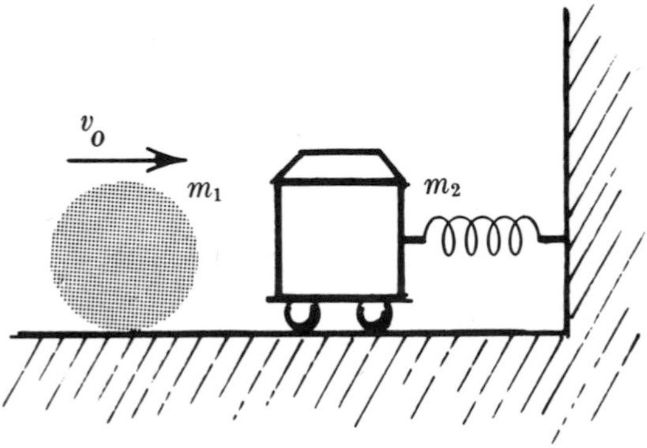

Figure Prob. 7-9

7-10. A 1000-lb pile driver falls 10 ft onto a 500-lb pile. The pile driver does not rebound after the impact. What is the average resistance force that the ground offers to the pile if the pile penetrates a distance of 5 ft?

7-11. By throwing a ball against a barrier and recording its speed of encounter and rebound speed, the experimental data in the accompanying table were obtained.

As one might suspect, the coefficient of restitution is a function of the velocity of encounter. Make a plot of the coefficient of restitution versus the velocity of encounter from the given data. Then state any physical implications of the data that you can conclude.

Encounter Speed (fps)	*Rebound Speed (fps)*
20	19
40	38
60	56
80	70
100	80

7-12. The bar shown in Fig. P.7–12 is rotating with an angular velocity of 2.0 radians/sec counterclockwise. Point O, the axis of rotation for the bar, is moving

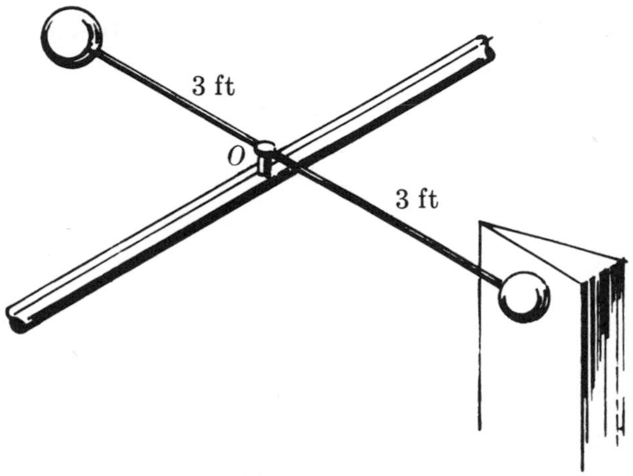

Figure Prob. 7-12

to the right with a velocity of 4.0 fps. One of the masses strikes the barrier. If the coefficient of restitution between the masses and the barrier is 0.70, what is the angular velocity of the bar immediately after impact?

7-2. MOTION OF A BODY OF VARIABLE MASS

We shall consider here the problem of trying to describe the motion of a body that is either gaining or losing mass. The rocket vehicle, for instance, obtains its thrust by expelling burned fuel at a high velocity.

In order to establish the equation of motion for a vehicle that is gaining or losing mass, we shall consider the problem of a rocket and its exhausted fuel and assume that the two masses constitute a "system of particles." It will be further assumed that the system is operating in a vacuum.

Shown in Fig. 7–5 is the rocket vehicle of mass m, with an element of fuel Δm, which is burned and expelled during an increment of time Δt.

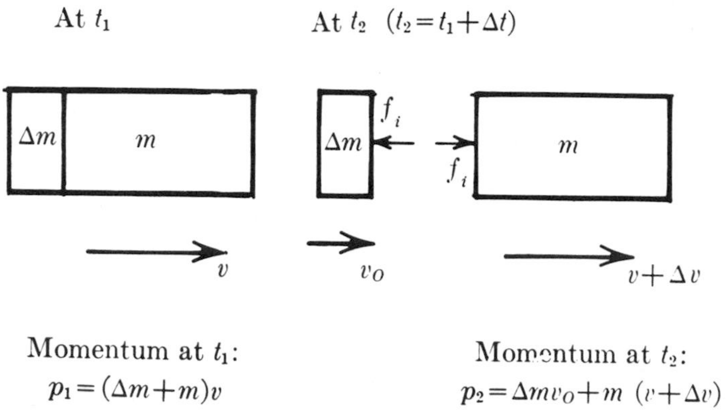

Figure 7-5

The equation of motion for a system of particles is

$$F = ma_C = \frac{d}{dt}(mv_C) \tag{7.13}$$

where mv_C is the total momentum of the system. In this case, the change in momentum during Δt is $p_2 - p_1$, and the change in momentum per change in time (or the time derivative of the momentum) is

$$\frac{d}{dt}(mv_C) = \lim_{\Delta t \to 0} \frac{p_2 - p_1}{\Delta t} \tag{7.14}$$

$$= \lim_{t \to 0} \frac{\Delta m\, v_O + mv + m\,\Delta v - (\Delta m)v - mv}{\Delta t}$$

It follows that

$$F = ma - \dot{m}(v - v_O) \tag{7.15}$$

The term $\dot{m}(v - v_O)$ may be interpreted as the thrust due to the expelled gases, and written as T. The term $v - v_O$ is the "exhaust" velocity, the velocity of the gas relative to the rocket, and is written as ΔV. Thus,

$$F + T = ma \tag{7.16}$$

where: $T = \dot{m}\,\Delta V$, rocket engine thrust.
F = force external to the system. This includes aerodynamic forces on the vehicle and pressure on the exhaust gas.
$m = m(t)$, the mass of the vehicle (a function of time).
a = acceleration of the vehicle.

It goes without saying that it is desirable to make the thrust of the engines as large as possible. This may be accomplished by:

1. Making $\dot{m}$ large by expelling a large amount of gas per unit time.
2. Making (ΔV) very large (maximizing the velocity of the expelled gases).

Since present-day propellants have a maximum exhaust velocity of about 12,000 fps and since the rate of mass flow must be relatively small for the simple reason that a given rocket cannot carry an infinite amount of fuel, the amount of thrust for a given engine is limited.

Because both $\dot{m}$ and ΔV are restricted by the properties of the known propellants, a very large amount of fuel is required to put a relatively small payload into orbit around the earth. The plasma jet and ion accelerator are able to attain very high exhaust velocities, but the particles ejected are so small that $\dot{m}$ is also very small and the resulting thrust of the engines is correspondingly small.

Example 7-3. An air-to-air missile weighing 200 lb is launched from an aircraft that is moving with a velocity of 400 fps. The missile burns 2 lb of fuel per second and ejects it with a velocity of 2000 fps with respect to the rocket. Determine the velocity of the missile 10 sec after it has been launched. Neglect any drag forces on the missile.

Solution: First the equation of motion of the missile is written:

$$F + \dot{m}(\Delta V) = m(t)a$$

Assuming that there is no aerodynamic drag on the missile and that the force of the atmosphere on the exhaust gases is negligible, the net external horizontal force on the missile system is equal to zero. It is assumed that the weight of the missile is balanced by the aerodynamic lift on the missile so that the missile is flying on a horizontal path. This means, then, that the total force acting on the system is zero. Since the missile is going to move in a horizontal path only, then the equation of motion may be written (with no force on the system) as

$$\dot{m}(\Delta V) = m(t)a$$

The relative velocity of the exhaust gases is

$$\Delta V = 2000 \text{ fps}$$

The rate of mass flow, since the missile is burning 2 lb/sec, is

$$\dot{m} = \frac{2}{32.2} = 0.062 \text{ slug/sec}$$

At $t = 0$, the missile weighs 200 lb; therefore the mass of the missile as a function of time may be written as

$$m(t) = \frac{200}{32.2} - 0.062t = (6.2 - 0.062t) \quad \text{slugs}$$

The equation of motion may then be written as

$$0.062(2000) = (6.2 - 0.062t)a$$

Solving for the acceleration,

$$a = \frac{124}{6.2 - 0.062t}$$

Since the acceleration is a function of time only, we may hope to perform a direction integration to determine the velocity of the vehicle as a function of time:

$$v = v_O + \int_0^t a\,dt$$

$$= 400 + \int_0^{10} \frac{124dt}{6.2 - 0.062t}$$

and, upon integrating,

$$v = 400 - \frac{124}{0.062}\,[\ln{(6.2 - 0.062t)}]_0^{10}$$

Then the velocity of the missile after 10 sec becomes

$$v = 608 \text{ fps}$$

PROBLEMS

7-13. Show that it is possible for a rocket vehicle to have the absolute velocity of the exhaust gases in the same direction as the motion of the vehicle and still produce a thrust. Give a numerical example, and explain physically why this is possible.

7-14. A rocket vehicle is traveling in outer space with an absolute velocity of 500 fps. The rate at which the engines are burning fuel is 16 lb/sec. The exhaust gases are expelled with a velocity of 5000 fps with respect to the rocket. Determine the thrust that the engines are imparting to the rocket at this instant of time.

7-15. Consider Problem 7–14. If, at the instant that the rocket is moving with a velocity of 500 fps, the weight of the rocket is 2000 lb, determine the acceleration of the rocket 1 min later. Note that at the rate the rocket is burning the fuel, it would not be able to continue much longer.

7-16. A water truck weighing 8000 lb is able to carry 4000 lb of water. As the truck moves, it is able to eject water out of both sides at a rate of 50 lb/min. If the motor of the truck is able to develop a maximum of 1000 lb of motive force supplied by the rear wheels, determine the acceleration of the truck (a) when it is full of water, (b) 5 min after it starts ejecting water, and (c) when the truck is empty. Assume that the relative velocity of the ejected water with respect to the truck is zero.

7-17. A light airplane weighing 4000 lb is traveling in bad weather at a constant velocity of 120 mph when the pilot notices that ice is beginning to form on the plane. If the airplane slows from 120 mph to 100 mph in 4 min with a constant deceleration, make an estimate of the rate at which ice is forming on the plane (in pounds per minute). *Hint:* Assume that the thrust of each engine is equal to the drag and that the mass of the plane is essentially constant. Use the average velocity of the plane for the calculation of ΔV.

7-18. Consider a rocket type of vehicle that is traveling in space essentially free from the gravitational field of any planet and which has a constant absolute velocity of 500 fps. If at a given instant of time, when the engines are ignited, the weight of the rocket is 2000 lb, what is the velocity of the rocket 5 sec after its rocket engines have been fired? The engines burn fuel at the rate of 10 lb/sec and expell the gases with a velocity of 7000 fps with respect to the vehicle.

7-19. A rocket weighing originally 96,000 lb is to be launched in a vertical position from the surface of the earth. A flow meter, which records the rate of flow of fuel to the engines, gives the data shown in Fig. P.7–19. If the engines expel the exhaust gas at a velocity of 800 fps, how much time will elapse before the rocket thrust overcomes gravity and begins to lift the rocket? Neglect the force of the atmosphere on the exhaust gases.

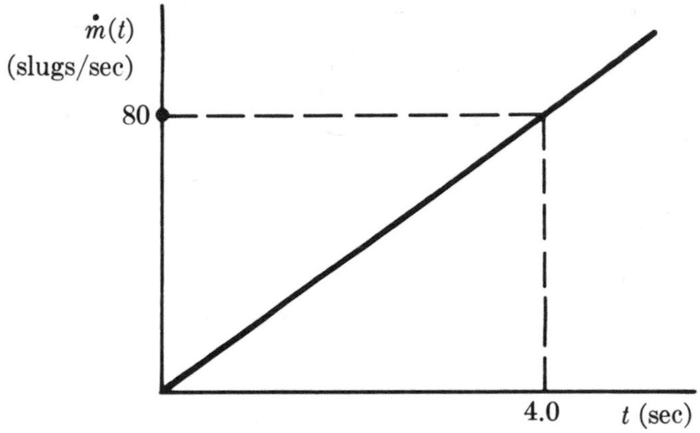

Figure Prob. 7-19

7-20. A rocket weighing initially 64,000 lb is to be launched in a vertical position from the surface of the earth. If the maximum velocity of the exhaust gases is 6000 fps, what must be the rate of flow of mass in pounds per second so that the rocket engine thrust is just enough to overcome gravitational force on the rocket at launch?

7-3. VIBRATIONS

Introduction. Analysis and control of vibrating systems are two of the most common areas of investigation for the professional dynamicist. A vibration problem exists wherever there is an external source for the vibration, and where an accompanying elastic system will oscillate in the presence of the source.

In this section we cannot hope to cover the whole spectrum of vibration problems, nor can we expect to present a very thorough treatment of the basic problems, but we shall attempt to introduce the reader to the basic problems involved and the methods of solving them. We shall also attempt in this section to present the basic terminology of engineering vibrations.

Kinematics of oscillatory motion. Suppose that there is only one coordinate, x, required to describe the motion of a single-degree-of-freedom system (Fig. 7–6). If x is given as a function of time by the function as shown in Fig. 7–6, the motion is said to be *periodic*, since the

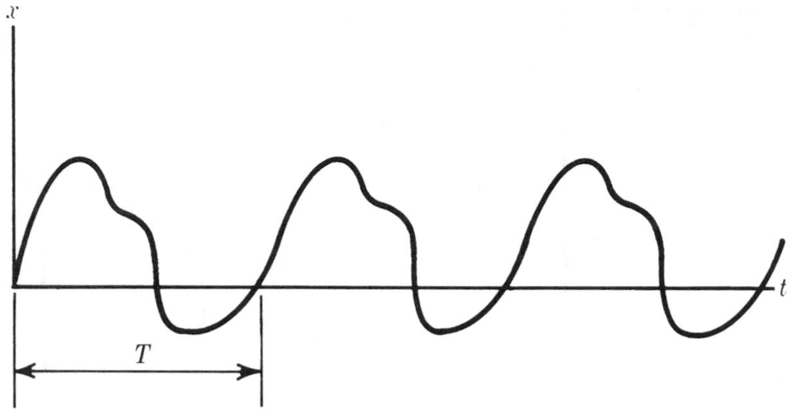

Figure 7-6

motion repeats itself in equal intervals of time. The time that the system takes to repeat itself is called the *period* of vibration, or the period of oscillation, and is expressed by the letter T. The motion of the body during one period is called 1 *cycle* of motion. The number of cycles of motion completed by a body per unit of time is known as the *frequency* of vibration. Thus, if a body makes 10 cycles in 1 sec, the frequency of vibration of the body is said to be 10 cps, and the period of vibration is said to be $\frac{1}{10}$ sec. Thus, it is seen that the frequency f and the period T are reciprocal:

$$f = \frac{1}{T} \tag{7.17}$$

If the motion is such (Fig. 7–7) that the displacement of the body as a function of time is either a sine or cosine function, then the motion is said to be *harmonic*. It is obvious that harmonic motion is also periodic motion, since the sine wave is a repeating function. The equation for the sine wave may be written as

$$x = X_O \sin \omega t \tag{7.18}$$

where X_O represents the amplitude of vibration. The term ω is as yet an unknown quantity. We find, however, that we may relate ω to the period T, since from Fig. 7–7, when t is equal to T, ωt must be equal to 2π. This implies that

$$\omega T = 2\pi \tag{7.19}$$

or

$$\omega = \frac{2\pi}{T} \tag{7.20}$$

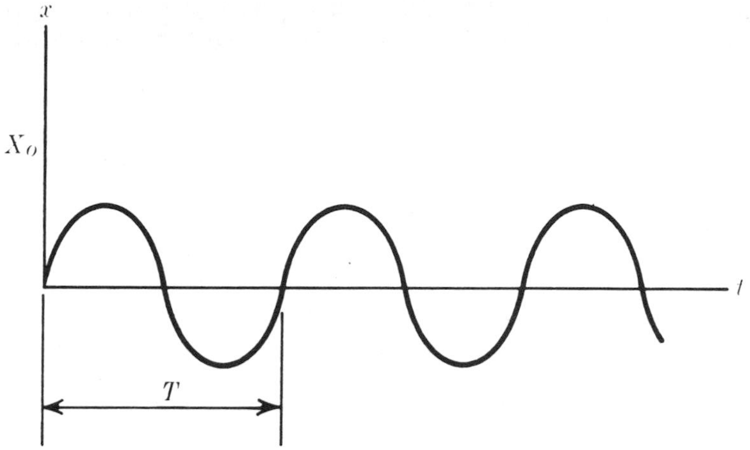

Figure 7-7

Since T is equal to $1/f$, it is seen that

$$\omega = 2\pi f \tag{7.21}$$

Therefore it appears that ω is also a measure of the frequency of the body, since it differs from f by only a factor of 2π. Thus, ω is called the *circular frequency*. The units of frequency are cycles per second, and it is seen from the definition of frequency that cycles are dimensionless. The units of ω are said to be radians per second. Radians are used because, from Eq. 7.21, 2π radians are equal to 1 cycle (or revolution). The units of radians are also dimensionless. In this application we do not really have to think of radians in terms of degrees of angle; here we are interested only in expressing a frequency of vibration, which we may do by either specifying ω or f.

Now consider motion that is harmonic. The displacement of the body as a function of time is given as

$$x = X_O \sin \omega t \tag{7.22}$$

The velocity and acceleration of the body as functions of time may be determined by differentiating the displacement. Thus,

$$\dot{x} = X_O\omega \cos \omega t \tag{7.23}$$

$$\ddot{x} = -X_O\omega^2 \sin \omega t \tag{7.24}$$

It is seen that the velocity and acceleration of a vibrating body depends upon the frequency of motion of the body to the extent that a body with high frequencies is likely to have a very high acceleration.

Example 7–4. The spring-mass system shown in Fig. 7-8 is oscillating harmonically; it makes 1 cycle of motion for every 1/4 sec. What is the velocity and acceleration of the body, as a function of time, if the amplitude of motion is 0.5 ft?

Solution: In order to write the displacement of the body as a function of time (Eq. 7.22), the value of ω must be known. Since the period of motion is 1 sec, the frequency of motion is

$$f = \frac{1}{T}$$

$$= \frac{1}{\frac{1}{4}} = 4 \text{ cps}$$

and the circular frequency is

$$\omega = 2\pi f = 2\pi(4) = 8\pi \quad \text{radians/sec}$$

The displacement of the mass as a function of time is

$$x = 0.5 \sin 8\pi t$$

and the velocity is obtained by differentiating the displacement:

$$\dot{x} = 4\pi \cos 8\pi t$$

The acceleration is obtained by differentiating the velocity:

$$\ddot{x} = -32\pi^2 \sin 8\pi t$$

Free vibration of single-degree-of-freedom systems. Consider the single-degree-of-freedom system shown in Fig. 7–8. If the

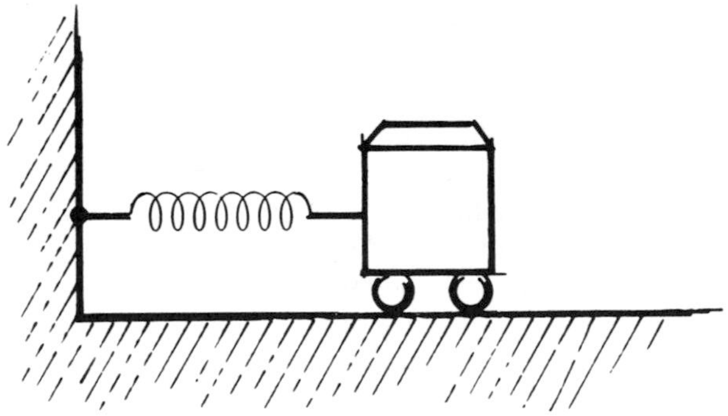

Figure 7-8

system is disturbed from its equilibrium position (for instance, by pulling the mass down a certain distance and then releasing it), it will oscillate; and if the system is free from any energy-dissipating or damping forces, the system will continue to oscillate. The frequency of oscillation of the system is called the *natural frequency* of the system. It is of immediate interest to determine the natural frequency of oscillation of certain mechanical systems.

Shown in Fig. 7–9 is a single spring-mass system. When the mass m is placed on the spring, the spring will deflect a distance Δ, the static

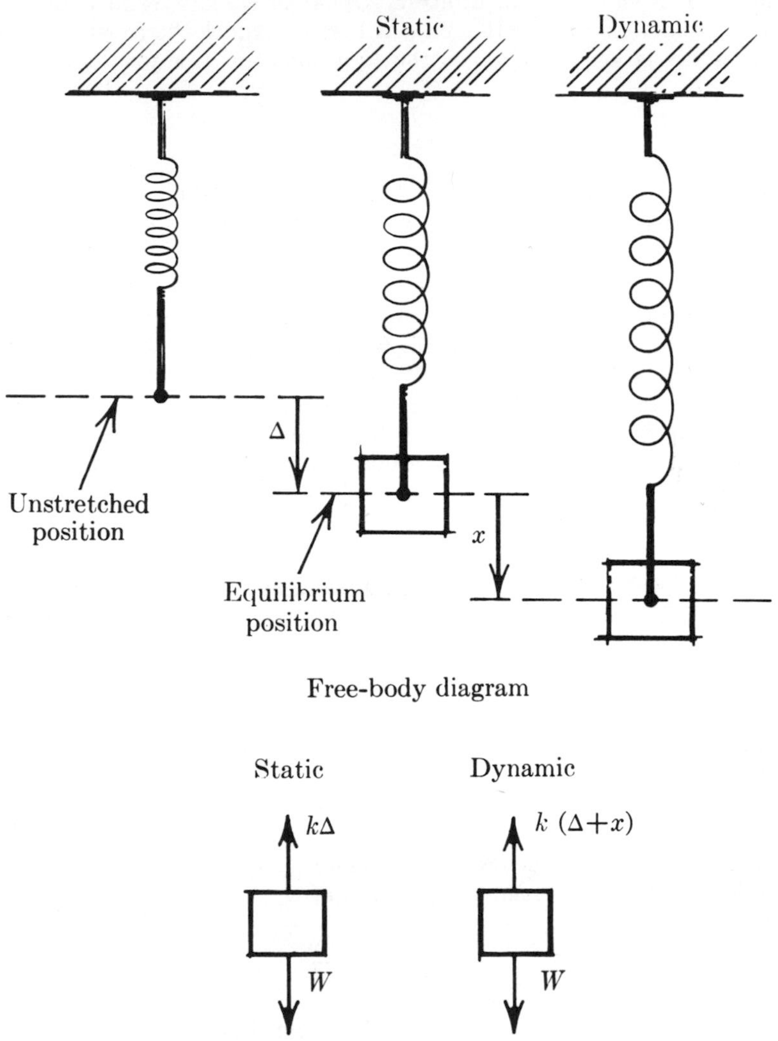

Figure 7-9

deflection of the system. If the mass and the spring constant are known quantities, then the static deflection may be determined by imposing upon the mass the condition of equilibrium that the sum of the forces in the vertical direction be equal to zero:

$$\begin{aligned} F_x &= 0 \\ W - k\Delta &= 0 \end{aligned} \tag{7.25}$$

The coordinate x, representing the displacement of the system at any time t, is defined as being measured from the equilibrium position as shown.

The mass is shown in an arbitrary dynamic configuration together with the free-body diagram of the mass in Fig. 7–9. Since the free-body diagram gives a tabulation of the forces, the equation of motion for the system may be written as

$$\begin{aligned} F_x &= m\ddot{x} \\ W - k(\Delta + x) &= m\ddot{x} \end{aligned} \tag{7.26}$$

But note that upon examination of Eq. 7.25, the value of the static deflection Δ is such that the equation of motion reduces to

$$m\ddot{x} + kx = 0 \tag{7.27}$$

At this point we should like to determine the solution to this second-order differential equation, for this would then give us the displacement of the mass as a function of time. We know, just by looking at the system, that the mass will oscillate in some fashion. The two simplest functions that we know to be oscillatory are the harmonic sine and cosine functions. Therefore, in an attempt to seek a function that will satisfy the differential equation of motion, we shall assume a general solution of the form

$$x(t) = A \cos \omega t + B \sin \omega t \tag{7.28}$$

Upon substituting into the differential equation, it is seen that the assumption is indeed a solution to the differential equation of motion as long as

$$\omega^2 = \frac{k}{m} \tag{7.29}$$

The constants A and B represent the two arbitrary constants of integration, which are necessary in the solution of a second-order differential equation; these constants are determined for a given case by the initial conditions of the system.

Now that the frequency of the oscillating system has been established, it follows that the frequency of motion of the spring-mass system will be

$$f = \frac{1}{2\pi}\sqrt{\frac{k}{m}} \tag{7.30}$$

It is also curious to note that the frequency of oscillation is not dependent upon the amplitude of motion or upon how the system was made to oscillate in the first place. This frequency, then, is the natural frequency of the spring-mass system, and it is the frequency with which the system will oscillate in the absence of any forces external to the system.

Example 7–5. Determine the natural frequency of oscillation for the simple pendulum shown in Fig. 7–10(a). The only coordinate required to represent the motion of the system is the angle θ.

Solution: In order to write the equation of motion of the system, a free-body diagram of the mass should be drawn. Polar coordinates will be used in this problem, because the mass is moving in a circular path; the unit vectors are shown in the

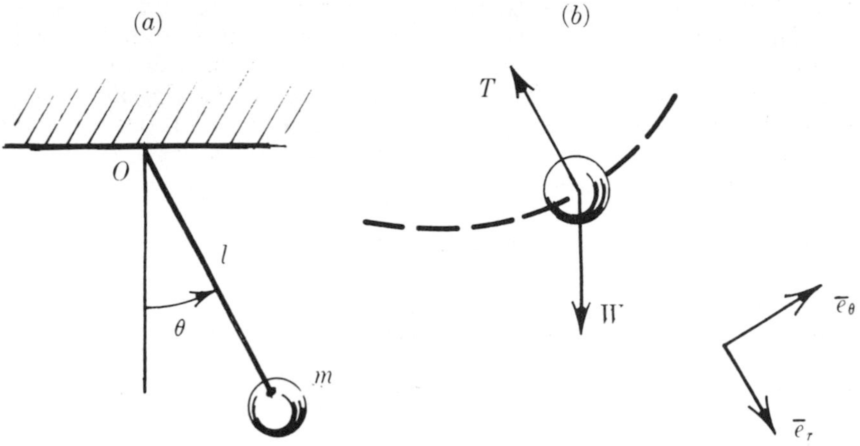

Figure 7-10

free-body diagram in Fig. 7–10(b). The equation of motion of the mass in the θ direction is

$$F_\theta = m(r\ddot{\theta} + 2\dot{r}\dot{\theta})$$

From the free-body diagram, the net force in this direction is

$$F_\theta = -W \sin \theta$$

so that the equation of motion then becomes (noting that $\dot{r} = 0$, $r = 1$, and $W = mg$)

$$l\ddot{\theta} + g \sin \theta = 0$$

Since the equation of motion for the pendulum does not compare with Eq. 7.27, it is seen that the system is not harmonic. However, if we restrict the motion of the system to small angles so that the sine of θ is approximately equal to θ, it is seen that the preceding equation reduces to

$$\ddot{\theta} + \frac{g\theta}{l} = 0$$

The natural frequency of the system may be determined by simply observing the equation. Upon comparison of the preceding equation of motion to Eq. 7.27 and the solution (Eq. 7.30), it follows that the solution for the frequency of the pendulum is

$$f = \frac{1}{2\pi}\sqrt{\frac{g}{l}}$$

It is curious to find that the natural frequency of the pendulum depends only upon the length of the pendulum and not at all upon the mass of the system. It should also be noted again that this solution is restricted to small angles of motion of the pendulum.

Damped vibration. A pendulum, when set in motion, does not continue to oscillate with the same constant amplitude; in fact, the amplitude of vibration decreases with time until the system comes to a rest. The force that causes the system to come to a rest is called a *damping force*, and in this case the damping force is the force of the atmosphere acting on the moving body. The damping force is an energy-dissipating force. Originally, the pendulum has a given energy (that is, $T + V$), but when the system comes to rest, the total energy is not the same as when the system started. Thus, it appears that the system is not conservative and that energy has been lost from the system. Hence this damping force is nonconservative and is responsible for the energy loss.

In this discussion, we shall be concerned only with damping that is proportional to velocity. Motion of systems subjected to other types of damping is discussed in any text on mechanical vibrations.

Consider now the system shown in Fig. 7–11. The dashpot shown in the figure represents the damping in the system regardless of whether the

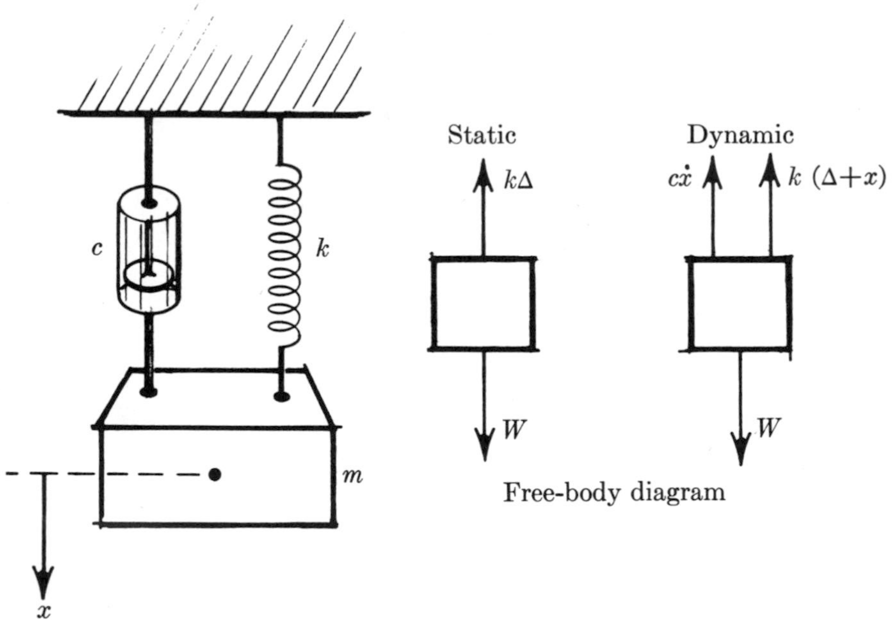

Figure 7-11

damping is due to the presence of the atmosphere, the energy dissipation in the spring, or an actual shock absorber (as shown). The free-body diagram of the mass in both the static and dynamic case is shown. The equation of motion of the mass is

$$F_x = m\ddot{x} = c\dot{x} - k(\Delta + x) + W \qquad \textbf{(7.31)}$$

The *damping coefficient* c is a measure of the amounts of damping in the system. If c is very large, the damping is large, and thus little or no oscillations will take place. But when the system is in static equilibrium, the condition that there will be no motion of the mass is

$$W - k\,\Delta = 0 \tag{7.32}$$

Therefore the equation of motion becomes

$$m\ddot{x} + c\dot{x} + kx = 0 \tag{7.33}$$

This is a linear, second-order differential equation. It is shown in any text on differential equations that solutions of this equation are of the form

$$x = e^{\alpha t} \tag{7.34}$$

where α is a parameter that is determined by substituting the solution into the equation. Upon substituting Eq. 7.34 into Eq. 7.33, it is seen that

$$(m\alpha^2 + c\alpha + k)e^{\alpha t} = 0 \tag{7.35}$$

If the equation is to be satisfied for all values of time, then

$$\alpha^2 + \frac{c}{m}\alpha + \frac{k}{m} = 0 \tag{7.36}$$

Solving for α,

$$\alpha_{1,2} = \frac{-c}{2m} \pm \sqrt{\left(\frac{c}{2m}\right)^2 - \frac{k}{m}} \tag{7.37}$$

Thus, it is seen that there are two values for which the assumed solution is an actual solution of Eq. 7.33. Now the general solution of the equation may be written as

$$x = Ae^{\alpha_1 t} + Be^{\alpha_2 t} \tag{7.38}$$

The constants A and B are the constants of integration. Solving a second-order differential equation is equivalent to integrating the equations twice. Since there must be a constant introduced with each integration, it follows that the solution of a second-order differential equation requires the introduction of two arbitrary constants.

In order to write the solution to the equation of motion in a simpler form, the following definitions will be made:

1. Undamped natural frequency. This is the frequency of the free vibrations of the system in the absence of damping.

$$\omega_n = \sqrt{\frac{k}{m}} \tag{7.39}$$

2. Critical damping coefficient. The critical damping coefficient c_c is that value of c that will make the radical of Eq. 7.37 go to zero. Thus,

$$c_c = 2m\left(\frac{k}{m}\right)^{1/2} = 2m\omega_n \tag{7.40}$$

3. The damping factor. The damping in a system may be specified in terms of a ratio of the actual damping to the critical damping coefficients.

$$\zeta = \frac{c}{c_c} \tag{7.41}$$

Upon making these substitutions, the solution becomes

$$x = Ae^{(-\zeta - \sqrt{\zeta^2 - 1})\omega_n t} + Be^{(-\zeta + \sqrt{\zeta^2 - 1})\omega_n t} \tag{7.42}$$

The form of the solution depends a good deal upon the value of the damping factor ζ. We shall consider here the form of the solution when ζ is equal to, greater than, or less than 1.

Case 1. $\zeta = 1.0$. The damping in the system is equal to the critical damping coefficient. If this is true, then the motion of the system (Eq. 7.42) becomes

$$x = X_O e^{-\omega_n t} \tag{7.43}$$

where X_O is equal to $A + B$. This function is shown in Fig. 7–12.

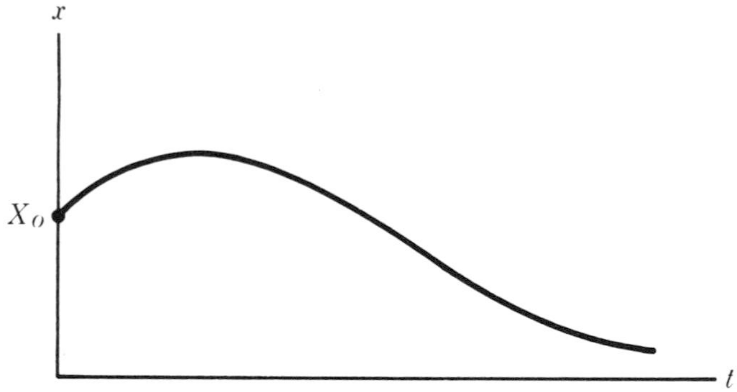

Figure 7-12

It is seen that the damping is large enough so that the system, when given an initial displacement and velocity, will eventually sink into its equilibrium position without any oscillations.

Case 2. $\zeta > 1.0$. Here the damping in the system is greater than in Case 1, so that again we should suspect that there will be no oscillations of the system. Specifically, the motion of the system (Fig. 7–13) is of the form given by Eq. 7.42. Since it is evident that both exponents of the e term will be negative, it follows that the form of the displacement-time curve is much the same as in Case 1.

Case 3. $\zeta < 1.0$. In this case, the actual damping is less than the critical damping in the system. Since ζ is less than 1, the imaginary number may be introduced in the solution, which can be written as

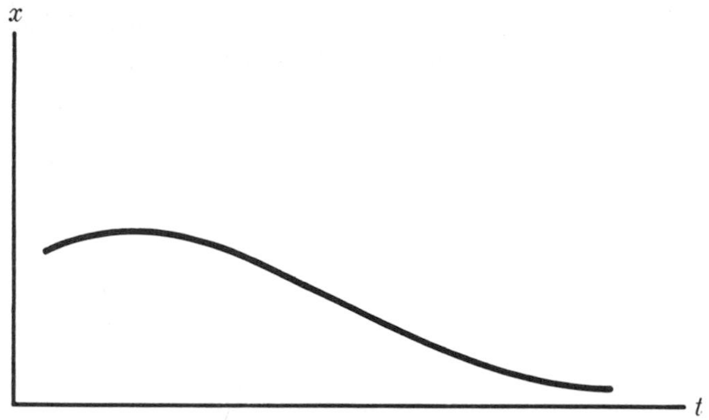

Figure 7-13

$$x = Ae^{(-\zeta - i\sqrt{1-\zeta^2})} + Be^{(-\zeta + i\sqrt{1-\zeta^2})} \tag{7.44}$$

Since

$$e^{i\theta} = \cos\theta + i\sin\theta \tag{7.45}$$

it follows that (by writing the sum of two harmonic functions with the same argument as one harmonic function with a phase ϕ)

$$x = X_O e^{-\zeta\omega_n t} \sin[\sqrt{1-\zeta^2}\,\omega_n t + \phi] \tag{7.46}$$

The total coefficient of the sine term may be thought of as an attenuating factor for the harmonic function. As time gets larger, the coefficient of the sine term will become smaller so that we have a sine wave with a progressively smaller amplitude. This is exactly what we know is going to happen physically. The plot of the motion of the system versus $\omega_n t$ is given in Fig. 7–14.

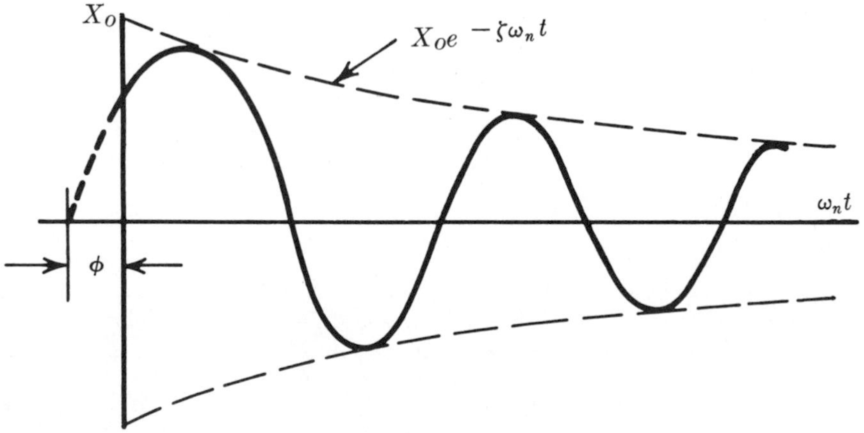

Figure 7-14

We can make a few interesting conclusions from the analysis. First, we note that the frequency of damped vibrations may be written as

$$\omega = \sqrt{1 - \zeta^2}\,\omega_n \tag{7.47}$$

Even though oscillatory motion results when ζ is less than 1, the oscillations will die out quickly when ζ is greater than 0.10. When $\zeta = 0.10$, for instance, there is a 50-percent decay in the amplitude of oscillations after only 1 cycle. Thus, a system that completes 3 or 4 cycles of measurable oscillation will have a ζ that is of the order of 0.10 or less. For this type of light damping, the radical of Eq. 7.47 is approximately equal to 1, and hence it is seen that the damped natural frequency of the system is equal to the undamped natural frequency of the system. Thus, we may conclude that damping has little effect on the natural frequency of the system as long as the damping is light. If the damping is heavy (less than 1.0, but greater than 0.10), the system will oscillate, but the decay is so rapid that there will be no observable period.

Forced vibration. In this section we shall consider the motion of a vibrating system under the influence of some external excitation force. Here we shall restrict the discussion to the response of vibrating systems to a harmonic force, although the response to other types of loading (such as shock loading) are also of interest to the dynamicist.

Consider now the one-degree-of-freedom spring-mass system shown in Fig. 7–15. The system has a harmonic force, $F_0 \sin \omega t$ applied to it. If the motion of the mass is measured from the equilibrium position, then the equation of motion of the system may be written as

$$\begin{aligned} F_x &= m\ddot{x} \\ F_0 \sin pt - c\dot{x} - kx &= m\ddot{x} \end{aligned} \tag{7.48}$$

or

$$m\ddot{x} + c\dot{x} + kx = F_0 \sin pt \tag{7.49}$$

The complete formal solution to this equation is discussed in any text on vibrations or differential equations. However, we are able to construct a partial solution from intuition. If the force has a frequency of p, then it stands to reason that the response of the system will have the same frequency. It also stands to reason that the amplitude of the response will not vary with time. With these assumptions, we may assume that the solution of the equation of motion for the response of the system as a function of time may be written as

$$x(t) = X_O \sin(pt - \phi) \tag{7.50}$$

It is further assumed that the phase of the displacement is not the same as the phase of the force; this phase difference is introduced by the angle ϕ. Upon substituting the assumed solution into the original differential equation of motion, we are able to determine the values of X_O and ϕ for which the assumed solution is a possible solution to the equation:

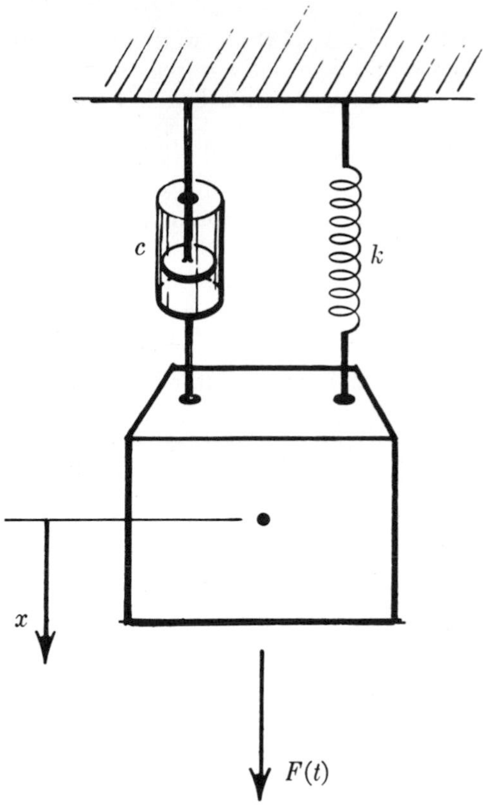

Figure 7-15

$$-mX_Op^2 \sin(pt - \phi) + cX_Op \cos(pt - \phi) + kX_O \sin(pt - \phi) = F_0 \sin pt \qquad (7.51)$$

Since this equation must be satisfied for all values of time, we may choose two specific values of time to give us two equations of motion that, presumably, we can solve for X_O and ϕ. First let $t = 0$; then

$$mX_Op^2 \sin \phi + cX_Op \cos \phi - kX_O \sin \phi = 0 \qquad (7.52)$$

Divide both sides by the cosine of ϕ and then solve for the tangent of ϕ:

$$\tan \phi = \frac{cp}{k - mp^2} \qquad (7.53)$$

This determines the phase angle between the external force on the system and the response of the system. It is seen from the form of the equation that the reason the displacement is not in phase with the force is that there is damping in the system. If there were no damping, then the displacement of the mass would be exactly in phase with the force.

To determine X_O, let $t = \pi/2$. Then Eq. 7.51 becomes

$$-mX_Op^2 \cos \phi + cpX_O \sin \phi + kX_O \cos \phi = F_0 \qquad \textbf{(7.54)}$$

After considerable reduction, which involves the substitution of Eq. 7.53 into Eq. 7.54, we are able to show that the magnitude of the displacement X_O, in terms of the force, is

$$X_O = \frac{F_0}{\sqrt{(k - mp^2)^2 + (cp)^2}} \qquad \textbf{(7.55)}$$

By dividing the numerator and denominator by k, we get

$$X_O = \frac{F_0/k}{\sqrt{[1 - (mp^2/k)]^2 + (cp/k)^2}} \qquad \textbf{(7.56)}$$

and, by making the following substitutions,

$$\begin{aligned} \omega_n^2 &= k/m \\ r &= p/\omega_n = \text{frequency ratio} \\ \zeta &= c/c_c \\ X_s &= F_0/k \end{aligned}$$

the equation for the amplitude of motion becomes

$$\frac{X_O}{X_s} = \frac{1}{\sqrt{(1 - r^2)^2 + (2\zeta r)^2}} \qquad \textbf{(7.57)}$$

The ratio of X_O to X_s is known as the *magnification factor*. In Fig. 7–16, the magnification factor is plotted versus the frequency ratio for various values of the damping factor.

It is most interesting to find that when there is no damping and when the frequency ratio is equal to 1 (meaning that the forcing frequency is equal to the natural frequency of the system), then the system will oscillate with an infinite amplitude (assuming, of course, that there are no physical constraints on the system). When the frequency ratio is equal to 1 and the motion of the system becomes large, a condition of *resonance* occurs.

The phase angle between the displacement of the system and the force, given by Eq. 7.51, may be written as

$$\tan \phi = \frac{2\zeta r}{1 - r^2} \qquad \textbf{(7.58)}$$

This gives the phase angle in terms of the frequency ratio. Note that when there is a resonant condition, there is a 90-deg phase difference between the force and the displacement.

Example 7–6. Shown in Fig. 7–17 is a schematic diagram of an electrical machine that has an unbalanced rotor. The unbalance is represented schematically by a mass m, removed at a distance e from the axis of rotation. The machine is operating

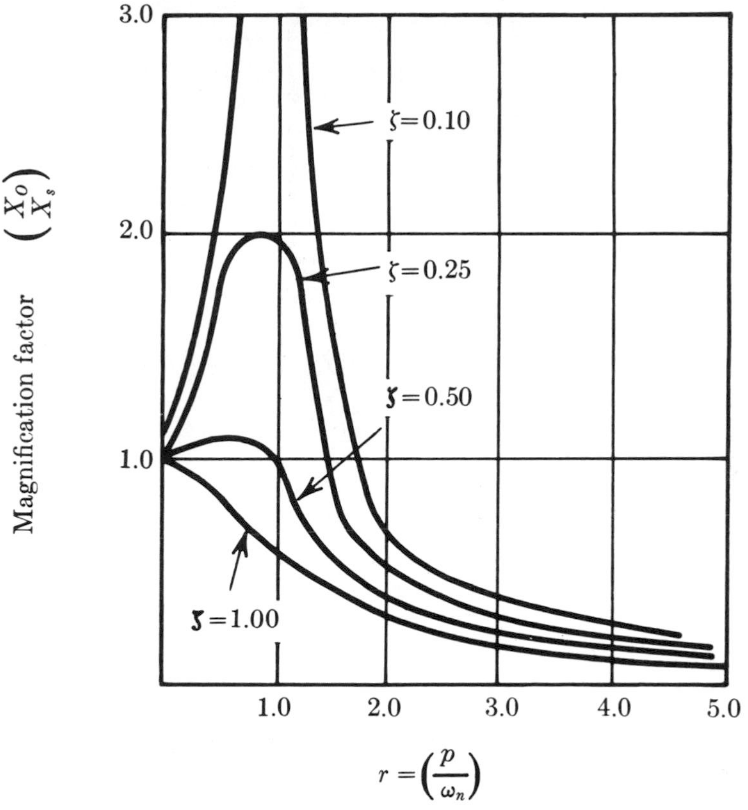

Figure 7-16

at a frequency of p radians per second, that is, the angular velocity of the rotor is equal to $2\pi p$ revolutions/sec. Write the equation of motion of the mass m of the engine block. Neglect weight in the free-body diagrams.

Solution: First a free-body diagram of the engine block and the rotor system will be drawn (Fig. 7–18). The coordinate y_1 represents the absolute displacement of M from its equilibrium position, and the coordinate y_2 is the absolute displacement of m.

The force that the engine block is exerting on the rotor in the y direction is given by $F_y(t)$. By Newton's second law, this force may be determined if the acceleration of the mass m is known. Thus,

$$F_y = m\ddot{y}_2$$

But, employing the relative acceleration equation for motion in a plane,

$$\ddot{y}_2 = \ddot{y}_1 + \ddot{y}_{2/1}$$

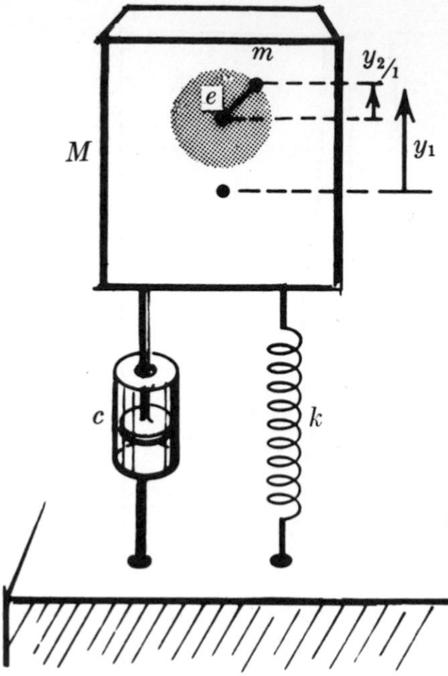

Figure 7-17

The acceleration in the y direction of the second mass with respect to the first is equal:

$$\ddot{y}_{2/1} = -ep^2 \sin pt$$

so that the force on the unbalance in the y direction is equal to

$$R_y = m(\ddot{y}_1 - ep^2 \sin pt)$$

Now, by Newton's third law, the force that the engine block exerts on the

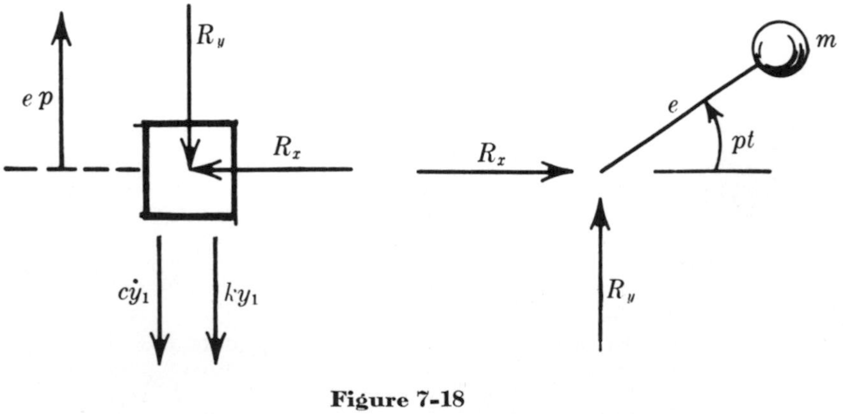

Figure 7-18

rotor must be equal in magnitude and opposite in direction to the force that the rotor exerts on the engine block. This was assumed in drawing R_y in the free-body diagrams of Fig. 7–18. Therefore the equation of motion of the engine block is

$$F_y = M\ddot{y}_1$$
$$-R_y - c\dot{y}_1 - ky_1 = M\ddot{y}_1$$

or, by using the determined value of R_y,

$$(M + m)\ddot{y}_1 + c\dot{y}_1 + ky_1 = mep^2 \sin pt$$

If the unbalance is fairly small, the magnitude of m will be small in comparison to the magnitude of M, so that the equation may be written as

$$M\ddot{y}_1 + c\dot{y}_1 + ky_1 = mep^2 \sin pt$$

The solution to this equation for the amplitude F_0 of the motion is indicated by the solution of the forced vibration equation given by Eq. 7.57:

$$Y_O = \frac{F_0/k}{\sqrt{(1 - r^2)^2 + (2\zeta r)^2}}$$

In this case, however, the magnitude of the force F_0 is equal to mep^2, so that the solution for the amplitude of motion of the engine block becomes

$$Y_O = \frac{e(m/M)r^2}{\sqrt{(1 - r^2) + (2\zeta r)^2}}$$

Note that $\omega_n^2 = k/M$ and $r = p/\omega_n$.

PROBLEMS

7-21. If the magnitude of oscillation of a body is 0.30 in. and the period of oscillation is 1/50 sec, what is the magnitude of the acceleration (in ft/sec²)?

7-22. A simple pendulum has a length of 2.0 ft and a mass of 3.0 slugs. If the frequency of oscillation of the pendulum is $2/\pi$ cps and the amplitude of motion is 10 deg what is the force in the rope when the angle θ is equal to zero?

7-23. A vibration table is able to put out 20 g of acceleration at 400 cps. What is the amplitude of motion at this condition?

7-24. Show that $X = A \cos \omega t + B \sin \omega t$ is a solution to the equation of motion of the harmonic oscillator ($m\ddot{x} + kx = 0$). What must be the value of ω for which this is a solution?

7-25. What is the natural frequency of a mass M attached to the end of a cantilever beam of length L and stiffness EI? It may be assumed that the weight of the beam is negligible in comparison with the weight W.

7-26. If the mass of a spring-mass system (the harmonic oscillator) weighs 60 lb and if it is known by experiment that it takes 10 lb to stretch the spring $\frac{1}{2}$ in., what will be the period of oscillation in free vibration?

7-27. A 10-lb weight is placed on a spring of unknown stiffness. If the period of oscillation is observed to be 0.70 sec, what is the static deflection of the spring when loaded, and what is the spring constant?

7-28. Show that $x = A \cos \omega t + B \sin \omega t$ may be written $x = C \sin(\omega t + \phi)$, and determine the values of C and ϕ.

7-29. The natural frequency of a spring-mass system is 4.0 cps. If the damping coefficient is 5.0 lb-sec/ft, determine the damping factor. The mass is equal to 2.0 slugs.

7-30. The mass of a damped spring-mass system is given an initial displacement of 2.0 in. and released. The amplitude is observed to decay to 1.2 in. in the first cycle. Determine the damping factor and the spring constant if the mass is equal to 0.12 slug and the period of oscillation is 0.80 sec.

7-31. The mass of a spring-mass system is given an initial displacement of 3.0 in. If after 5 sec the amplitude is 0.4 in., what is the damping factor? The frequency is observed to be equal to 2.0 cps.

7-32. For a vibrating body, the peak amplitude of the first cycle is observed to be equal to 6.0 in., and the peak amplitude of the second cycle is observed to be equal to 5.2 in. If the period is equal to 1.2 sec, how long will it take the amplitude of motion to be equal to $\frac{1}{10}$ of the original?

7-33. A harmonic force of $2.0 \sin 12.0t$ is acting on a spring-mass system. The mass is equal to 40 lb and the spring constant is 60 lb/in. What is the amplitude of the motion of the mass if the damping factor is equal to zero?

7-34. What is the amplitude of the system of Problem 7–33 if the damping coefficient is equal to 2.0 lb-sec/in.?

7-35. If the amplitude of a machine at resonance is not to exceed 0.01 in., what must be the damping factor and the damping coefficient? The weight of the machine is 400 lb, the spring constant is 250 lb/in., and the force is $5.0 \sin \omega t$.

7-4. INTRODUCTION TO ORBITAL MECHANICS

Introduction. With the development of large rockets, the possibility of not only sending a vehicle into earth orbit, but also of launching an interplanetary space vehicle became a distinct reality. The space age then introduced a new area of investigation for dynamicists. Satellite orbits and interplanetary space trajectories must be calculated in terms of the boost capacity before any project can be activated. The area of investigation in calculating these trajectories is usually called *astrodynamics*, or *celestial mechanics*.

The role of the astrodynamicist is to calculate the motion of a particle (that is, the space vehicle) subjected to forces of gravitational attraction of the earth, moon, sun, and other bodies, and any thrust forces that the vehicle might have. What he must do, then, is to solve the equation of motion of a particle subjected to very generally complicated forces.

Modern celestial mechanics has its origins in Kepler's laws of planetary motion. In 1609, Johannes Kepler, after years of astronomical observations, formulated the first two of his three laws of motion:

1. Every planet describes an ellipse with the sun at one of the foci.
2. The radius vector drawn from the sun to the planet sweeps out equal areas in equal amounts of time.

Ten years later, Kepler stated his third law:

3. The squares of the periods of the planets are proportional to the cubes of the semimajor axes of their elliptical orbits.

Sir Isaac Newton used Kepler's laws of motion and showed that if the planets move in elliptical paths about the sun, there must be an attractive force between the planets and the sun. Newton also observed that there must be attractive forces between terrestrial bodies and the earth, since free objects always fall toward the surface of the earth. Newton was able to resolve both problems when he formulated his law of universal gravitation. He stated that the force of attraction between any two bodies of the universe is equal to

$$F = \frac{GMm}{r^2} \tag{7.59}$$

where G is a proportionality constant, M and m are the masses of the two bodies, and r is the distance between their centers of mass. In the engineering system of units, G is equal to 3.38×10^{-8} ft^4/lb-sec^4; it is seen that this force of attraction is unmeasurable unless the mass of one of the bodies is very large.

It stands to reason that the gravitation problem and the satellite orbital problem are directly related. One knows from intuition that if he is able to throw a rock with enough initial velocity (assuming no atmospheric drag), as the rock starts falling toward the earth, the earth starts "falling away" because of its curvature. Thus the body keeps falling toward the surface of the earth, but since the earth is spherical, the rock will continue in a path about the earth (that is, if the rock is thrown at the correct velocity).

We are able to determine GM (where M is the mass of the earth) for the calculations of the motion of earth satellites. We are able to do this by noting that the gravitational force must be equal to the force of attraction of a body of mass m to the earth. Thus,

$$mg = \frac{GMm}{R^2} \tag{7.60}$$

where R is the radius of the earth.

Solving for GM,

$$GM = gR^2 \tag{7.61}$$

Since we know that the acceleration due to gravity is equal to 32.2 ft/sec^2 and that the radius of the earth is 3960 miles, we are able to calculate GM:

$$\begin{aligned} GM &= (32.2)(3960 \times 5280)^2 \\ &= 14.1 \times 10^{15} \text{ lb-ft}^2/\text{slug (or ft}^3/\text{sec}^2) \end{aligned} \tag{7.62}$$

Orbit determination. In this section, we shall attempt to verify Kepler's laws of planetary motion by using Newton's laws of motion (historically, it was Newton who formulated his law of universal gravitation on the basis of Kepler's observations), and we shall further attempt to determine the orbits of space vehicles in terms of the initial launch conditions. No mention will be made here, however, of the trajectories of powered spacecraft.

Since the mass of a space vehicle is so insignificant with respect to the mass of the earth, the earth may be considered to be a point that is absolutely fixed in space, and the motion of the vehicle may be assumed to have no effect on the motion of the earth.

Since the force that the earth exerts on the satellite will be radial, it follows that the equations of motion could best be expressed in polar coordinates. The unit vectors for this system are shown in Fig. 7–19 along with a free-body diagram of the vehicle.

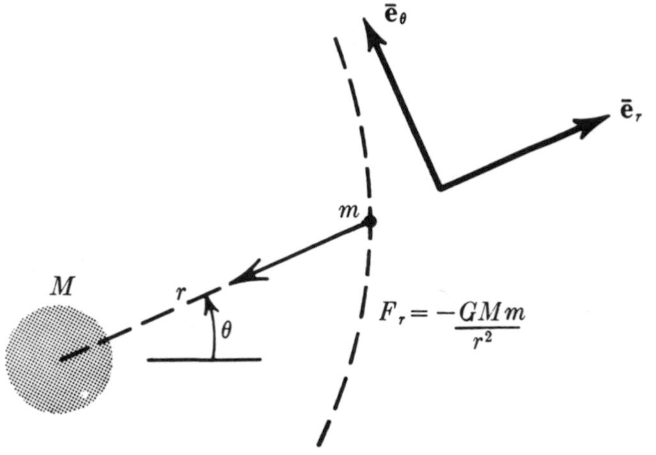

Figure 7-19

The equations of motion of the vehicle may be written as

$$\begin{aligned} F_r &= m(\ddot{r} - r\dot{\theta}^2) \\ -\frac{GMm}{r^2} &= m(\ddot{r} - r\dot{\theta}^2) \end{aligned} \tag{7.63}$$

$$\begin{aligned} F_\theta &= m(r\ddot{\theta} + 2\dot{r}\dot{\theta}) \\ 0 &= m(r\ddot{\theta} + 2\dot{r}\dot{\theta}) \end{aligned} \tag{7.64}$$

The second of the two equations of motion may be written as

$$\frac{1}{r}\frac{d}{dt}(r^2\dot{\theta}) = 0 \tag{7.65}$$

This may be easily verified by taking the time derivative of the term. In any case, Eq. 7.65 implies that

$$r^2\dot{\theta} = h \quad \text{(a constant)} \tag{7.66}$$

The term h has a physical significance. It is the magnitude of the moment of momentum about the point O per-unit mass of the particle. Since there is no moment of the particle about the point O (the center of the earth), it follows that the moment of momentum about O is conserved.

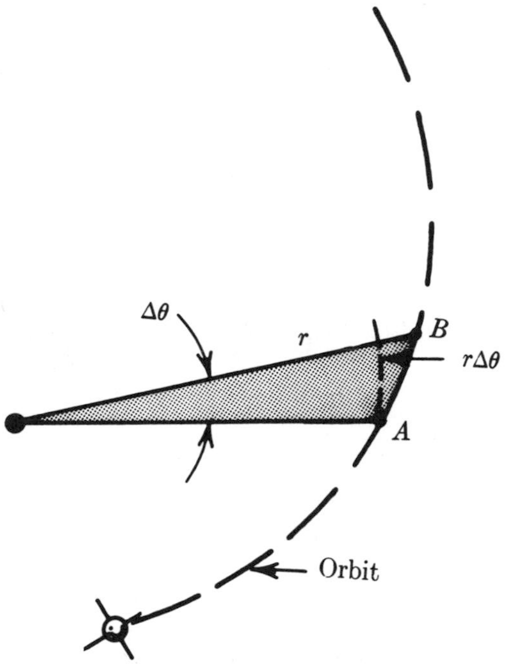

Figure 7-20

Here is verification of Kepler's second law of motion. In a small amount of time, Δt, the satellite will move from point A to point B, as shown in Fig. 7–20. The area swept out by the radius vector will be equal for small $\Delta\theta$:

$$\Delta A = \tfrac{1}{2}r(r\,\Delta\theta) \tag{7.67}$$

and the time rate of change of the area is determined by dividing both sides of the equation by dt and taking the limit as dt approaches zero to obtain

$$\frac{dA}{dt} = \frac{1}{2}r^2\dot{\theta} \tag{7.68}$$

If we compare Eq. 7.68 with Eq. 7.66, it follows that dA/dt must be a constant; this agrees with Kepler's second law.

The first equation of motion (Eq. 7.63) may be solved in the following manner: Time is eliminated from the equation of motion, and the variable θ is introduced by making the following substitutions:

$$\begin{aligned}\frac{dr}{dt} &= \frac{dr}{d\theta}\dot{\theta} = \frac{h}{r^2}\frac{dr}{d\theta} \\ &= -h\frac{d}{d\theta}\left(\frac{1}{r}\right)\end{aligned} \tag{7.69}$$

Letting $u = 1/r$,

$$\frac{dr}{dt} = -h\frac{du}{d\theta} \tag{7.70}$$

$$\begin{aligned}\frac{d^2r}{dt^2} &= -h\frac{d^2u}{d\theta^2}\dot{\theta} \\ &= -h^2u^2\frac{d^2u}{d\theta^2}\end{aligned} \tag{7.71}$$

Upon substitution into Eq. 7.63, the equation of motion becomes

$$\frac{d^2u}{d\theta^2} + u = \frac{GM}{h^2} \tag{7.72}$$

The general solution for this second-order differential equation is

$$u = \frac{GM}{h^2} + C\cos(\theta - \theta_0) \tag{7.73}$$

This may be verified by substituting this solution into the equation of motion. The two arbitrary constants are C and θ_0. The constant, θ_0, may be set equal to zero by measuring θ from the point of minimum distance from O. This equation gives the trajectory of the particle in terms of polar coordinates.

But the trajectory equation is the equation of a conic section. Recall that the equation for a conic section in polar form is

$$r = \frac{a(1 - e^2)}{1 + e\cos\theta} \tag{7.74}$$

and e is the eccentricity, where a is the semimajor axis. It is the value of e that determines the type of conic section. The rule for this is as follows:

$e > 1$: Hyperbola
$e = 1$: Parabola
$0 < e < 1$: Ellipse
$e = 0$: Circle

By letting $u = 1/r$, and reducing Eq. 7.73 to the form of Eq. 7.74, it is seen that

$$\epsilon = \frac{Ch^2}{GM} \tag{7.75}$$

Since we know that the orbits are conic sections, we should now like to determine the type of orbit that we can get by launching a vehicle with a velocity v_O and distance r_O from the center of mass of the earth.

Suppose that the vehicle is launched so that the velocity is perpendicular to the radius vector. Then Eq. 7.73 may be written as

$$u = \frac{1}{r_O} = \frac{GM}{h^2} + C \tag{7.76}$$

where

$$h = r_O^2\dot{\theta} = r_O^2\left(\frac{v_O}{r_O}\right) = r_Ov_O \tag{7.77}$$

Then

$$\frac{1}{r_O} = \frac{GM}{(r_Ov_O)^2} + C \tag{7.78}$$

Circular orbits. If we attempt to launch a vehicle into a circular orbit, $\epsilon = 0$, which implies that $C = 0$, it follows from Eq. 7.78 that

$$v_O = \sqrt{\frac{GM}{r_O}} \tag{7.79}$$

The distance r_O may be expressed as the distance R of the radius of the earth, plus the altitude h above the surface of the earth. The value of the launch velocity is given as a function of the altitude in Fig. 7–21.

Escape trajectories. If the vehicle is to be launched into a trajectory that will escape the gravitational field of the earth, we should like to launch the vehicle into either a parabolic or hyperbolic trajectory. The velocity required to achieve a parabolic trajectory is a transitional velocity, since any velocity smaller than the parabolic velocity will result in an elliptical orbit about the earth. Of course any velocity greater than the parabolic trajectory velocity will result in escape, since the vehicle will then go into a hyperbolic orbit.

For a parabolic orbit, $\epsilon = 1$ and $C = GM/h^2$. Thus, it follows from Eq. 7.78 that

$$v_O = \sqrt{\frac{2GM}{r_O}} \tag{7.80}$$

The escape velocity as a function of altitude is plotted in Fig. 7–21.

Figure 7–22 shows a launch at an altitude of 100 miles and the velocities associated with each type of orbit.

Period of rotation for a circular or elliptical orbit. The period for one rotation of a satellite may be determined in the following manner: From Eq. 7.66 and Eq. 7.68, the time rate at which the area is swept out by the radius vector to the particle may be written as

$$\frac{dA}{dt} = \frac{1}{2}h \tag{7.81}$$

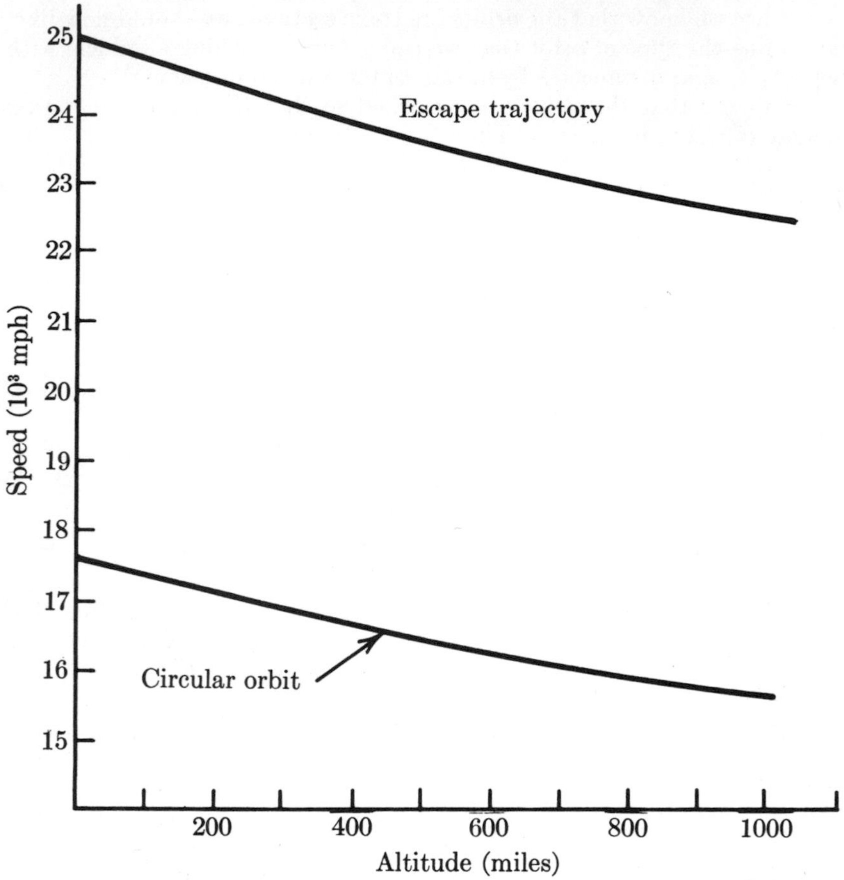

Figure 7-21

Integrating over one period of rotation,

$$A = \tfrac{1}{2}hT \tag{7.82}$$

where T is the period, or time, for one rotation.

But the area in an ellipse is equal to πab, where a and b are the semi-major and minor axes, respectively. The term h may be expressed in terms of the initial launch conditions, $h = r_O v_O$. Then the period may be written as

$$T = \frac{2\pi ab}{r_O v_O} \tag{7.83}$$

In case the vehicle is in circular orbit, the period reduces to

$$T = \frac{2\pi r_O}{v_O} \tag{7.84}$$

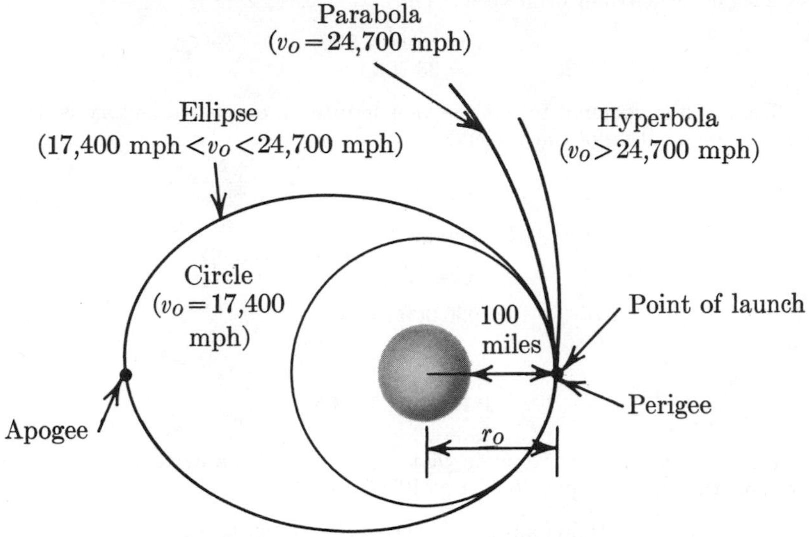

Figure 7-22. *Launch velocities at 100 miles*

Example 7–7. A 3000-lb space vehicle is to be launched into a circular parking orbit at an altitude of 100 miles. After making one revolution, a rocket engine on the vehicle fires and gives enough impulse to the vehicle so that it is put into a parabolic escape trajectory. Determine the velocity required to launch the vehicle into the circular orbit, the period of the orbit, the velocity required for escape, and the impulse that the rocket engines must impart to the vehicle in order to achieve the escape velocity.

Solution: The velocity required for a circular orbit is $\sqrt{GM/r_O}$. Using 4000 miles for the radius of the earth, and $GM = 14.1 \times 10^{15}$ ft³/sec²,

$$v_O = \sqrt{\frac{14.1 \times 10^{15}}{(4000 + 100)5280}}$$

$$= 25{,}500 \text{ fps}$$

The period for one rotation is

$$T = \frac{2\pi r_O}{v_O}$$

$$= \frac{(6.28)(4000 + 100)(5280)}{25{,}500}$$

$$= 5330 \text{ sec} \quad \text{(or 89 min, or 1 hr 29 min)}$$

The velocity required for escape is

$$v_e = \sqrt{\frac{2GM}{r_O}}$$

or $\sqrt{2}$ times the circular orbit speed. Thus,

$$v_e = 1.41(25{,}500)$$
$$= 35{,}700 \text{ fps}$$

The impulse required to put the vehicle into an escape trajectory is just the change in momentum of the vehicle:

$$\text{Impulse} = \int F\,dt = mv_e - mv_O$$
$$= \left(\frac{3000}{32.2}\right)(35{,}700 - 25{,}500)$$
$$= 950{,}000 \text{ lb-sec}$$

PROBLEMS

For your calculations, assume that the radius of the earth is equal to 4000 miles and that GM is equal to 14.1×10^{15} ft^3/sec^2.

7-36. How much work in foot-pounds is required to put an 85,000-lb Apollo spacecraft into an escape trajectory?

7-37. Determine for the 85,000-lb Apollo spacecraft, the energy required to put the vehicle into a circular orbit at 300 miles.

7-38. The period of the moon about the earth is 27.3 days. Using the equations for the circular orbit, determine the distance between the centers of mass of each and the velocity of the moon relative to the earth.

7-39. The period of rotation of the earth about the sun is approximately 365 days and the mean distance of the earth to the sun is 93 million miles. Calculate GM_s for the sun in cubic feet per square second.

7-40. If the mass of the earth is 81 times larger than the mass of the moon, what will be the escape velocity of a body at the surface of the moon?

7-41. When a vehicle is placed into an earth orbit, the plane of the orbit will maintain a constant orientation in space. Because of the spin of the earth, however, it appears that the orbit plane is regressing (this shift is obviously not apparent when the vehicle is in an equatorial orbit). The Project Mercury flights were 100-mile circular-orbit flights. What would be the apparent shift in the orbit plane in degrees for one orbit of a Project Mercury flight?

7-42. An observation satellite is to have an observed apogee of 10,000 miles and a perigee of 200 miles. Determine the launch velocity v_O and the period for one rotation.

8

The Equations of Motion of a Rigid Body

A *rigid body* is nothing more than a system of particles, defined so that any two of the particles are always at a constant distance from each other; that is, there is no relative movement or velocity between any two particles of the body. The particles of which the rigid body is composed (here the implication is that the particles are actually finite particles of mass, not atomic particles) usually lie adjacent to each other, and one observes the system of particles arranged such that there is no internal deformation or deflection. The student should recognize immediately that the assumption that a body is rigid is an idealization, since even the hardest metals are subject to deformation under loading. But except for highly flexible bodies, there is little error introduced in the dynamical analysis by assuming that the body is rigid.

8-1. PLANE MOTION

Description of the motion. The purpose here is to attempt to determine the number and type of coordinates required to define the position of a rigid body that is constrained to move in a plane. Consider the rigid body shown in Fig. 8–1. The body is constrained to move in such a manner that it will rotate only about the z axis and translate only in the x and y directions. The body is constrained to a two-dimensional space.

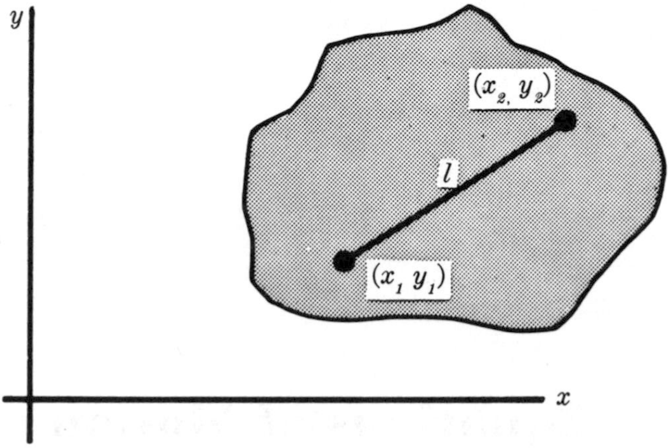

Figure 8-1

Two arbitrary points are picked on the body, as shown in the figure. The position of the body may be uniquely determined by specifying the x and y coordinates of both points. Thus the position of the rigid body moving in a plane may be specified by the four coordinates x_1, y_1, x_2, y_2. However, the four coordinates are not independent because the distance separating the two points is a constant (because the body is rigid). Thus,

$$l^2 = (x_1 - x_2)^2 + (y_1 - y_2)^2 \tag{8.1}$$

This implies that there are only three *independent* coordinates required to specify the position of the body. Because of convenience in writing the equations of motion of the body, it is customary to use, as the three independent coordinates, two coordinates to define the translation of the center of mass and one angular coordinate to define the rotation of the body.

Table 8–1 classifies the types of motion that a rigid body moving in a plane may experience.

The equations of motion: the force equations. In order to establish the equations of motion for a rigid body that is moving in a plane, the rigid body will be first thought of as consisting of a system of particles. The equation of motion of a typical particle will be written, and then the equations will be summed over the system in order to obtain a relationship that applies to the system.

Shown in Fig. 8–2 is a rigid body that is moving in a plane. The

TABLE 8-1. COORDINATES FOR THE PLANE MOTION OF A RIGID BODY

Translating Rigid Body

Only one coordinate is required to describe the motion.

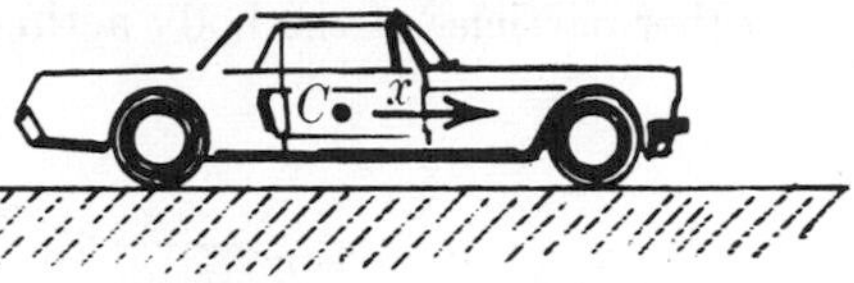

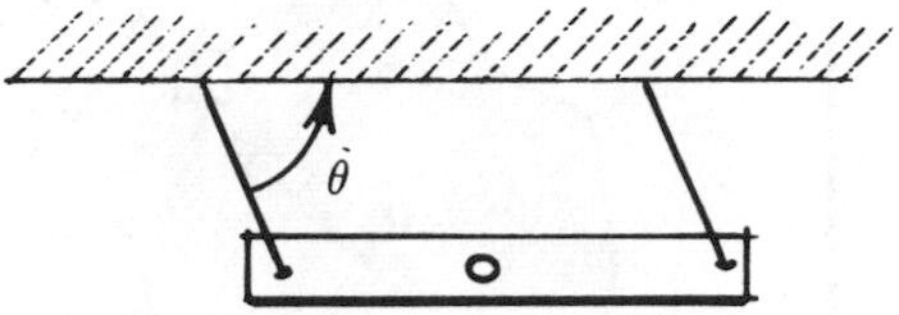

Rotating Rigid body (About a Fixed Point)

Only one coordinate is required to describe the motion.

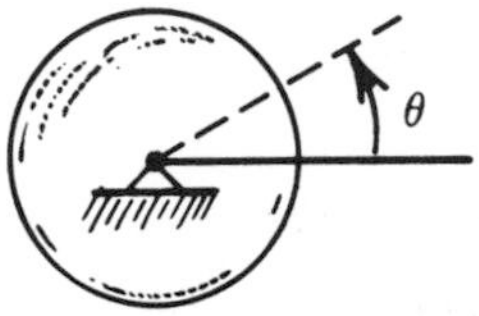

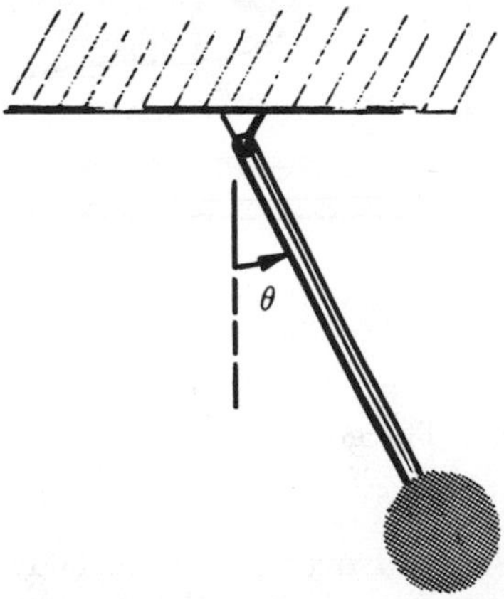

General Motion in a Plane

Three coordinates are generally required to describe the motion.

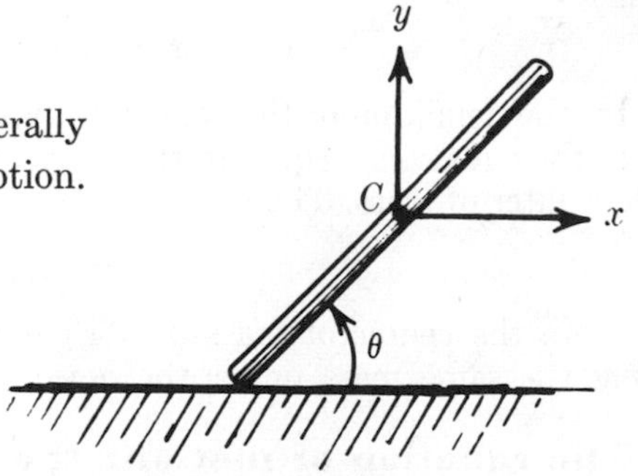

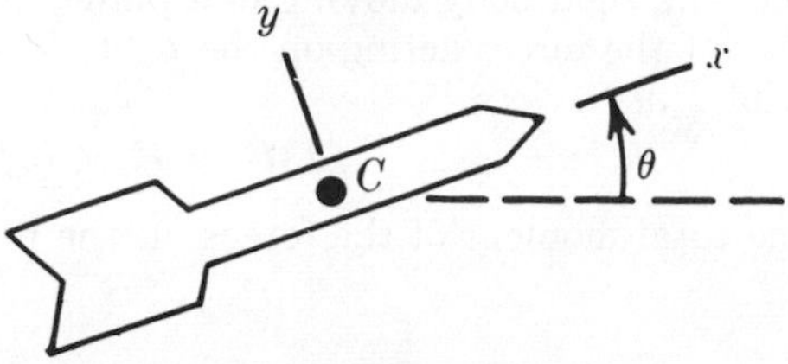

point C is the center of mass of the system, and the point P represents any convenient reference point. The force $d\boldsymbol{F}$ is the net external force acting on a particle of the body of mass dm. The force $d\boldsymbol{f}$ acting on the particle is the net internal force acting on the particle. This is the force of the other particles of the body acting on dm.

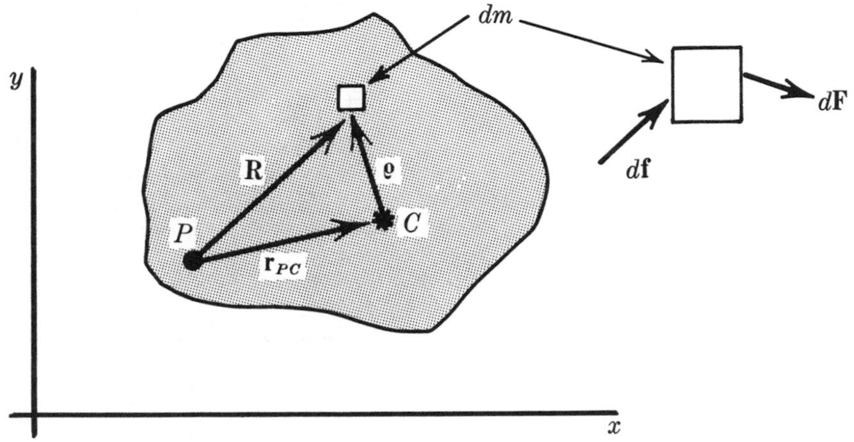

Figure 8-2

The equation of motion of the typical particle is

$$d\boldsymbol{F}_i + d\boldsymbol{f}_i = (dm)\boldsymbol{a} \tag{8.2}$$

Summed over the entire body, and noting that the sum of all internal forces equals zero, the equation of motion becomes

$$\boldsymbol{F} = \int \boldsymbol{a}\, dm \tag{8.3}$$

But by the definition of the center of mass, the integral on the right-hand side of the equation is equal to the mass of the body times the acceleration of the center of mass. Thus,

$$\boldsymbol{F} = m\boldsymbol{a}_c \tag{8.4}$$

Therefore the center of mass of a rigid body moves as a single particle having the same mass under the action of the same net external force.

The equation of motion: the moment equations. Consider the rigid body moving in a plane, as shown in Fig. 8–2. The moment $d\boldsymbol{M}_P$ of the forces acting on the particle dm about any arbitrary reference point P is

$$d\boldsymbol{M}_P = \boldsymbol{R} \times (d\boldsymbol{f} + d\boldsymbol{F}) \tag{8.5}$$

The total moment of the forces on the body acting about point P may be found by performing a summation (or integration) over the entire body. Noting that the sum of the moments of the internal forces equals zero, the summation becomes

$$\boldsymbol{M}_P = \int \boldsymbol{R} \times \boldsymbol{a}\, dm \tag{8.6}$$

But from relative acceleration concepts

$$\boldsymbol{a} = \boldsymbol{a}_P + \ddot{\boldsymbol{R}} \tag{8.7}$$

so that Eq. 8.6 may be written as

$$\boldsymbol{M}_P = \int (\boldsymbol{R} \times \boldsymbol{a}_P)\, dm + \int (\boldsymbol{R} \times \ddot{\boldsymbol{R}})\, dm \tag{8.8}$$

The first term on the right-hand side may be reduced in the following manner:

$$\int (\boldsymbol{R} \times \boldsymbol{a}_P)\, dm = \left\{ \int \boldsymbol{R}\, dm \right\} \times \boldsymbol{a}_P \tag{8.9}$$

since $\boldsymbol{a}_P$ is a constant quantity. From Fig. 8–2, $\boldsymbol{R}$ is equal to $\boldsymbol{r}_{pc} + \boldsymbol{\rho}$, and from the definition of the center of mass, $\int \boldsymbol{\rho}\, dm = 0$, so that

$$\begin{aligned} \left\{ \int \boldsymbol{R}\, dm \right\} \times \boldsymbol{a}_p &= \left\{ \int \boldsymbol{r}_{pc}\, dm \right\} \times \boldsymbol{a}_p \\ &= m(\boldsymbol{r}_{pc} \times \boldsymbol{a}_p) \end{aligned} \tag{8.10}$$

The second term in the right-hand side of Eq. 8.8 may be written as

$$\int (\boldsymbol{R} \times \ddot{\boldsymbol{R}})\, dm = \frac{d}{dt} \int (\boldsymbol{R} \times \dot{\boldsymbol{R}})\, dm \tag{8.11}$$

This may be verified by performing the differentiation. Define as the moment of momentum relative to the point P:

$$\boldsymbol{H}'_P = \int (\boldsymbol{R} \times \dot{\boldsymbol{R}})\, dm \tag{8.12}$$

Note that this will be equal to the moment of momentum as previously defined only if P is fixed in inertial space. Thus it follows from Eqs. 8.11 and 8.12 that the second term on the right-hand side of Eq. 8.8 becomes $\dot{\boldsymbol{H}}_P$. The moment equation then becomes, by combining Eqs. 8.8, 8.10, and 8.12,

$$\boldsymbol{M}_p = \dot{\boldsymbol{H}}'_p + m(\boldsymbol{r}_{pc} \times \boldsymbol{a}_p) \tag{8.13}$$

Examine $\boldsymbol{H}'_p$ as defined by Eq. 8.12; note that

$$\dot{\boldsymbol{R}} = \boldsymbol{\omega} \times \boldsymbol{R} \tag{8.14}$$

where $\boldsymbol{\omega}$ is the angular velocity of the body.

Since the body is moving in a plane, $\boldsymbol{\omega}$ is colinear with the z axis, which then implies that $\dot{\boldsymbol{R}}$ is in a direction shown in Fig. 8–3 and equal in magnitude to $R\omega$. Then $\boldsymbol{R} \times \dot{\boldsymbol{R}}$ is a vector in the positive z direction and equal to $R^2\omega$. Thus,

$$\boldsymbol{H}'_p = \omega \int R^2\, dm\bar{\boldsymbol{k}} \tag{8.15}$$

The integral in Eq. 8.15 is called the *moment of inertia* about point P and is written I_P. Then

$$\dot{\boldsymbol{H}}'_P = I_P\dot{\omega}\bar{\boldsymbol{k}} \tag{8.16}$$

By the definition of the cross-product, it is seen from Fig. 8–3 that

$$\begin{aligned} m(\boldsymbol{r}_{pc} \times \boldsymbol{a}_p) &= -m(r_{pc} \sin \theta)a_p\bar{\boldsymbol{k}} \\ &= -d(ma_p)\bar{\boldsymbol{k}} \end{aligned} \tag{8.17}$$

where d is the perpendicular distance between the line of action of a_p and the point C.

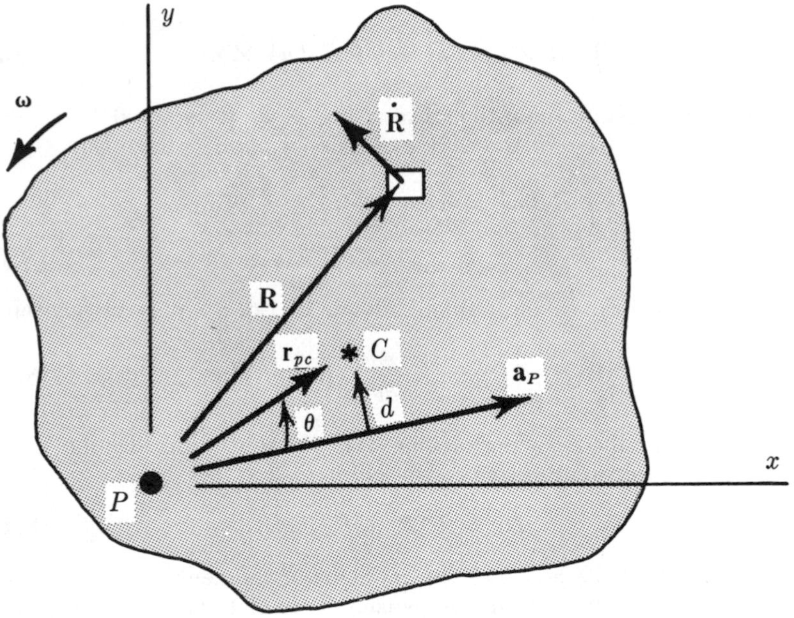

Figure 8-3

Since there will be moments only about the z axis, $\boldsymbol{M}_P = M_P\bar{\boldsymbol{k}}$, and the moment equation of motion may be written (from Eqs. 8.13, 8.16, and 8.17) as

$$\boxed{M_P = I_P\dot{\omega} - d(ma_P)} \tag{8.18}$$

This, then, is the general expression for the moment equation for a rigid body in a plane. Both M_P and ω are measured positive counterclockwise, and d is positive in the positive y direction when a_P is in the positive x direction.

8-2. THREE-DIMENSIONAL MOTION

It will be our purpose here to attempt to determine the number and types of coordinates required to define the position of a rigid body. Consider the body shown in Fig. 8–4. The x, y, and z axes are defined as inertial axes that are fixed in space. The three points P_1, P_2, and P_3 define a plane in the rigid body, a plane that moves with the body.

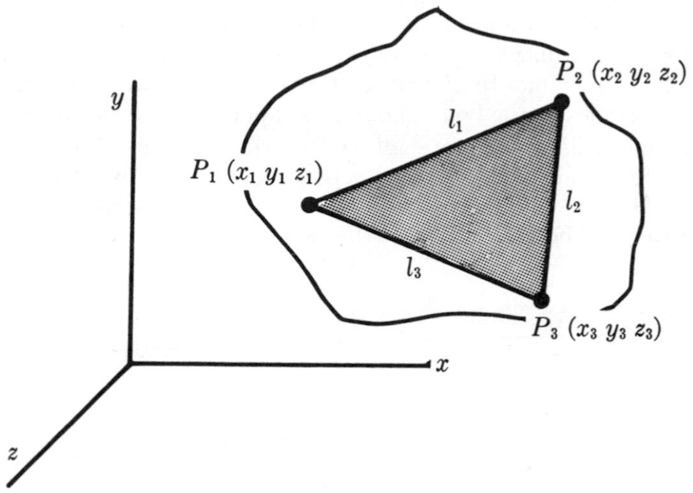

Figure 8-4

It is almost immediately obvious that we could uniquely determine the position of the rigid body by specifying the position of the three points. And since there are three coordinates associated with each point, there would then be a total of nine coordinates needed to determine the position of the body. However, it is noted that there are three equations relating the position of the three points. They are:

$$
\begin{aligned}
l_1^2 &= (x_2 - x_1)^2 + (y_2 - y_1)^2 + (z_2 - z_1)^2 \\
l_2^2 &= (x_3 - x_2)^2 + (y_3 - y_2)^2 + (z_3 - z_2)^2 \\
l_3^2 &= (x_1 - x_3)^2 + (y_1 - y_3)^2 + (z_1 - z_3)^2
\end{aligned} \tag{8.19}
$$

This implies that only six of the coordinates are independent and therefore *only a total of six independent coordinates are required to specify to position of a rigid body.* The problem now is to try to determine the six best independent coordinates to use. The problem is not so much to choose just any set of six coordinates, but to choose six coordinates for which six equations of motion, relating the forces to the motion, may be written.

Since we already have the equations of motion of the center of mass of a system of particles, $\boldsymbol{F} = m\boldsymbol{a}_c$, we may choose the center of mass as a reference point, and this gives us three equations for three of the six required coordinates. Once the center of mass has been specified, the other three coordinates are needed to define the orientation or rotation of the body in space. The center of mass of the body may be defined by one vector displacement, $\boldsymbol{r}_c$. On the other hand, since angular rotation cannot be defined by a vector, it is impossible to specify the rotation by one vector composed of the rotations about each coordinate axis and we find it somewhat difficult to find three angles to specify the orientation of the body. In general, however, we are not so much interested in the orientation of the body as we are in the angular velocity or motion of the body, and since the angular velocity may be specified as a vector, we find that it is quite convenient to choose as the remaining three coordinates the angular velocities of the body about the x, y, and z axes fixed in the body. Later on in the discussion, we shall see that the moment equations, $\boldsymbol{M} = \dot{\boldsymbol{H}}$, developed originally for a system of particles, may be written in terms of these angular velocities. Figure 8–5 shows the six coordinates that may be used to describe the motion of the body.

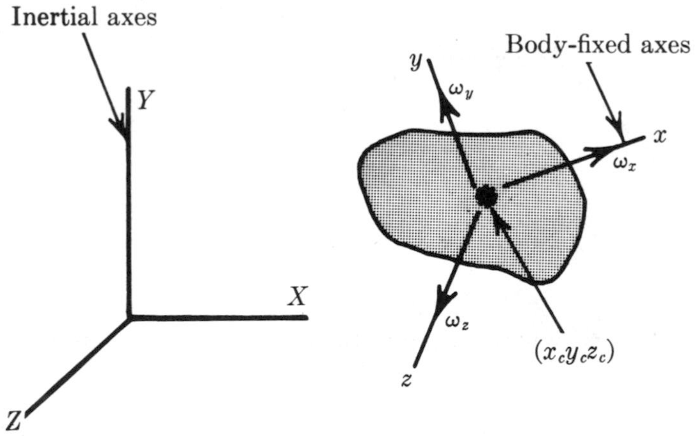

Figure 8-5

In this text, we shall be concerned primarily with the motion of a rigid body and not so much with the orientation or position of the body as a function of time. Often, however, it is necessary to describe not only the angular velocities about the body axes, but also the actual orientation of the body. To do this, we try to choose three independent angles that will completely define the position of the body relative to the inertial space. One of the most convenient schemes for doing this is the *Euler angles*. The Euler angles are defined as shown in Fig. 8–6. The xyz axes are fixed in the body, and the XYZ axes are inertial axes fixed in space.

The three Euler angles are defined by a combination of the three successive rotations, as shown:

1. Rotate the body axes about the z axis through an angle of ψ.
2. Rotate the body axes about the x' axis through an angle of θ.
3. Rotate the body axes about the z'' axis through an angle of ϕ.

These three angles are said to be independent of each other because any one of the angles may be changed without changing the other two. Now the three Euler angles and the three coordinates for the center of mass of the body may be used as the six parameters describing the position of the body.

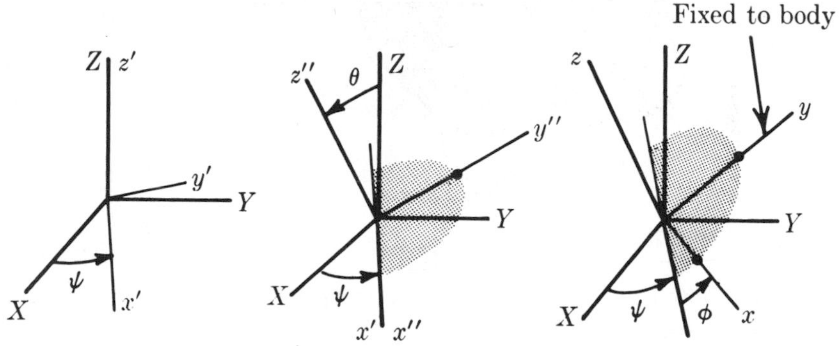

Figure 8-6

In summary, we have established two sets of six coordinates, which may be employed to specify the position and motion of a rigid body as it moves through space. The two sets are as follows:

1. The center of mass and the angular velocities about the three body axes: $(x_c, y_c, z_c, \omega_x, \omega_y, \omega_z)$.
2. The center of mass and the three Euler angles: $(x_c, y_c, z_c, \psi, \theta, \phi)$.

The first set of coordinates has the disadvantage that the position of the body cannot be specified. The second set has the disadvantage that the equations of motion often become somewhat more complex and difficult to establish. In most of the simpler problems of the dynamical analysis of the motion of rigid bodies, the first set is generally employed. The Euler angles are usually used in those cases where the rigid body has a large angular velocity of spin or where it is desired to specify the position of the body as a function of time.

In the special case where the body is moving in a plane, there are essentially three constraints, owing to the fact that the body is not allowed to move in a direction out of the plane and is not allowed to rotate about two of its three coordinate axes fixed in the body. Thus, the position of a rigid body moving in a plane may be described by three coordinates. Two coordinates are required to define the position of the center of mass of the body, and only one coordinate is required to define the orientation of the body. This coordinate may be an angle θ, as shown in Fig. 8–7. Chapter

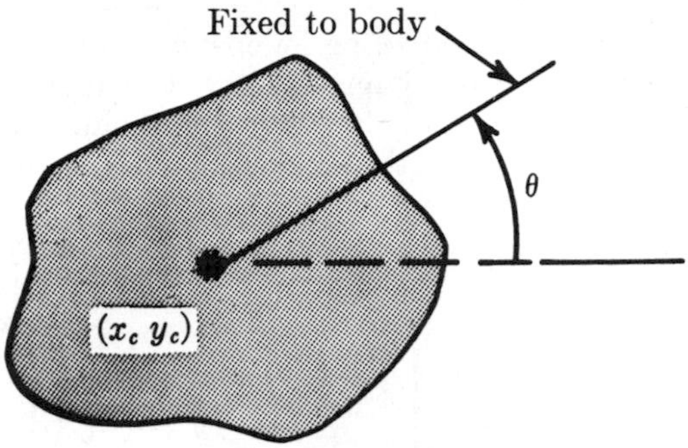

Figure 8-7

2 explained how to describe the angular motion of bodies, by specifying angular displacement, velocity, and acceleration.

8-3. THE EQUATIONS OF MOTION

Since there are six coordinates required to specify the position of a rigid body in space, there must be (if the body is moving) six equations of motion, which presumably can be solved to determine each of the six coordinates as a function of time. The six equations of motion developed in Chapter 6 for a system of particles, and which are available, are the three force equations with which the student is already familiar; the three moment equations were introduced in Sec. 6–2. In vector form, the force and the moment equations are

$$\boldsymbol{F} = m\boldsymbol{a}_c \tag{8.20}$$

$$\boldsymbol{M}_P = \dot{\boldsymbol{H}}_P \tag{8.21}$$

Examination of the moment equation: the moment of momentum. The moment equation $\boldsymbol{M} = \dot{\boldsymbol{H}}$ for a system of particles of a rigid body is referred to a point that either must be fixed in inertial space or must coincide with the center of mass of the body. In this section, we shall examine the moment of momentum about the center of mass or a fixed point for a rigid body, but we shall start out by choosing any reference point that is fixed in the body, and by writing the moment of momentum relative to that point.

Shown in Fig. 8–8 is a body that is moving through space and is both translating and rotating at the instant shown. At this instant, the body has an angular velocity given by the vector $\boldsymbol{\omega}$. The point O is any reference point that is fixed in the body. The mass dm is a small representative particle of the system of particles of which the body is constituted.

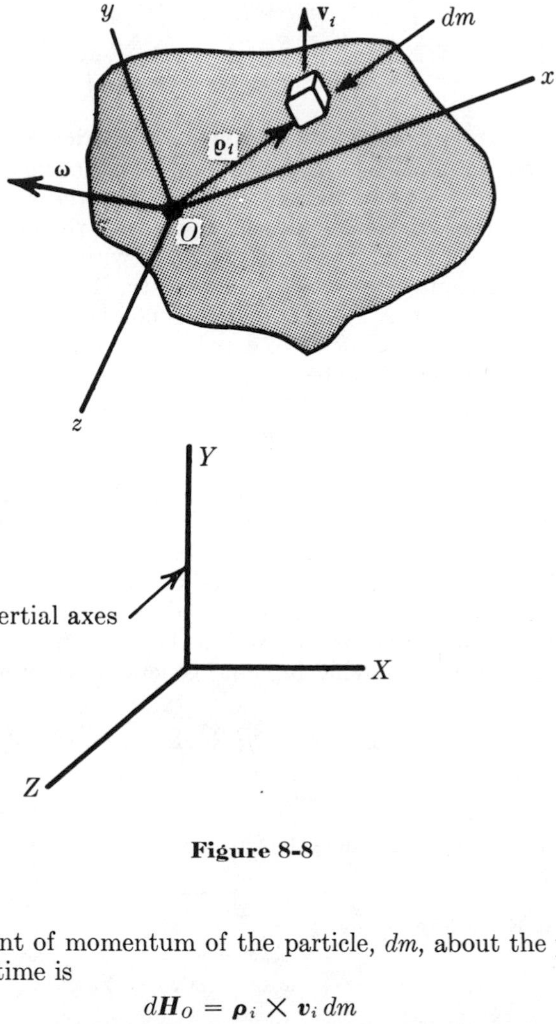

Figure 8-8

The moment of momentum of the particle, dm, about the point O at this instant of time is

$$d\boldsymbol{H}_O = \boldsymbol{\rho}_i \times \boldsymbol{v}_i\, dm \tag{8.22}$$

where $\boldsymbol{v}_i$ is the absolute velocity of the particle at this instant, and $\boldsymbol{\rho}_i$ is the radius vector from O to the particle. The velocity of the particle may be expressed in terms of the velocity of point O by the relative velocity equation (Eq. 3.23)

$$\boldsymbol{v}_i = \boldsymbol{v}_O + \boldsymbol{\omega} \times \boldsymbol{\rho}_i + \boldsymbol{v}_r \tag{8.23}$$

Since the velocity of dm relative to O, $\boldsymbol{v}_r$, is zero, the moment of momentum becomes

$$d\boldsymbol{H}_O = \boldsymbol{\rho}_i \times (\boldsymbol{v}_O + \boldsymbol{\omega} \times \boldsymbol{\rho}_i) \tag{8.24}$$

The total moment of momentum of the body about the point O is obtained by summing the moment of momentum of all elements about that point. In this case, the summation will be performed by an integration:

$$\begin{aligned} \boldsymbol{H}_O &= \int_v \{\boldsymbol{\rho} \times (\boldsymbol{v}_O + \boldsymbol{\omega} \times \boldsymbol{\rho})\}\, dm \\ &= \int_v \boldsymbol{\rho} \times (\boldsymbol{\omega} \times \boldsymbol{\rho})\, dm - \boldsymbol{v}_O \times \int_v \boldsymbol{\rho}\, dm \end{aligned} \tag{8.25}$$

Now, since the reference point O must be restricted to either a fixed point in the body or to the moving center of mass of the body if the moment equation (Eq. 8.21) is to be used, it follows that the second integral of Eq. 8.25 will be zero. If point O is a fixed point in the body, the velocity of point O will be zero, and if point O coincides with the center of mass of the body, then the integral $\int \boldsymbol{\rho}\, dm$ will be zero. The latter follows from the definition of the center of mass. Then, if point O is either the moving center of mass of the body or a fixed point in the body, the moment of momentum about the point O becomes

$$\boldsymbol{H}_O = \int_v \boldsymbol{\rho} \times (\boldsymbol{\omega} \times \boldsymbol{\rho})\, dm \tag{8.26}$$

Consider now the vector expansion of both the radius vector and the angular velocity vector. Both vectors are written in terms of the unit vectors defined in the x, y, z axes shown in Fig. 8–8. (It is important to note that the only restriction on the axes at this point is that the origin coincides with the center of mass of a fixed point in the body; it is not known as yet whether the axes are fixed in the body, fixed with a constant orientation in space, or moving in some general manner with respect to the body.)

$$\boldsymbol{\rho} = x\bar{\boldsymbol{i}} + y\bar{\boldsymbol{j}} + z\bar{\boldsymbol{k}} \tag{8.27}$$

$$\boldsymbol{\omega} = \omega_x\bar{\boldsymbol{i}} + \omega_y\bar{\boldsymbol{j}} + \omega_z\bar{\boldsymbol{k}} \tag{8.28}$$

By evaluating the cross-products that appear in the moment-of-momentum equation, we have

$$\begin{aligned} \boldsymbol{\rho} \times (\boldsymbol{\omega} \times \boldsymbol{\rho}) = & [\omega_x(y^2 + z^2) - \omega_y xy - \omega_z xz]\bar{\boldsymbol{i}} \\ & + [-\omega_x yx + \omega_y(z^2 + x^2) - \omega_z yz]\bar{\boldsymbol{j}} \\ & + [-\omega_x zx - \omega_y zy + \omega_z(x^2 + y^2)]\bar{\boldsymbol{k}} \end{aligned} \tag{8.29}$$

Upon substitution of Eq. 8.29 into the equation for the moment of momentum of the body, given by Eq. 8.26, the moment of momentum may be written as

$$\boldsymbol{H} = H_x\bar{\boldsymbol{i}} + H_y\bar{\boldsymbol{j}} + H_z\bar{\boldsymbol{k}} \tag{8.30}$$

where

$$\begin{aligned} H_x &= \omega_x \int_v (y^2 + z^2)\, dm - \omega_y \int_v xy\, dm - \omega_z \int_v xz\, dm \\ H_y &= -\omega_x \int_v yx\, dm + \omega_y \int_v (z^2 + x^2)\, dm - \omega_z \int_v yz\, dm \qquad \textbf{(8.31)} \\ H_z &= -\omega_x \int_v zx\, dm - \omega_y \int_v zy\, dm + \omega_z \int_v (x^2 + y^2)\, dm \end{aligned}$$

The equations for the components of the moment of momentum may be reduced considerably by making the following definitions:

Moment of inertia about the x axis:

$$I_{xx} \equiv \int_v (y^2 + z^2)\, dm$$

Moment of inertia about the y axis:

$$I_{yy} \equiv \int_v (z^2 + x^2)\, dm$$

Moment of inertia about the z axis:

$$I_{zz} \equiv \int_v (x^2 + y^2)\, dm$$

Product of inertia with respect to the xy axes:

$$I_{xy} \equiv \int_v xy\, dm$$

Product of inertia with respect to the yz axes:

$$I_{yz} \equiv \int_v yz\, dm$$

Product of inertia with respect to the zx axes:

$$I_{zx} \equiv \int_v zx\, dm$$

The method of evaluation of these integrals is a complete study in itself. For this reason, Sec. 8-4 is devoted to the discussion of the moment and product of inertia integrals.

Upon examination of the preceding six integrals, it is seen that both the moments and the products of inertia depend upon not only the geometry of the body but also the definition of the coordinate axes. Two points that directly affect the equations of motion should be emphasized:

1. The moments and products of inertia will be a function of time unless the reference axes are fixed in the body (except in the case of a symmetrical body). Thus the reference axes should always be fixed in the body.
2. It is possible to choose the reference axes so that all products of inertia are equal to zero. If this is possible, then the equations of motion may be considerably reduced by proper choice of reference

axes. The axes that have this property are called the *principal axes.*

Assuming now that the reference axes are not the principal axes, the moment of momentum of the body may be written as

$$\begin{aligned} H_x &= I_{xx}\omega_x - I_{xy}\omega_y - I_{xz}\omega_z \\ H_y &= -I_{yx}\omega_x + I_{yy}\omega_y - I_{yz}\omega_z \\ H_z &= -I_{zx}\omega_x - I_{zy}\omega_y + I_{zz}\omega_z \end{aligned} \tag{8.32}$$

and if the reference axes are the principal axes, the moment of momentum reduces to

$$\boldsymbol{H}_O = I_{xx}\omega_x\bar{\boldsymbol{i}} + I_{yy}\omega_y\bar{\boldsymbol{j}} + I_{zz}\omega_z\bar{\boldsymbol{k}} \tag{8.33}$$

Examination of the moment equation: the moment related to the moment of momentum. The next step in relating the moment to the moment of momentum of the body is to take the time derivative of the moment of momentum:

$$\boldsymbol{M} = \dot{\boldsymbol{H}}$$

$$\begin{aligned} M_x\bar{\boldsymbol{i}} + M_y\bar{\boldsymbol{j}} + M_z\bar{\boldsymbol{k}} &= \frac{d}{dt}(H_x\bar{\boldsymbol{i}} + H_y\bar{\boldsymbol{j}} + H_z\bar{\boldsymbol{k}}) \\ &= \dot{H}_x\bar{\boldsymbol{i}} + \dot{H}_y\bar{\boldsymbol{j}} + \dot{H}_z\bar{\boldsymbol{k}} + H_x\dot{\bar{\boldsymbol{i}}} + H_y\dot{\bar{\boldsymbol{j}}} + H_z\dot{\bar{\boldsymbol{k}}} \end{aligned} \tag{8.34}$$

Since the reference axes are fixed in the body, the unit vectors will be changing direction as the body moves, thus implying that the unit vectors will have time derivatives. The time derivatives of the x unit vectors may be evaluated by noting that the angular velocity of the body (and thus the reference coordinate system and the unit vectors) is equal to $\boldsymbol{\omega}$. The time derivatives of the unit vectors may then be evaluated in the following manner:

$$\begin{aligned} \dot{\bar{\boldsymbol{i}}} &= \boldsymbol{\omega} \times \bar{\boldsymbol{i}} = \omega_z\bar{\boldsymbol{j}} - \omega_y\bar{\boldsymbol{k}} \\ \dot{\bar{\boldsymbol{j}}} &= \boldsymbol{\omega} \times \bar{\boldsymbol{j}} = \omega_x\bar{\boldsymbol{k}} - \omega_z\bar{\boldsymbol{i}} \\ \dot{\bar{\boldsymbol{k}}} &= \boldsymbol{\omega} \times \bar{\boldsymbol{k}} = \omega_y\bar{\boldsymbol{i}} - \omega_x\bar{\boldsymbol{j}} \end{aligned} \tag{8.35}$$

Therefore the moment equation becomes, when expanded into scalar form,

$$\begin{aligned} M_x &= \dot{H}_x - \omega_z H_y + \omega_y H_z \\ M_y &= \dot{H}_y - \omega_x H_z + \omega_z H_x \\ M_z &= \dot{H}_z - \omega_y H_x + \omega_x H_y \end{aligned} \tag{8.36}$$

The moment of momentum of the body with respect to its three coordinate axes is given by Eq. 8.32 or Eq. 8.33 if the reference axes are the principal axes. The complete set of moment equations could be written by substituting Eq. 8.32 into Eq. 8.36, but since the resulting expression is so lengthy, it will not be carried out here.

These three moment equations, then, along with the three force equations, form the six equations needed to describe the motion of a rigid body.

Method of establishing moment equation for a given problem. The moment equation may be established for a given problem from a combination of Eqs. 8.32 and 8.36. However, the author feels that perhaps the student derives more benefit by developing each problem from the beginning, as outlined below. There is more work involved, but it is not necessary to memorize a set of complex equations.

1. *Define the reference coordinate system.* Define the origin of the coordinate system (and the point to which the moment equation is referred) at either a point in the body that is fixed in inertial space or in the moving center of mass of the body. Generally, the following rules, when observed, will yield the best results:

(*a*) If the body is moving through space in some arbitrary manner, we have no other choice but to fix the origin of the reference system at the center of mass.

(*b*) If the body is rotating about a fixed point or axis, fix the origin of the moving reference system to the fixed point and refer the moment equation to that point.

(*c*) Fix the reference axes to the body. This is done to ensure that the moments and products of inertia are constants and not functions of time. In the case of a body of revolution, it is possible and often quite convenient to fix the system in space with assurance that the moments and products of inertia do not change with time.

(*d*) If possible, try to choose the reference axes as the principal axes of the body. This simplifies the equations considerably, since all products of inertia are zero.

2. *Evaluate the moments and products of inertia.*

3. *Write the moment of momentum for the body.* Once the reference point and the reference axes have been defined, the moment of momentum of the body about the reference point may be written (from Eq. 8.32) as

$$\begin{aligned} \boldsymbol{H} = {} & [I_{xx}\omega_x - I_{xy}\omega_y - I_{xz}\omega_z]\bar{\boldsymbol{i}} \\ & + [-I_{xy}\omega_x + I_{yy}\omega_y - I_{yz}\omega_z]\bar{\boldsymbol{j}} \\ & + [-I_{xz}\omega_x - I_{yz}\omega_y + I_{zz}\omega_z]\bar{\boldsymbol{k}} \end{aligned} \tag{8.37}$$

4. *Take the time derivative of the moment of momentum equation.* Since the reference axes are fixed to the body (in order to ensure that the moments and products of inertia are constants), the reference axes move with the body, implying that the unit vectors of the reference axes have time derivatives. In any case, the time derivative of the moment of momentum may be determined in one of two ways:

(*a*) Differentiate the moment of momentum equation directly, noting that both angular velocities and unit vectors will have time derivatives. (Note how large the equation would become if the moments and products of inertia were functions of time.)

(*b*) Use the form developed in Sec. 3–2 for determining the time derivative of the vector, which is defined in a coordinate system that is moving as

$$\dot{\boldsymbol{H}} = \dot{\boldsymbol{H}}_{xyz} + \boldsymbol{\omega} \times \boldsymbol{H} \tag{8.38}$$

where

$$\dot{\boldsymbol{H}}_{xyz} = \dot{H}_x\bar{\boldsymbol{i}} + \dot{H}_y\bar{\boldsymbol{j}} + \dot{H}_z\bar{\boldsymbol{k}} \tag{8.39}$$

Both methods listed above will give the same results.

5. *Equate the time derivative of the moment of momentum to the moment on the body.* Then separate the vector equation into the three scalar equations. In general, the three equations will be highly nonlinear, and it is only with some difficulty (usually requiring the aid of a computer) that the equations can be solved. But in any case, one now has three moment equations, in combination with the three force equations, for the required set of six equations from which the motion of the rigid body may be determined.

8-4. EVALUATION OF MOMENTS AND PRODUCTS OF INERTIA

Before the motion of a given body can be determined, the moments and products of inertia of that body about the chosen reference axes must be established. Specifically, we must determine the following integrals:

$$\begin{aligned} I_{xx} &= \int_v (y^2 + z^2)\, dm & I_{xy} &= \int_v xy\, dm \\ I_{yy} &= \int_v (z^2 + x^2)\, dm & I_{yz} &= \int_v yz\, dm \\ I_{zz} &= \int_v (x^2 + y^2)\, dm & I_{zx} &= \int_v zx\, dm \end{aligned} \tag{8.40}$$

It will be useful in the tabulation to consider the integrals written in summation form. If the rigid body is divided into n particles, each of mass Δm, the moment of inertia about the x axis and the product of inertia with respect to the xy axes may be determined by performing the following summations, from i equal to 1 to i equal to n:

$$\begin{aligned} I_{xx} &= \sum_i (y_i^2 + z_i^2)\, \Delta m_i \\ I_{xy} &= \sum_i x_i y_i\, \Delta m_i \end{aligned} \tag{8.41}$$

Tabulated below are some of the properties of moments and products of inertia:

1. Both the moment and product of inertia are completely dependent upon the position and orientation of the coordinate system relative to the body. This will become quite obvious upon examination of some of the examples given subsequently.

2. The moment and product of inertia is a measure of not only the mass of a body but also of the distribution of that mass. If the mass of a body is such that it lies some distance from the reference axes, it will have a larger moment of inertia than will a body with the same mass clustered about the axes.

3. The moment of inertia will always be a positive number. This is apparent from examination of the definition of moment of inertia. It is impossible for any of the terms in the definition to be negative.

4. The product of inertia may be any number: positive, negative, or zero. If one of the reference axes of a body is an axis of symmetry, then the product of inertia will be zero. This may be seen from Fig. 8–9.

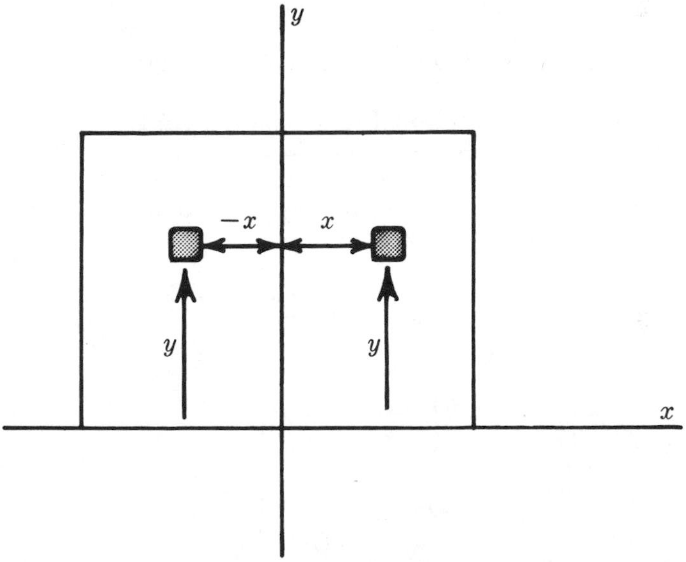

Figure 8-9

For every element in the first quadrant with an incremental product of inertia of $xy(\Delta m)$, there is a mirror image in the second quadrant with a product of inertia of $(-x)y(\Delta m)$. In the summation, these will all add to zero. Also, it follows that if the concentration of mass is in the first or third quadrants, the product of inertia will be positive, and if the concentration is in the second or fourth quadrants, then the product of inertia will be negative.

5. Given a reference point in the body that defines the origin of the reference system, it is possible to orient the reference axes in the body so

that the products of inertia are all equal to zero. These axes are the *principal axes.*

6. The *radius of gyration* of a body is defined as

$$r_{xx} = \sqrt{\frac{I_{xx}}{m}} \tag{8.42}$$

Units. It is seen from the definition of the moment of inertia that the moment of inertia will have units of mass times a length squared. In the engineering system of units, mass has units of pound-second² per foot and units of length of feet. Thus, the units for the moment of inertia are pound-second²-feet. The product of inertia by inspection has the same units.

The moment of inertia is usually expressed in the following form:

I = (a fraction)(mass of the body)(a significant dimension of the body)²

This will be demonstrated in examples in the next discussion.

The analytical method for determining the moment and product of inertia. If the geometry and the density of a body are defined analytically, it is often possible that the moment and product of inertia integrals may be evaluated directly. The examples below show how a direct integration may be performed.

Example 8–1. For the cylinder shown in Fig. 8–10, determine the moment of inertia about the y axis and the product of inertia about the xy axis.

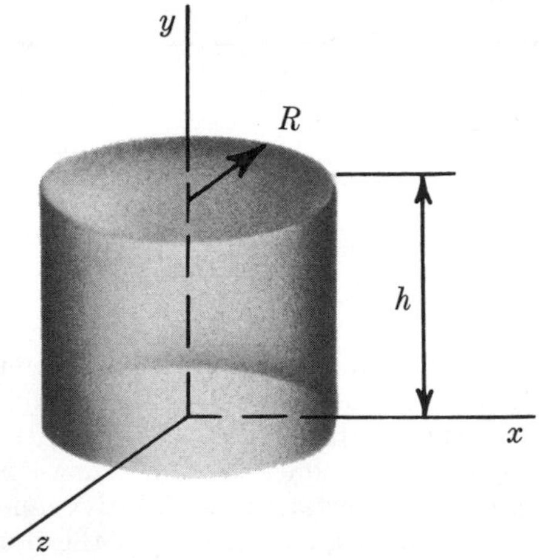

Figure 8-10

Solution: First the moment of inertia about the y axis will be determined. The integral to be evaluated is

$$I_{yy} = \int_v \gamma(x^2 + z^2)\, dV$$

where γ is the mass density and $dm = \gamma\, dV$. Because of the circular symmetry in this problem, one might be tempted to try using polar coordinates. The cylinder, as viewed by looking down the y axis, is shown in Fig. 8-11.

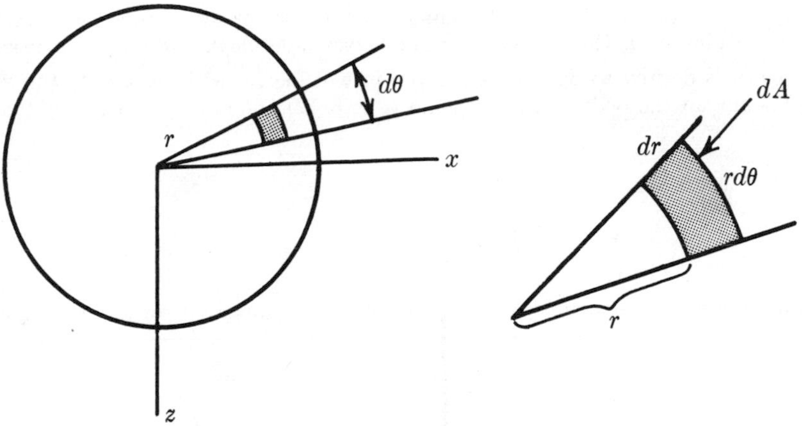

Figure 8-11

If polar coordinates are to be used,

$$x^2 + z^2 = r^2$$

The increment of volume is

$$dV = hr\, dr\, d\theta$$

By substituting into the integral for the moment of inertia,

$$I_{yy} = \int_A \gamma r^3 h\, dr\, d\theta$$

or

$$I_{yy} = \int_0^R \int_0^{2\pi} \gamma h r^3\, d\theta\, dr$$

and

$$I_{yy} = \int_0^R \gamma 2\pi h r^3\, dr$$

$$= \frac{\gamma \pi h R^4}{2}$$

The moment of inertia may be determined as a function of the mass of the cylinder. The mass of the cylinder may be determined by integrating the volume:

$$M = \int_V \gamma\, dV$$

Thus,

$$M = \int_0^R \int_0^{2\pi} \gamma(hr\, d\theta\, dr)$$

and

$$M = \gamma\pi h R^2$$

Therefore the moment of inertia as a function of the mass is

$$I_{yy} = \frac{MR^2}{2}$$

This is an important relationship to remember because this problem appears very often in dealing with the motion of rigid bodies, specifically wheels and disks.

Now it is desired to determine the product of inertia with respect to the xy axes. Looking at the body in the xy plane (Fig. 8–12) one notes immediately that

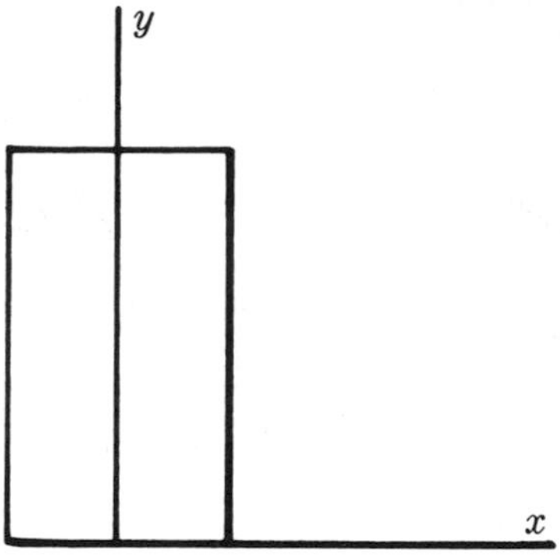

Figure 8-12

the y axis is an axis of symmetry, so that the product of inertia with respect to the xy axes will be zero.

Example 8–2. Determine the moment of inertia about the x axis for the solid rectangular body shown in Fig. 8–13.

Solution: The moment of inertia about the x axis is the integral

$$I_{xx} = \int_v \gamma(y^2 + z^2)\, dV$$

The integral can be rewritten as

$$I_{xx} = \int_V \gamma y^2\, dV + \int_V \gamma z^2\, dV$$

Figure 8–14 shows the yz plane. The first integral could be evaluated if the increment of volume could be expressed as a function of y and the second integral could be evaluated if the increment of volume could be expressed as a function of z.

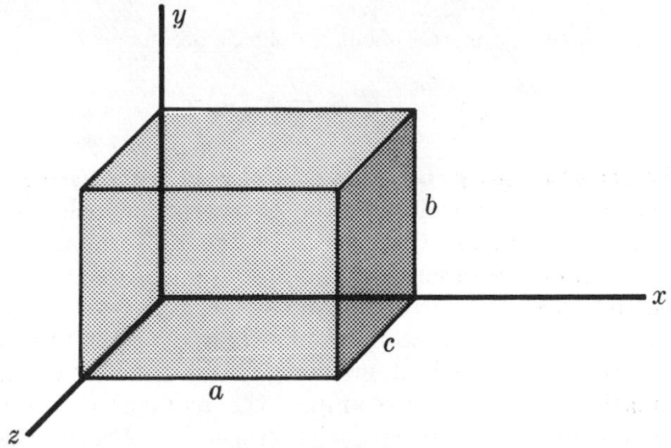

Figure 8-13

This may be done by choosing a horizontal and vertical strip, respectively, as shown in Fig. 8–14. Thus,

$$dV = ca\,dy$$

and

$$dV = ba\,dz$$

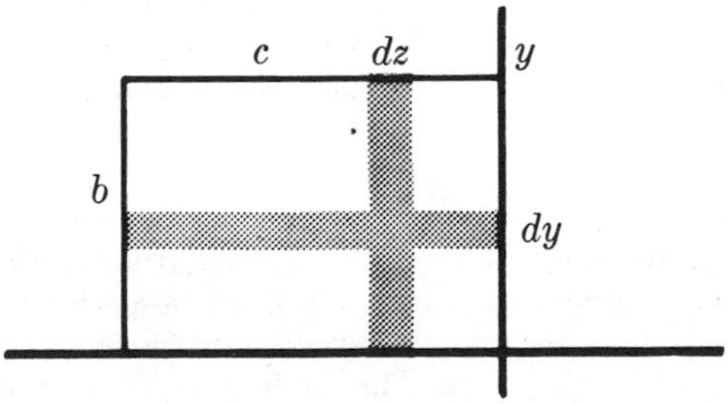

Figure 8-14

Then the moment of inertia becomes

$$I_{xx} = \int_0^b \gamma y^2 ca\,dy + \int_0 \gamma baz^2\,dz$$

or

$$I_{xx} = \frac{\gamma abc}{3}(b^2 + c^2)$$

Here, again, the moment of inertia may be expressed in terms of the mass. The total mass is nothing more than

$$M = \gamma abc$$

so that the moment of inertia about the x axis becomes

$$I_{xx} = \frac{M}{3}(b^2 + c^2)$$

Moments and products of inertia by numerical methods. In almost every practical case, the body with which one is dealing is a nonhomogeneous body, that is, a body whose mass distribution and geometry cannot be described conveniently as an analytical function of time. In this case, it is virtually impossible to perform a direct integration over the body to determine its moments and products of inertia. But we may perform a numerical integration. This is done by writing the integrals in summation form. As an example, the moment of inertia about the x axis and the product of inertia with respect to the xy axes are written in summation form as

$$I_{xx} = \int_V (y^2 + z^2)\, dm = \sum_i (y_i^2 + z_i^2)m_i \tag{8.43}$$

$$I_{xy} = \int_V xy\, dm = \sum_i x_i y_i m_i \tag{8.44}$$

The body is assumed to be split into n small elements, and the mass of each of the elements is known and given as m_i. The coordinates associated with each m_i are given as x_i, y_i, and z_i. The evaluation of the product of inertia with respect to the xy axes, for instance, is made by determining the product of $x_i y_i m_i$ for each of the elements and then adding this product of all the masses. The numerical integration is demonstrated by Example 8–3.

Example 8–3. It is desired to determine the moment and product of inertia of an artificial earth satellite about each of the centroidal axes. Since the body is not at all homogeneous, a numerical integration must be performed, and this is done by breaking the body up into a number of discrete parts and tabulating the mass and coordinate of each of the parts. This is done in Table 8–2. For this problem, determine the moment of inertia about the z axis and the product of inertia about the yz axes.

TABLE 8–2. NUMERICAL INTEGRATION

n	m_i	x_i	y_i	z_i
1	2	2	3	1
2	3	3	4	−2
3	1	2	−1	−2
4	2	1	−3	2
5	1	−3	−2	1
6	3	−2	3	4
7	3	−4	2	−3
8	2	−2	−3	−1

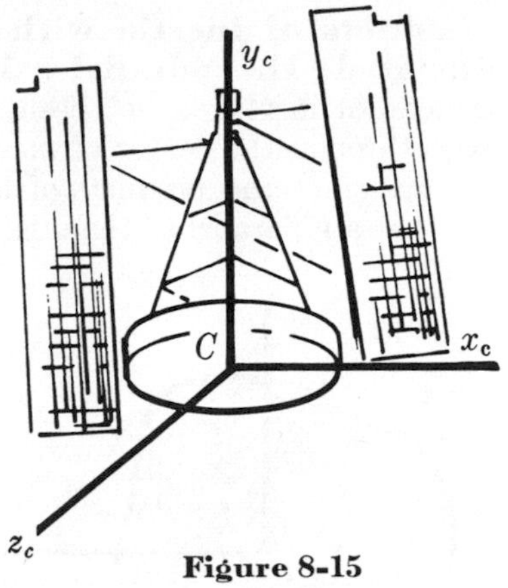

Figure 8-15

The moment of inertia about the z axis is, in summation form,

$$I_{zz} = \sum_i (x_i^2 + y_i^2)m_i$$

and the products of inertia with respect to the yz axes are

$$I_{yz} = \sum_i y_i z_i m_i$$

In order to perform the summation, it might be best to establish Table 8–3.

TABLE 8-3

For I_{zz}					For I_{yz}	
n	x_i^2	y_i^2	$(x_i^2 + y_i^2)$	$m_i(x_i^2 + y_i^2)$	$z_i y_i$	$m_i z_i y_i$
1	4	9	13	26	3	6
2	9	16	25	75	−8	−24
3	4	1	5	5	2	2
4	1	9	10	20	−6	−12
5	9	4	13	13	2	2
6	4	9	13	39	12	36
7	16	4	20	60	−6	−18
8	4	9	13	26	3	6
				264		−2

In this way, the moment and product of inertia are obtained by simply performing the desired summations. Thus,

$$I_{zz} = 264$$

and

$$I_{yz} = -2$$

Moments and products of inertia with respect to axes that have been translated: the parallel axis theorem. Once the moments and products of inertia have been determined for a given set of axes that pass through the center of mass of the body, it is possible to determine the moments and products of inertia of that same body with respect to axes that are parallel to the original axes.

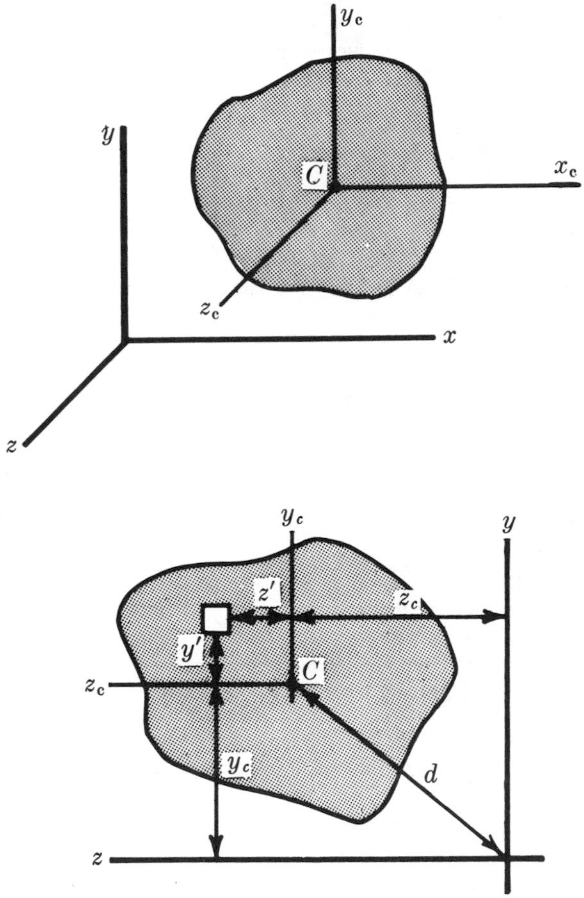

Figure 8-16

Suppose that the moment of inertia about the x_c axis of the body shown in Fig. 8–16 is known, and it is desired to determine the moment of inertia about the x axis. The moment of inertia about the x axis may be written as

$$I_{xx} = \int_V (y^2 + z^2)\, dm \tag{8.45}$$

But, from Fig. 8–16,

$$\begin{aligned} y &= y_c + y' \\ z &= z_c + z' \end{aligned} \tag{8.46}$$

so that

$$\begin{aligned} I_{xx} = \int (y'^2 + z'^2)\, dm + \int (y_c^2 + z_c^2)\, dm + 2y_c \int y'\, dm \\ + 2z_c \int z'\, dm \end{aligned} \tag{8.47}$$

But it is known that

$$\int y'\, dm = 0 \quad \text{and} \quad \int z'\, dm = 0$$

since y' is measured from the center of mass. Noting that

$$\int_V (y'^2 + z'^2)\, dm = I_{xx_c} \quad \text{(the moment of inertia about the } x_c \text{ axis)}$$

$$d^2 = y_c^2 + z_c^2$$

$$\int dm = m$$

it follows that the moment of inertia about the x axis is

$$I_{xx} = I_{xx_c} + d^2 m \tag{8.48}$$

This is the *parallel axis theorem.*

By a similar argument, the product of inertia with respect to the yz axes may be determined:

$$\begin{aligned} I_{yz} &= \int yz\, dm \\ &= \int (y_c + y')(z_c + z')\, dm \\ &= \int y_c z_c\, dm + \int y'z'\, dm + y_c \int z'\, dm + z_c \int y'\, dm \end{aligned} \tag{8.49}$$

Hence the parallel axis equation for the product of inertia becomes

$$I_{yz} = I_{yz_c} + y_c z_c m \tag{8.50}$$

The parallel axis equations for the moments and products of inertia with respect to the other axis may be easily formed by using the preceding results for the x and y axes.

Example 8–4. Using the parallel axis theorem, determine the moment of inertia about the y axis of the right circular cylinder shown in Fig. 8–17.

Solution: The moment of inertia is known for the vertical axis y_c that passes through the center of mass. This was shown in Example 8–1 to be equal to

$$I_{yy_c} = \frac{MR^2}{2}$$

The parallel axis theorem states that

$$I_{yy} = I_{yy_c} + d^2 M$$

where d is the perpendicular distance between the y_c and the y axis; in this case, d is equal to R. Therefore

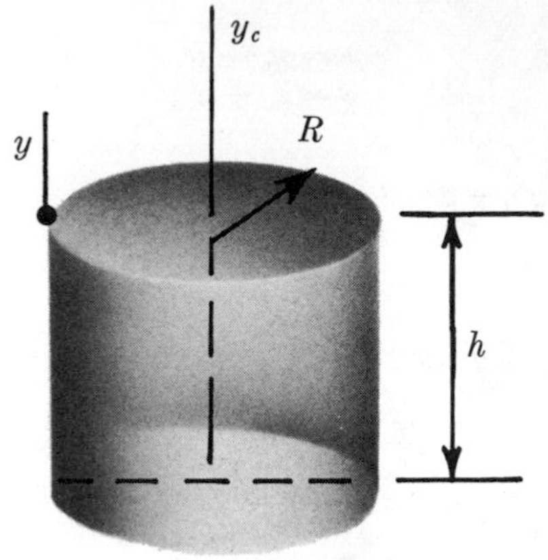

Figure 8-17

$$I_{yy} = \frac{MR^2}{2} + R^2M$$

or

$$I_{yy} = \frac{3MR^2}{2}$$

Example 8–5. Determine the moment of inertia about the z axis of the body shown in Fig. 8–18. Both the rod and the block are homogeneous. The rod weighs 8 lb and the block weighs 16 lb.

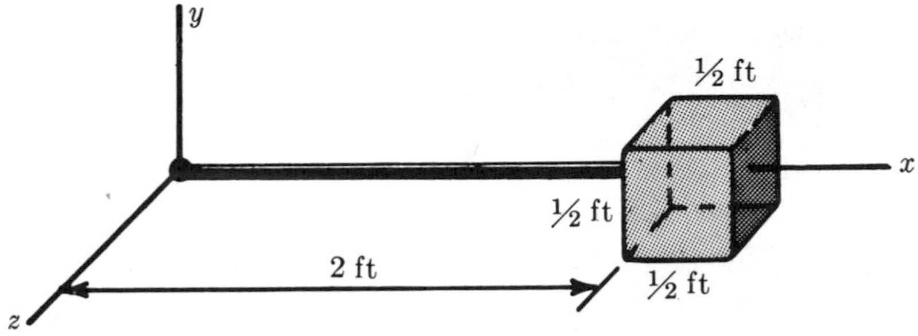

Figure 8-18

Solution: Both the rod and the block will be considered separately. From Appendix I, it is noted that the moment of inertia of the rod about the z axis is

$$I_{zz} = \frac{Ml^2}{3}$$

and in this case,

$$I_{zz} = \frac{(8/32.2)(2)^2}{3}$$

$$= 0.33 \text{ lb-sec}^2\text{-ft}$$

It is also noted in Appendix I that the moment of inertia of the block about an axis through its centroid is equal to

$$I_{zz_c} = \frac{Ma^2}{6}$$

$$= \frac{(16/32.2)(0.5)^2}{6} = 0.21$$

Now the parallel axis theorem may be employed to determine the moment of inertia of this block about the z axis:

$$I_{zz} = I_{zz_c} + d^2M$$

or, in this case,

$$I_{zz} = 0.21 + (2.25)^2 \frac{16}{32.2}$$

$$= 2.43 \text{ lb-sec}^2\text{-ft}$$

The moment of inertia of the whole body about the z axis will be simply the algebraic sum of the moment of inertia of each of the bodies. Thus,

$$I_{zz} = 0.33 + 2.43$$
$$= 2.76 \text{ lb-sec}^2\text{-ft}$$

Moments and products of inertia with respect to a rotated set of axes and the principal axis problem. We shall now consider the problem of determining the moments and products of inertia with respect to a set of axes that have been rotated relative to a set of axes whose moments and products of inertia are known. We shall also consider the method of determining the rotated axes for which the products of inertia are equal to zero (the principal axes). These problems are somewhat outside the scope of this text, but they are included here in order to complete the discussion.

Matrix algebra will be used because of the simplicity of the presentation. We suggest that the curious student who is interested in this topic, but who is not familiar with the fundamentals of matrix algebra, consult an applied mathematics text.* An introduction to matrix algebra, sufficient for this discussion, is given in Appendix II.

Given the moments and products of inertia with respect to the x, y, z axes as shown in Fig. 8–19, the first problem is: What are the moments and products of inertia with respect to the x', y', z' axes?

It is known that a vector expressed in the x, y, z system may also be expressed in the x', y', z' system by premultiplying the x, y, z matrix by the appropriate transformation matrix.

$$\{A'\} = [a]\{A\} \qquad \textbf{(8.51)}$$

* For example, L. Pipes, *Matrix Methods for Engineering*, Prentice-Hall, 1963.

The a matrix is a matrix of cosines of the angles between the axes. The element a_{12}, for instance, is the cosine of the angle between the x axis and the y' axis. This is a "linear transformation."

Since the moments and products of inertia cannot be thought of as a vector (as moments and angular velocities are), it appears that we cannot

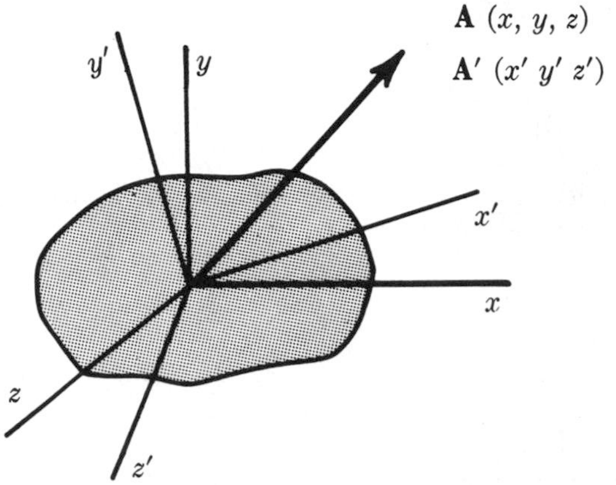

Figure 8-19

perform a similar operation on the moments and products of inertia. We can, however, transform the moments and products of inertia from the x, y, z system to the x', y', z' system in the following manner: By observation of Eq. 8.32 it is seen that the moment of momentum equation may be written as

$$\{H\} = [I]\{\omega\} \tag{8.52}$$

where

$$\{H\} = \begin{bmatrix} H_x \\ H_y \\ H_z \end{bmatrix} \qquad [I] = \begin{bmatrix} I_{xx} & -I_{xy} & -I_{xz} \\ -I_{xy} & I_{yy} & -I_{yz} \\ -I_{xz} & -I_{yz} & I_{zz} \end{bmatrix} \qquad \{\omega\} = \begin{bmatrix} \omega_x \\ \omega_y \\ \omega_z \end{bmatrix}$$

By premultiplying Eq. 8.52, the transformation matrix $[a]$ from the unprimed coordinates to the primed coordinates is

$$[a]\{H\} = [a][I]\{\omega\} \tag{8.53}$$

Then premultiplying the angular velocity vector by $[a]^{-1}[a]$, which is equal to the unit matrix, we have

$$[a]\{H\} = [a][I][a]^{-1}[a]\{\omega\} \tag{8.54}$$

Now, since the moment of momentum and angular velocity are vectors, they may be transformed into the primed system of coordinates by the transformation matrix $[a]$:

$$\begin{aligned} \{\omega'\} &= [a]\{\omega\} \\ \{H'\} &= [a]\{H\} \end{aligned} \tag{8.55}$$

so that the moment of momentum equation in the primed system reads

$$\{H'\} = [I']\{\omega'\} \tag{8.56}$$

where (the inverse of the transformation matrix is equal to the transpose)

$$[I'] = [a][I][a]^T \tag{8.57}$$

Hence the inertia matrix may be transformed from one set of coordinates, to a set of coordinates that has been rotated with respect to the first. The type of transformation indicated by Eq. 8.57 is called a *similarity transformation.*

The principal axis problem. In the moment equations, a reduction of two-thirds of the size of the equations may be realized if it is possible to orient the axes in such a manner that all products of inertia are equal to zero. We are interested in both the orientation of the axes and the moments of inertia of the body about these axes. The set of axes for which the products of inertia are equal to zero are the *principal axes,* and the moments of inertia with respect to these principal axes are the *principal moments of inertia.*

Given the moments and products of inertia of a body with respect to a given set of axes, the problem is: What is the transformation matrix a so that

$$[I'] = \begin{bmatrix} I_1 & 0 & 0 \\ 0 & I_2 & 0 \\ 0 & 0 & I_3 \end{bmatrix} \tag{8.58}$$

and what are the values of I_1, I_2, and I_3? To obtain the required results, postmultiply both sides of the similarity transformation, given by Eq. 8.57, by $[a]$:

$$[I'][a] = [a][I] \tag{8.59}$$

By equating the elements in the first column of the left-hand side of the preceding equation with the elements in the first column of the term on the right-hand side, it can be shown that

$$I'\{a\} = [I]\{a\} \tag{8.60}$$

This is the *eigenvalue problem.* An abundant amount of information may be found in the literature concerning this problem.*

PROBLEMS

Assume that all solids have a homogeneous mass distribution unless otherwise stated.

8-1. Determine by integration the moment of inertia about the y axis for the solid rectangular body (Fig. P.8–1).

* See Pipes, *ibid.*, or H. Goldstein, *Classical Mechanics,* Addison-Wesley, 1957.

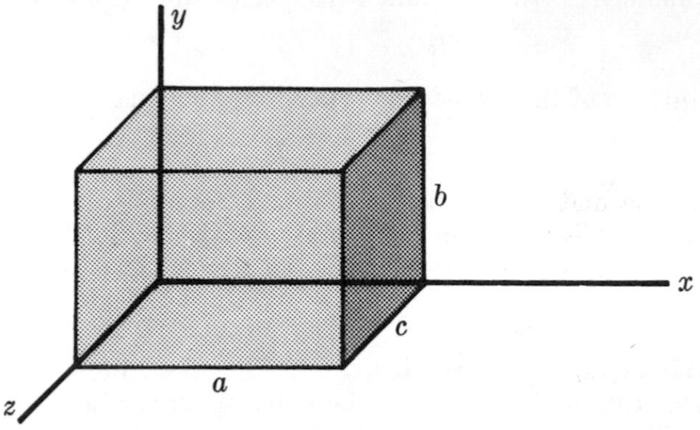

Figure Prob. 8-1

8-2. Determine the product of inertia of the body of Problem 8–1 about the *yz* axes.

8-3. Determine by integration the moment of inertia of the right circular cylinder about the x axis (Fig. P.8–3).

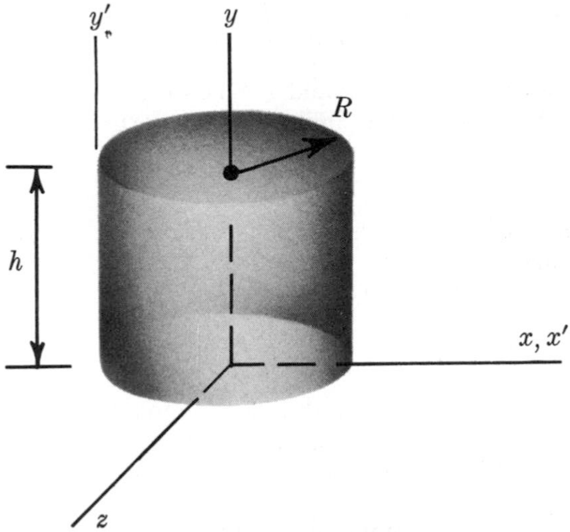

Figure Prob. 8-3

8-4. Show, using the integral definition of the product of inertia, that the product of inertia about the *zy* axes of the preceding problem is equal to zero.

8-5. Determine by integration the moment of inertia about the centroidal axis of a sphere. *Hint:* Use spherical coordinates from your integration.

8-6. Determine, using the integral form for the moment of inertia, the moment of inertia about the x axis of the solid shown in Fig. P.8–6. The solid is formed by rotating the curve $y = x^2$ about the x axis. The solid is bounded by the plane $x = 0$ and $x = 2$.

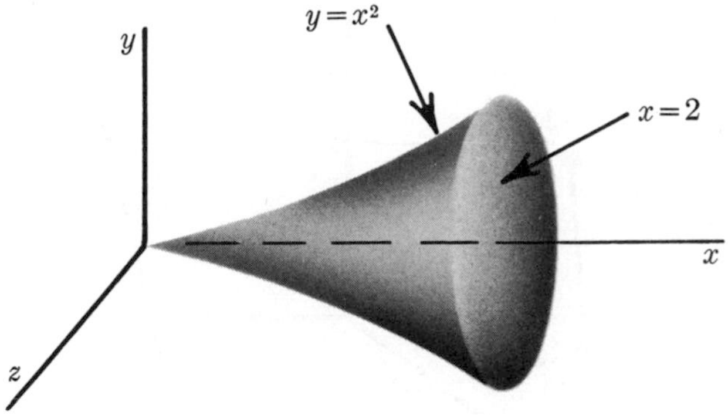

Figure Prob. 8-6

8-7. A slender rod of length l lies along the x axis (Fig. P.8–7). Determine its moment of inertia. Here assume in your integration that an increment of length corresponds to an increment of mass, that is, $dm = m\,dx$, where m is mass/length, and M is the total mass.

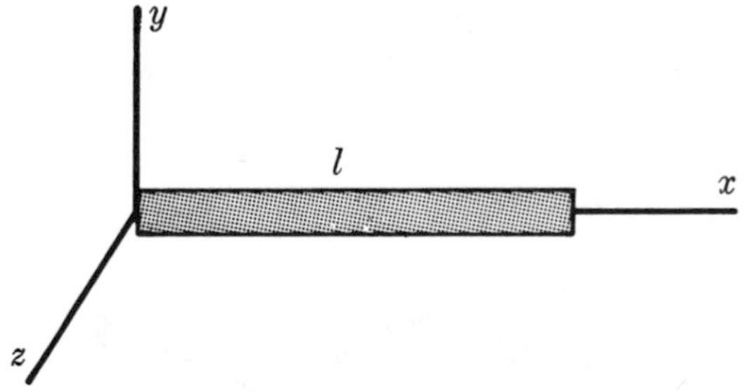

Figure Prob. 8-7

8-8. For Problem 8–7, determine by integration the moment of inertia of the slender rod about a z axis that passes through the center of mass of the body. Then use the parallel axis theorem to determine the moment of inertia of the rod about the end.

8-9. Determine the product of inertia about the $y'x'$ for the cylinder of Problem 8-3. Use the parallel axis theorem.

8-10. Determine the moment of inertia about the y axis for the system of particles shown in Fig. P.8–10. Assume that the connecting rods are weightless. The masses are equal to 2, 3, 1, and 4, respectively.

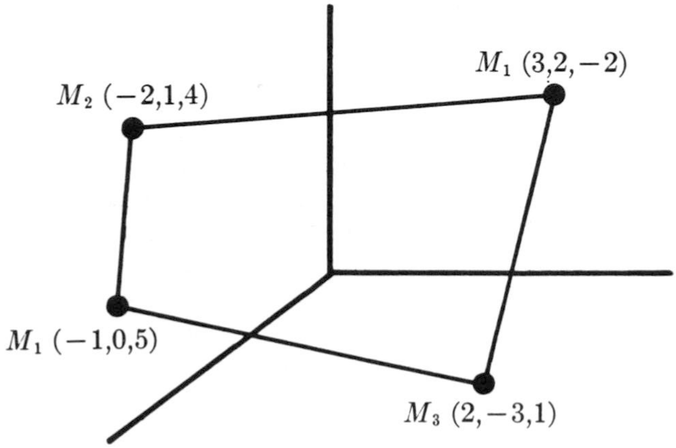

Figure Prob. 8-10

8-11. Determine the product of inertia about the yz axes for Problem 8–10.

8-12. Given a body with a set of reference axes fixed to the body with the origin at the center of mass. It is desired to determine the moment of inertia about the x axis for the nonhomogeneous body shown in Fig. P.8–12. To do this, a numerical integration can be performed, and as a start, the incremental masses with their

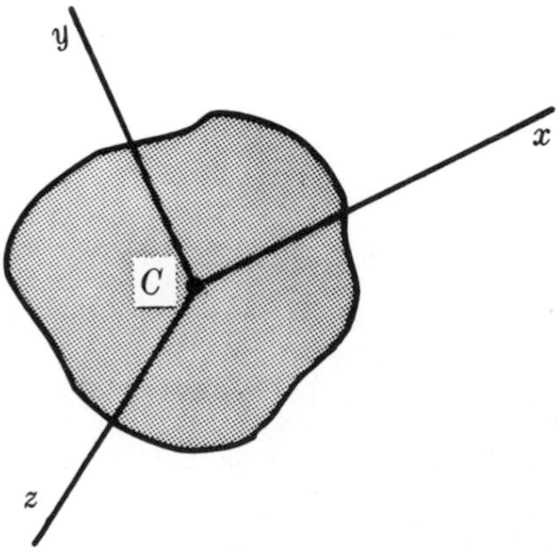

Figure Prob. 8-12

corresponding coordinates are tabulated in Table 8-4. What is the moment of inertia of the body about the x axis?

TABLE 8-4. INERTIA IN A NONHOMOGENEOUS BODY

n	m_i	x_i	y_i	z_i
1	1	4	5	2
2	2	3	2	−2
3	4	2	−4	−3
4	3	1	−3	2
5	5	−1	−2	1
6	2	−3	2	4
7	4	−2	1	−3
8	3	−4	−2	−1

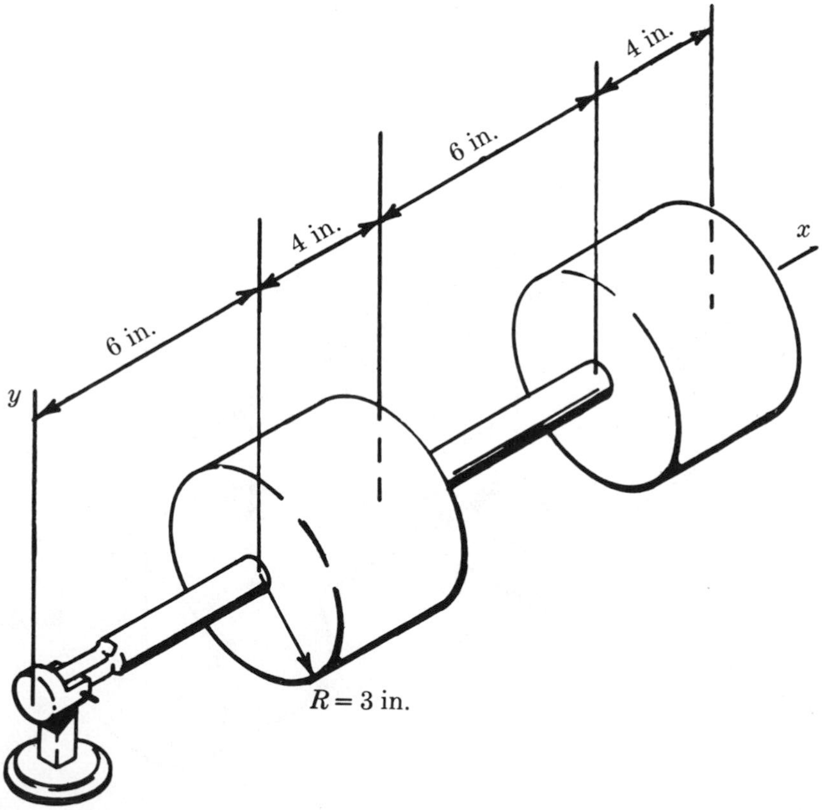

Figure Prob. 8-16

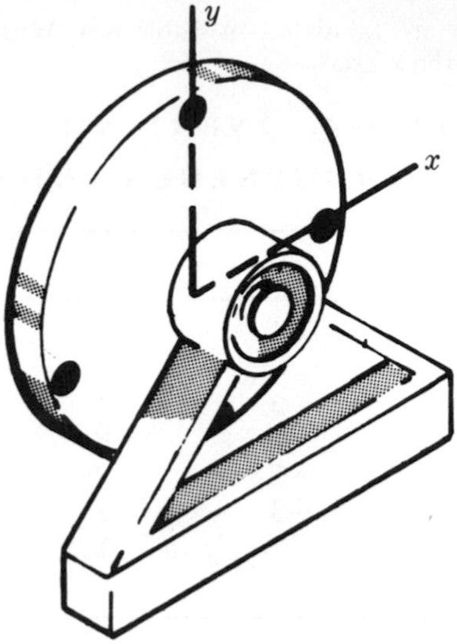

Figure Prob. 8-17

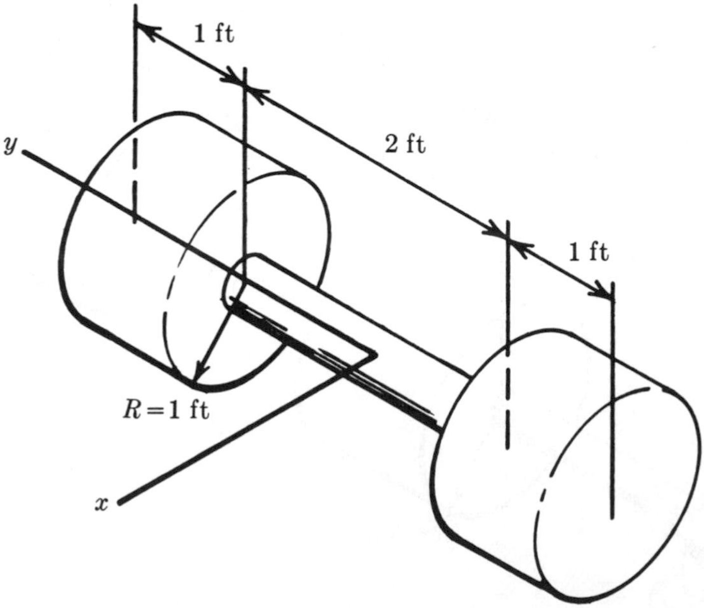

Figure Prob. 8-18

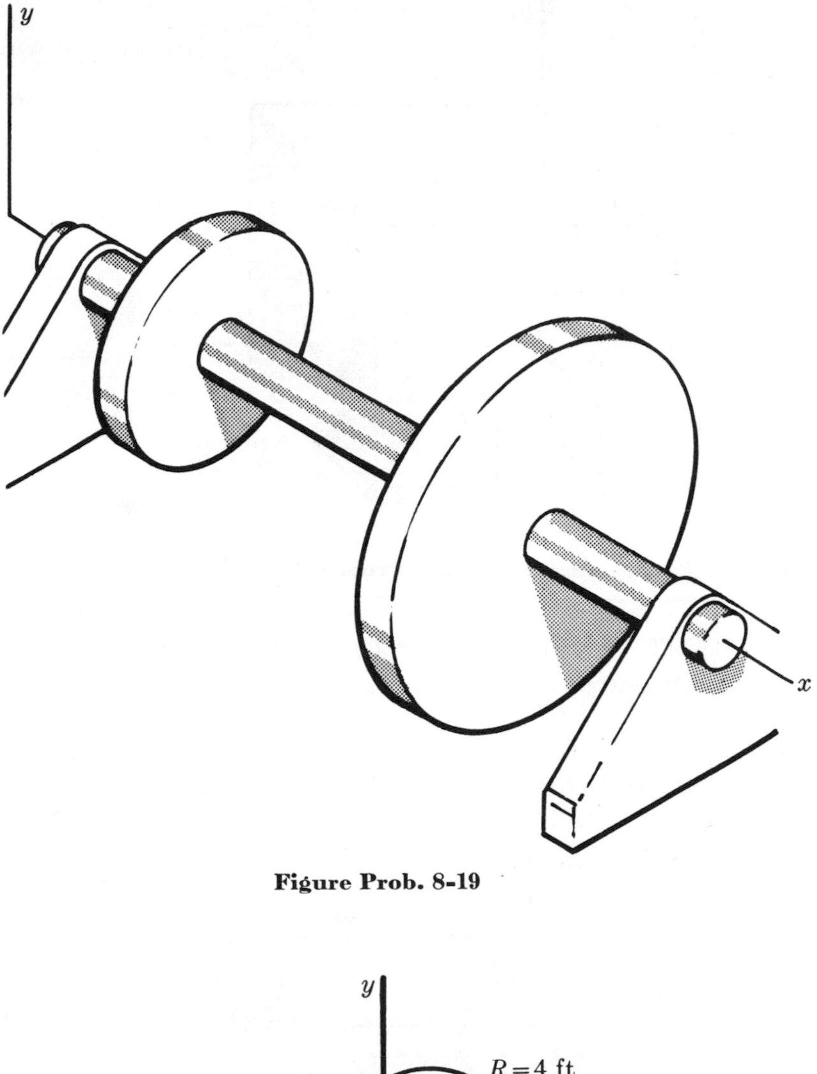

Figure Prob. 8-19

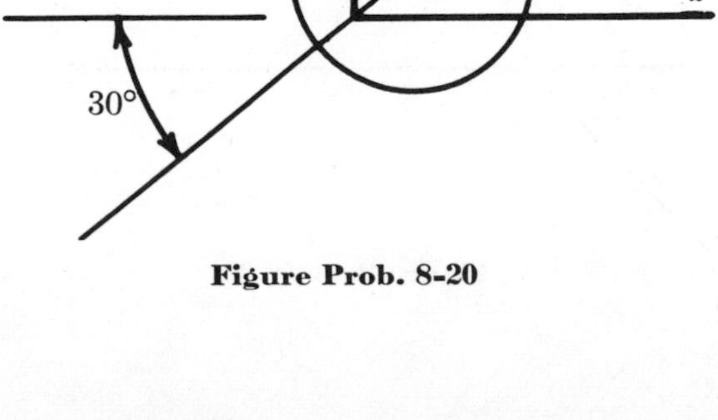

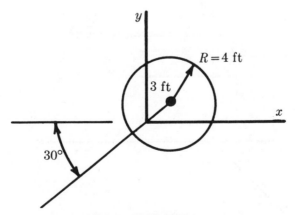

Figure Prob. 8-20

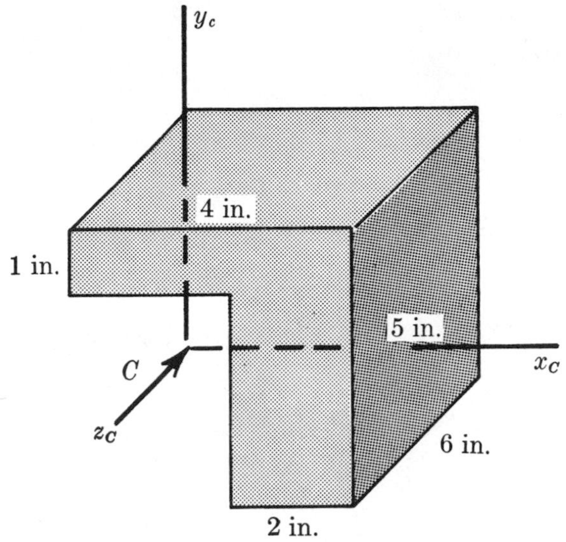

Figure Prob. 8-21

8-13. For Problem 8–12, determine the product of inertia about the xz axes.

8-14. For Problem 8–12, determine the moment of inertia of the body about the z axis.

8-15. Determine, using the parallel axis theorem, the product of inertia about the xy axes for a sphere that is mutually tangent to the xy, xz, and yz planes. The sphere has a mass M.

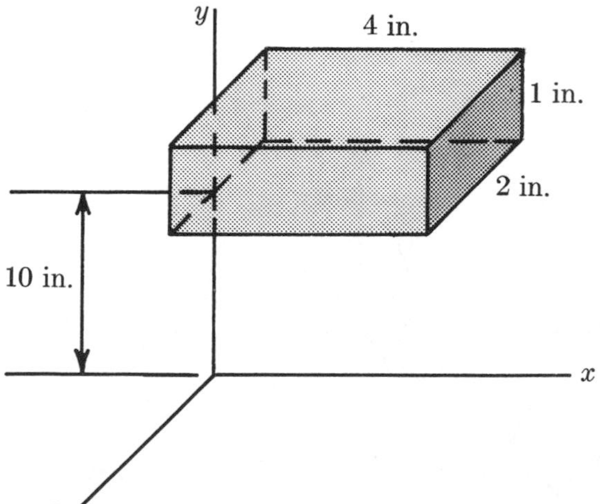

Figure Prob. 8-22

8-16. Determine, using the tables in Appendix I and the parallel axis theorem, the moment of inertia about the z axis for each of the composite bodies in Problems 8–16 to 8–19. The bar in Fig. P.8–16 weighs 3 lb and each block weighs 10 lb.

8-17. The wheel in Fig. P.8–17 has a mass of 3.0 slugs, and each of the concentrated masses is 0.20 slug. The radius of the wheel is 2.0 ft.

8-18. The 2-ft bar in Fig. P.8–18 weighs 10 lb and each of the blocks weighs 50 lb.

8-19. The wheel on the left in Fig. P.8–19 weighs 32.2 lb, and the one on the right weighs 128.8 lb. The radii of the wheels are 18 and 36 in., respectively.

8-20. Determine the product of inertia about the xy axes for the cylinder (Fig. P.8–20), using the parallel axis theorem. The weight of the body is 80 lb.

8-21. Determine the moment of inertia about the centroidal z axis for the body shown (Fig. P.8–21) if the mass density (slugs/ft^3) is 1.4.

8-22. Determine the product of inertia of the rectangular solid (Fig. P.8–22) about the xy axes if the mass density in slugs/in.^{3} is 0.003.

9

Dynamics of Rigid Bodies

The equations of motion for a rigid body have been established in Chapter 8. This chapter will be devoted to the discussion of the practical applications of the equations of motion. The classes of problems that will be discussed, in the order in which they appear in this chapter, are translation of a rigid body, rotation of a rigid body about a fixed axis, plane motion of a rigid body, the impulse-momentum and work-energy equations for a rigid body, gyroscopic motion, and finally, the general motion of a rigid body.

9-1. TRANSLATION OF A RIGID BODY

The moment equation. A translating, rigid body is characterized by the fact that its total angular velocity vector, $\boldsymbol{\omega}$, is equal to zero. This implies that each and every point in the body has the same velocity and acceleration. A sled that is moving along a straight-line track is a translating, rigid body. In a preliminary analysis, an automobile moving on a smooth road may be considered to be a rigid body; even though some of the components of the automobile, such as the wheels and the piston rods, do not experience translational motion, the majority of the mass does; therefore the assumption that the whole body translates will yield some useful results.

The relationship between the forces and associated response of a translating, rigid body that experiences a general three-dimensional motion may be established by considering projections of the body in three orthogonal planes and by treating motions in these three directions independently. Generally speaking, however, situations that occur will involve the motion of the body in a plane, which is usually along a straight-line path.

To describe the motion, there are two force equations and one moment equation available. As was the common practice in equilibrium studies in statics, more than one moment equation may be used, but there are only three independent equations of motion.

In the case of the translating, rigid body, which has an acceleration a, the moment equation for the motion of a body in a plane (given by Eq. 8.18) reduces to

$$M_P = -d(ma) \tag{9.1}$$

and may be rewritten as

$$M'_P = 0 \tag{9.2}$$

where the term $d(ma)$ may be thought of as an inertia moment, that is, the moment due to the inertia force ma acting through the center of mass of the body. Then the moment M_P represents the moment of all forces, including the inertia force about any convenient reference point P.

The method of problem solution. The following procedure should be followed in dealing with problems relating the forces to the motion of a translating, rigid body:

1. Draw a free-body diagram of the body.
2. Choose a convenient reference point in the body, that is, a point about which you should like to take moments. Then define the reference system, with the origin as this point, and one of the axes (usually the x axis) aligned in the direction of the motion of the body. It is possible in the same problem to choose a different reference point for each moment equation.
3. Then write the force equation,

$$\boldsymbol{F} = m\boldsymbol{a}_c$$

and the moment equation,

$$M_P + d(ma) = 0 \qquad \text{or} \qquad M'_P = 0$$

The force $\boldsymbol{F}$ is the sum of all forces that are acting on the body, and the moment M_P is the sum of all moments on the body acting about the z axis. (This assumes that the axes are aligned such that the motion of the body is in the xy plane.) It must also be pointed out that the moments must be taken as positive when they are counterclockwise.

The preceding three rules apply to a body that can be assumed to be two-dimensional. If the body must be treated as the three-dimensional body, then the rules listed above must be applied to each of the three planes.

Example 9–1. At a certain instant of time, the 3600-lb automobile (Fig. 9–1) has an acceleration to the right of 10 ft/sec². Determine the normal reaction of the road on both the front and the rear wheels at this instant of time.

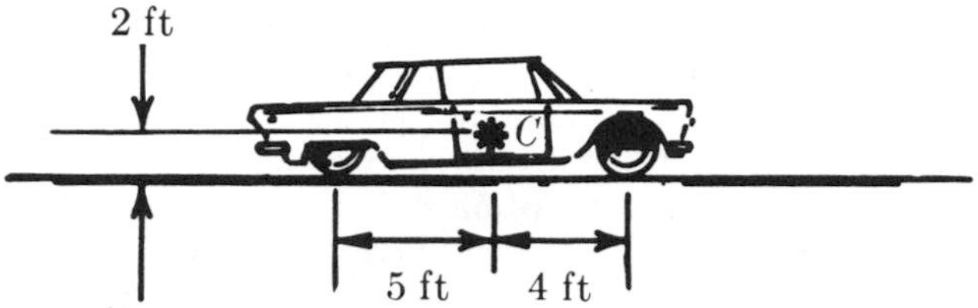

Figure 9-1

Solution: The first step in the solution for the forces is to draw a free-body diagram of the body. It should be noted that if the body is accelerating and if the auto has a rear-wheel drive, then the motive force (that is, frictional force) f of the road on the rear wheels must be included in the free-body diagram (Fig. 9–2).

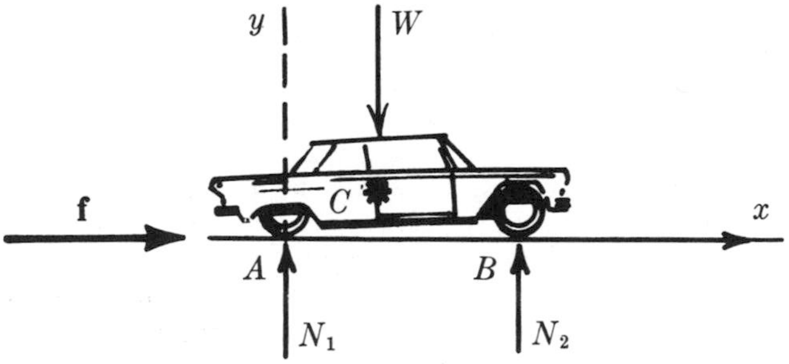

Figure 9-2

In order to determine the normal force, N_2, the point A may be considered as a moment center. Then

$$M_A + d(ma) = 0$$

$$9N_2 - 3600(5) + (2)\left(\frac{3600}{32.2}\right)(10) = 0$$

Note that all counterclockwise moments are positive and all clockwise moments are negative. Then

$$N_2 = 1750 \text{ lb}$$

To determine N_1, the force equation for motion in the y direction may be used:

$$F_y = m\ddot{y}_c = 0$$
$$N_1 + 1750 - 3600 = 0$$

and

$$N_1 = 1850 \text{ lb}$$

As a check on your calculations, the moment equation referred to point B may be used:

$$M_B + d(ma) = 0$$

$$-9N_1 + 3600(4) + (2)\left(\frac{3600}{32.2}\right)(10) = 0$$

$$N_1 = 1850 \text{ lb}$$

Here the result is the same as obtained for the force N_1. The results indicate that the normal force between the rear wheels and the road for an accelerating vehicle are larger than the normal forces on the front wheels. This is intuitively obvious, since we know that an accelerating vehicle tends to rock backward under the action of the inertia force.

Example 9–2. The bar AB in Fig. 9–3 is hinged at point A so that it is free to move in a circular path about the point A. In the position shown, the bar is resting

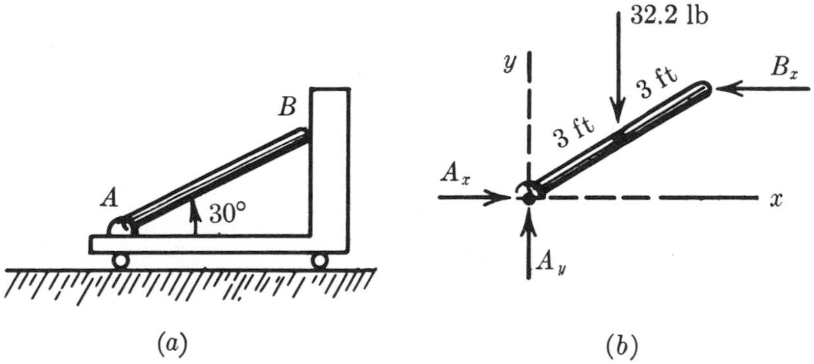

Figure 9-3

on the cart at point B. If the cart were given an acceleration to the right, one might suspect that the normal reaction of the bar on the cart at B would get smaller. In fact, if the acceleration were great enough, there would be no normal reaction at B, and the bar would thus rotate about A. Determine the acceleration for which the normal reaction at B is zero. The bar is 6 ft long and weighs 32.2 lb.

Solution: First draw a free-body diagram of the bar (Fig. 9–3b). Since the pin forces A_x and A_y are unknown quantities, and since it is not desired in this case to determine these quantities, it follows that the most logical equation to write would be a moment equation referred to the point A:

$$M_A + d(ma) = 0$$

Since we wish to determine the acceleration for which the force B_x is equal to zero, we may set B_x equal to zero in the free-body diagram and thus obtain one moment equation in which the only unknown is the acceleration of the bar. Thus,

$$-32.2(3\cos 30) + (3\sin 30)\left(\frac{32.2}{32.2}\right)(a) = 0$$

and

$$a = 55.8 \text{ fps}^2$$

Example 9–3. It is desired to determine the angle θ of the grade of a road, as a function of the velocity V of an automobile, so that there will be no frictional forces between the car and the road. The road has a radius of curvature, R; the car has a weight W; and the distance between the center of mass of the car and the wheel is the distance b shown in Fig. 9–4.

Solution: A free-body diagram of the auto is shown along with a diagram of fixed values and a set of moving axes. Frictional forces between the wheels and the

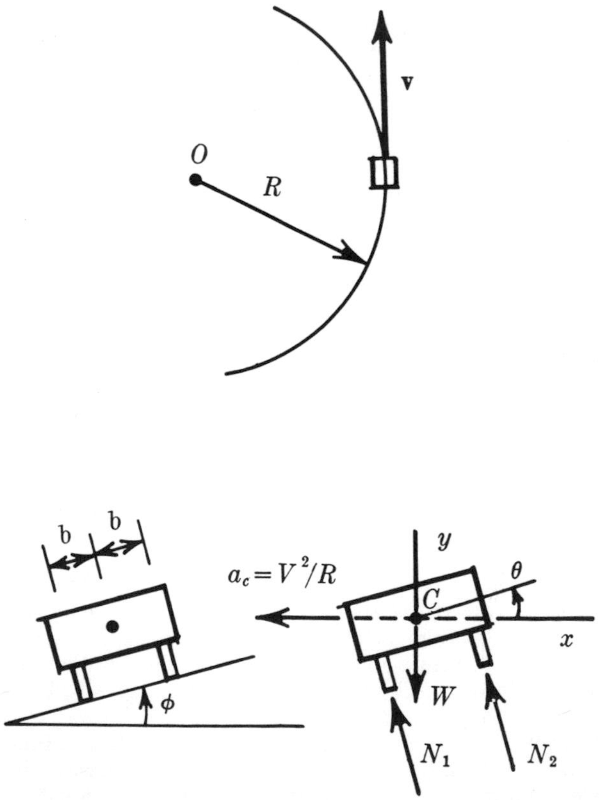

Figure 9-4

road are shown in the free-body diagram, but since it is stipulated in the problem that they are equal to zero, they will be ignored in the equations of motion.

If it is desired to determine the velocity of the automobile as a function of the angle ϕ, one should first try to write an equation that will relate the two quantities. Since the automobile is moving on a circular path, one notes that the acceleration of the center of mass of the automobile will be of magnitude V^2/R and in the negative x direction. Since the x components of the two normal forces are functions of the angle ϕ, an equation that will relate the angle to the velocity of the auto is the force equation for the x direction:

$$F_x = m\ddot{x}_c$$
$$-N_1 \sin \phi - N_2 \sin \phi = \frac{-MV^2}{R}$$

But, unfortunately, the force equation introduces two undesired unknowns, N_1 and N_2. In order to determine N_1 and N_2, two other equations will be needed. The force equation for the y direction and the moment equation for the z axis may be used:

$$F_y = m\ddot{y}_c$$
$$N_1 \cos \phi + N_2 \cos \phi - W = 0$$

and

$$M_c = 0$$
$$N_2 b - N_1 b = 0$$

The moment equation shows that N_1 and N_2 are equal and the force equation for the y direction then shows that

$$N_1 = N_2 = N = \frac{W}{2 \cos \phi}$$

Finally, substituting this into the force equation for the x direction, the relationship between the velocity and the angle becomes

$$\tan \phi = \frac{V^2}{Rg}$$

One notes that as V^2/Rg gets larger, so does the angle ϕ. This means that for relatively fast speeds, the angle of grade must be relatively large if there is to be no friction. This also implies that the angle must be large for a relatively small radius of curvature.

PROBLEMS

9-1. If the 3220-lb automobile (Fig. P.9-1) accelerates from rest to a velocity of 60 mph in 12 sec with a constant acceleration, what is the normal force between the wheels and the ground?

9-2. Consider Problem 9-1. The velocity of the auto is given as a function of time, as shown in Fig. P.9-2. Determine the maximum force of the rear wheels on the road for the period shown in the graph.

9-3. The uniform bar in Fig. P.9-3 weighs 16.1 lb and is 48 in. long. Determine the force in the cable AB as a function of the acceleration of the cart.

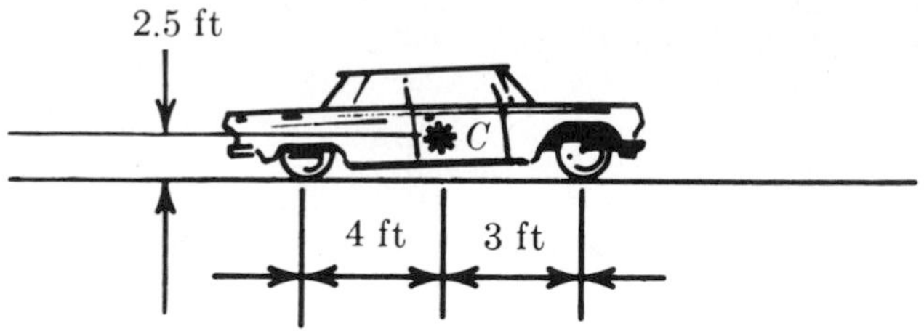

Figure Prob. 9-1

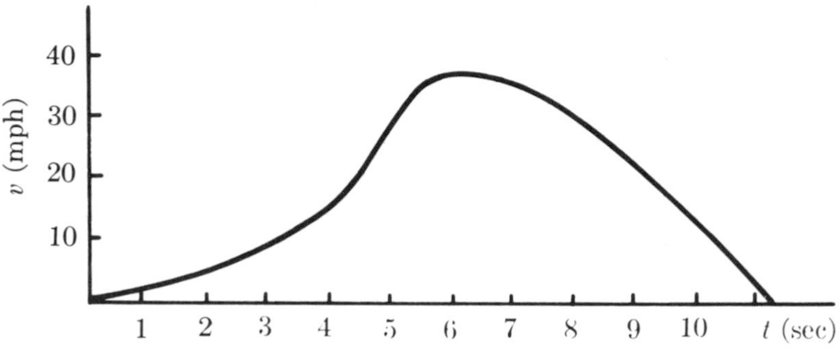

Figure Prob. 9-2

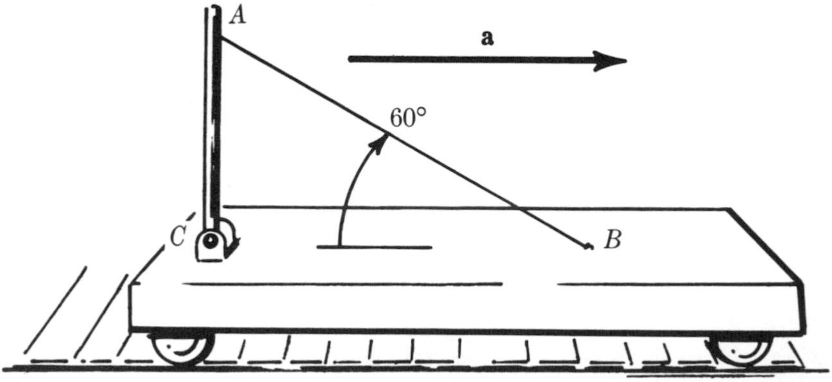

Figure Prob. 9-3

9-4. Consider Problem 9-3. Suppose the pin at C has a maximum shearing strength of 100 lb. What would be the maximum acceleration that the car could be subjected to?

9-5. An automobile pulling the 600-lb trailer in Fig. P.9-5 is accelerating at a rate of 3 ft/sec². Determine the reactions of the car acting on the trailer at point A,

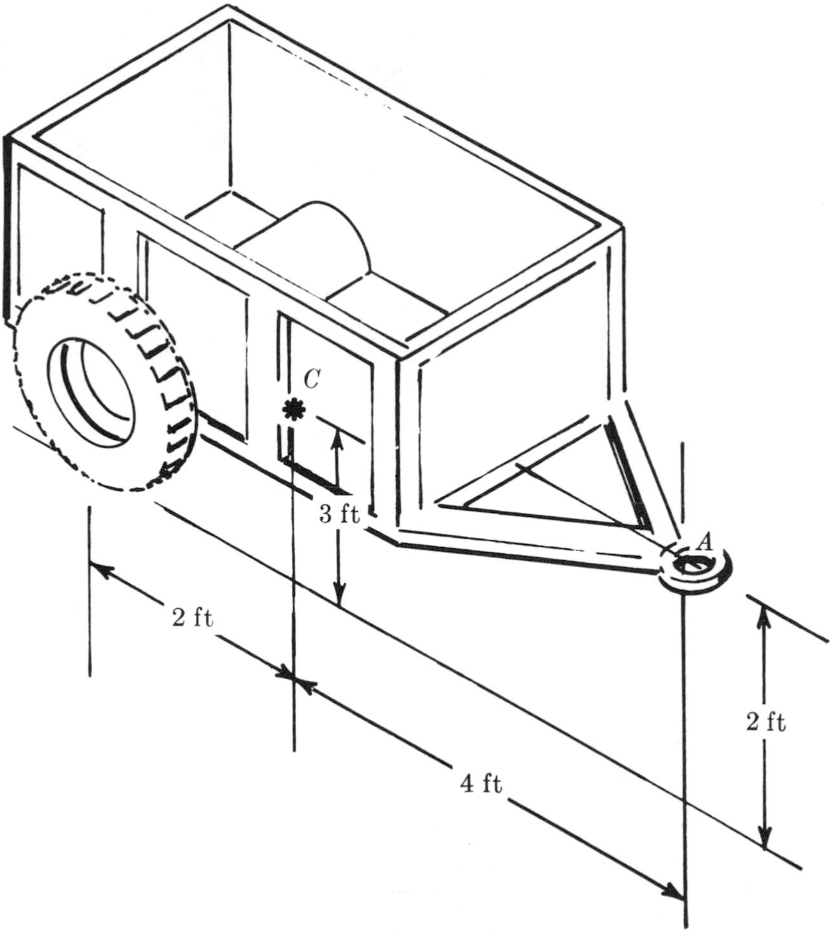

Figure Prob. 9-5

the point where the trailer is attached to the car. Assume that the weight of the wheels of the trailer is negligible.

9-6. The radius of curvature of a certain highway is 1500 ft. If the average speed of automobiles traveling on this highway is 60 mph, what must be the angle of grade of the highway if there is to be no friction between the car and the road?

9-7. A plane (Fig. P.9-7) weighing 32,200 lb lands with a velocity of 120 mph. The plane is stopped by brakes in the wheels under the wing. If the plane comes to rest with a constant acceleration after traveling 1 mile down the runway, what is the normal force of the ground on the front wheel?

9-8. For Problem 9-7, draw a sketch of the work (W ft-lb) done by the brakes in bringing the aircraft to rest, and the normal force N lb of the front wheels, versus the landing velocity V of the aircraft (assume that deceleration in 1 mile is constant).

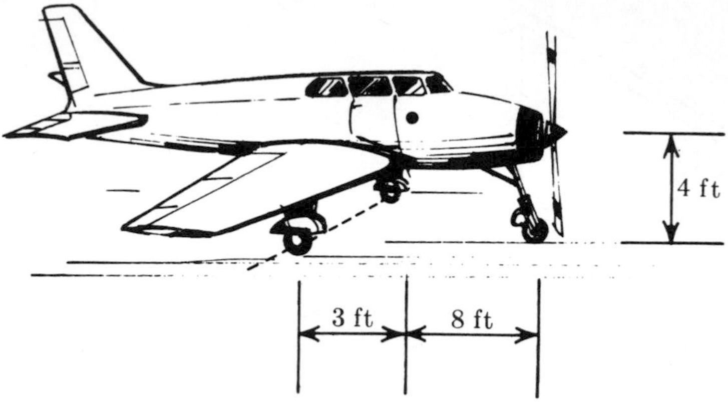

Figure Prob. 9-7

9-9. The 100-lb box in Fig. P.9-9 is resting on the flat bed of an accelerating vehicle. The frictional force between the box and the floor is large enough that the box will tip before it will slide. What must be the acceleration of the vehicle before the box will tip?

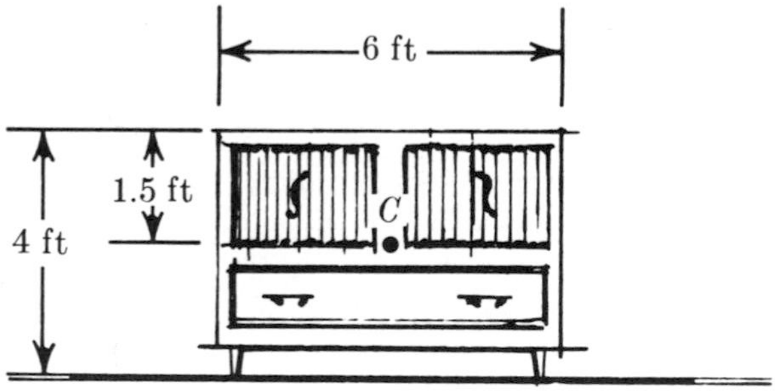

Figure Prob. 9-9

9-10. An automobile is moving on a curve of a highway (Fig. P.9-10). The curve, which has a radius of curvature of 500 ft, is not banked. If the automobile weighs 3220 lb, how fast can it go through the curve before it will tip over?

9-11. A piece of furniture weighing 120 lb (Fig. P.9-11) is tied onto the bed of a truck by a rope connected at points A and B. Assuming that there are no frictional forces between the furniture and the bed of the truck, determine the force in the rope as a function of the acceleration of the truck and the normal reactions as a function of the acceleration.

9-12. Determine the maximum value of W (Fig. P.9–12) so that the body will not tip about its front wheels. The weight of the trailer is 200 lb. The system is initially at rest.

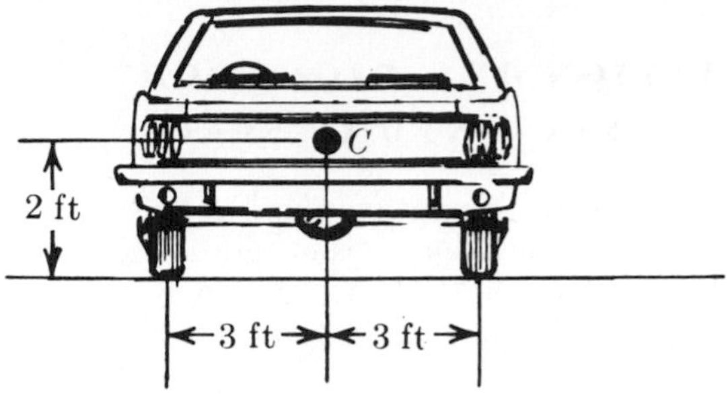

Figure Prob. 9-10

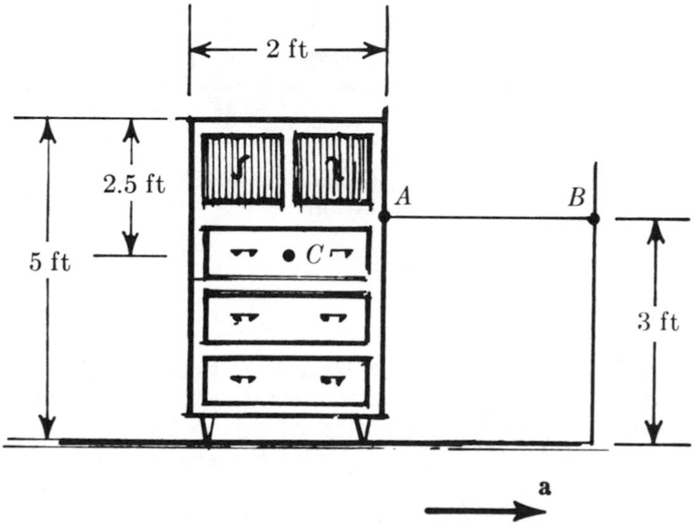

Figure Prob. 9-11

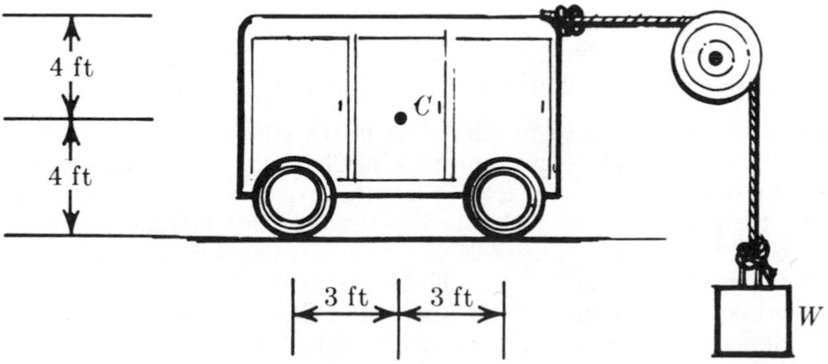

Figure Prob. 9-12

9-2. ROTATION OF A RIGID BODY ABOUT AN AXIS FIXED IN SPACE

Consider a rigid body rotating about a line or axis that is fixed in inertial space, that is, the line or axis of rotation is neither translating nor rotating with respect to inertial space. Figure 9–5 shows a free-body diagram of a rigid body that is rotating about a fixed axis AB. The body has

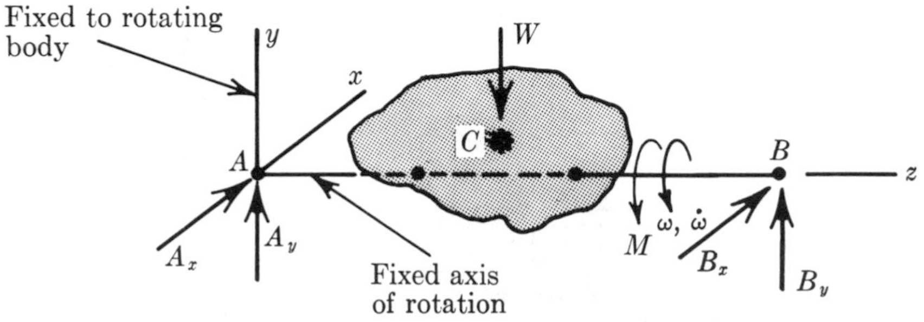

Figure 9-5

an angular velocity of ω_z and an angular acceleration of $\dot{\omega}_z$. The moment M is the external moment about the axis of rotation that is causing the rotational motion. The body is supported at two points (often called the "bearings") A and B, and at points A and B there are reactive forces, as shown.

There are two basic problems of interest for the case of the body rotating about the fixed axis. We shall try to determine:

1. The relationship between the moment M about the axis of rotation, the angular acceleration, and velocity of the body about the axis of rotation.
2. The relationship between the motion of the body and the magnitude of the reactions at points A and B.

We shall consider both cases separately in the ensuing discussion.

Following the procedure outlined in Chapter 8, we must establish a reference coordinate system for the moment equation. As indicated previously, it is generally best to locate the origin of the reference system at a fixed point in the system, if possible. Here it is possible, since every point on the axis of rotation is fixed. Therefore we shall fix the origin of the reference system on the axis of rotation of the body and let the z axis coincide with the axis of rotation, as shown in Fig. 9–5.

If the z axis coincides with the axis of rotation, there is no angular velocity of the body about either the x or the y axes, even though the x and y

axes must be fixed to the body. Thus ω_x and ω_y are equal to zero. The moment of momentum of the body becomes (from Eqs. 8.30 and 8.32)

$$\boldsymbol{H}_O = -I_{xz}\omega_z\bar{\boldsymbol{i}} - I_{yz}\omega_z\bar{\boldsymbol{j}} + I_{zz}\omega_z\bar{\boldsymbol{k}} \tag{9.3}$$

The time derivative of the moment of momentum equation may be determined by direct differentiation:

$$\dot{\boldsymbol{H}}_O = -I_{xz}\dot{\omega}_z\bar{\boldsymbol{i}} - I_{xz}\omega_z\dot{\bar{\boldsymbol{i}}} - I_{yz}\dot{\omega}_z\bar{\boldsymbol{j}} - I_{yz}\omega_z\dot{\bar{\boldsymbol{j}}} + I_{zz}\dot{\omega}_z\bar{\boldsymbol{k}} \tag{9.4}$$

and the time derivatives of the unit vectors are determined by noting that the system is rotating about the z axis with an angular velocity of $\boldsymbol{\omega} = \omega_z\bar{\boldsymbol{k}}$. Thus the time derivatives of the unit vectors become

$$\begin{aligned} \dot{\bar{\boldsymbol{i}}} &= \boldsymbol{\omega} \times \bar{\boldsymbol{i}} = \omega_z\bar{\boldsymbol{j}} \\ \dot{\bar{\boldsymbol{j}}} &= \boldsymbol{\omega} \times \bar{\boldsymbol{j}} = -\omega_z\bar{\boldsymbol{i}} \end{aligned} \tag{9.5}$$

Finally, the time derivative of the moment of momentum is

$$\dot{\boldsymbol{H}}_O = [-I_{xz}\dot{\omega}_z + I_{yz}\omega_z^2]\bar{\boldsymbol{i}} + [-I_{yz}\dot{\omega}_z - I_{xz}\omega_z^2]\bar{\boldsymbol{j}} + I_{zz}\omega_z\bar{\boldsymbol{k}} \tag{9.6}$$

Since $M_O = \dot{H}_O$, we may set the moment equal to the time derivative of the moment of momentum and separate the corresponding components. Thus,

$$M_x = -I_{xz}\dot{\omega}_z + I_{yz}\omega_z^2 \tag{9.7a}$$

$$M_y = -I_{yz}\dot{\omega}_z - I_{xz}\omega_z^2 \tag{9.7b}$$

$$M_z = I_{zz}\dot{\omega}_z \tag{9.7c}$$

These, then, are the moment equations for a rigid body rotating about a fixed axis. The reference coordinate system is defined so that the origin of this moving system is on the fixed axis and the z axis coincides with the axis of rotation.

The relationship between the moment and the motion about the axis of rotation. In this section we are interested in determining the relationship between the angular velocity and acceleration of the body rotating about the axis of rotation and the moment about that axis which causes that rotation.

Upon examining the moment equations for the motion of a rigid body about a fixed axis of rotation, we note that the moment equation that relates the moment about the axis of rotation to the motion about the axis of rotation is Eq. 9.7(c):

$$\boxed{M_z = I_{zz}\dot{\omega}_z} \tag{9.8}$$

Equation 9.8 relates the applied moment to the angular acceleration in the same way as Newton's second law relates force to linear acceleration. By knowing the external forces acting on a body (and thus the external moments), the angular motion of the body can be determined by Eq. 9.8.

This moment equation, as is the force equation, is a differential equation of the second order; in general, a solution to this differential equation is required to determine the motion of the body.

The procedure used in trying to determine the motion of a body about the axis of rotation is as follows:

1. Looking into the plane of motion, draw a free-body diagram of the body, showing all forces and moments acting on the body.
2. Define a coordinate system for the moment equation. Place the origin of this system at the axis of rotation and fix the axes to the body. Figure 9–6 shows a typical free-body diagram for this situation.
3. The motion of the body about the axis of rotation is related to the moment of the forces about the axis by the equation $M_O = I_O\dot{\omega}$. (The z axis which appears as a point in the xy plane is now referred to as point O.) By defining the coordinate system as indicated, I_O is the moment of inertia of the body about the axis of rotation.
4. If the force equation is needed, write the force equation $\boldsymbol{F} = m\boldsymbol{a}_c$ in terms of the xy axes.

By the right-hand rule, counterclockwise moments and angular velocities will be positive. If the moments and angular velocities about the z axis were described as vectors, a counterclockwise moment (for instance, about the z axis), when represented by a vector, would be a vector in the positive z direction. It is usually best in dealing with this class of problem to define the reference system as shown in Fig. 9–6.

Example 9–4. The 64.4-lb armature of a large electric motor is shown schematically in Fig. 9–7. If a constant moment of 40 ft-lb is applied to the armature, what will be the angular velocity of the armature (in rpm) 3 sec after the armature starts from rest?

Solution: The free-body diagram of the armature is drawn in Fig. 9–9(b). The angular acceleration of the body about the axis of rotation may be determined from the moment equation $M_O = I_O\dot{\omega}$. Once the angular acceleration has been determined, presumably the angular velocity can be obtained by an integration. First, however, the moment of inertia of the body about the axis of rotation must be calculated. From Appendix I it is seen that the moment of inertia of the cylinder about its longitudinal axis is $mR^2/2$. Thus,

$$I = \frac{1}{2}\left(\frac{64.4}{32.2}\right)(2)^2$$

$$= 4.0 \text{ lb-sec}^2\text{-ft}$$

therefore the moment equation becomes

$$40 = 4.0\dot{\omega}$$

and it is seen that the angular acceleration of the armature is a constant:

$$\dot{\omega} = 10 \text{ radians/sec}^2$$

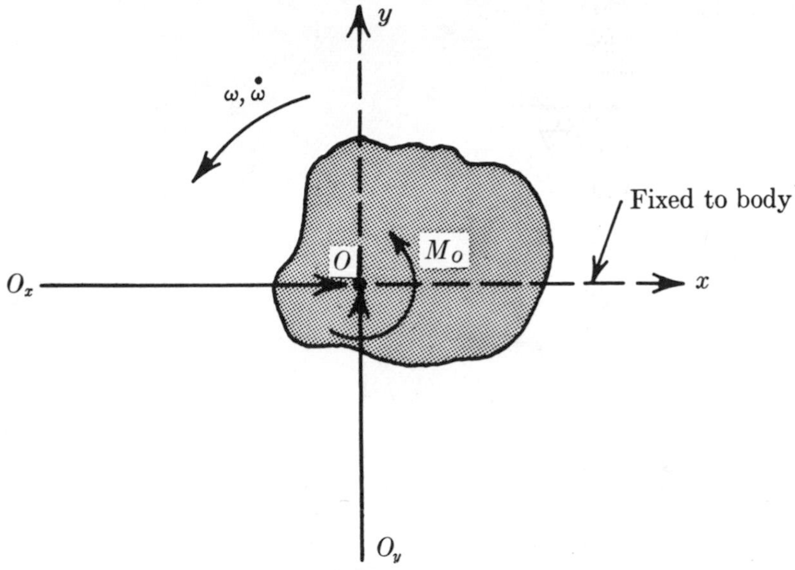

Figure 9-6

The angular velocity is obtained by an integration:

$$\omega = \omega_0 + \int_0 \dot{\omega}\, dt$$

$$= 10t \quad \text{radians/sec}$$

At $t = 3$ sec,

$$\omega = 30 \text{ radians/sec}$$

$$= \frac{30(60)}{2\pi}$$

$$= 287 \text{ rpm}$$

Example 9-5. Two large circular spur gears are shown in Fig. 9-8. A motor drives the first gear by applying the moment M as shown in the figure. If the first gear weighs 28 lb and the second gear weighs 48 lb, what will be the angular acceleration of the second gear if the moment M is equal to $0.2t$ ft-lb?

Solution: First draw a free-body diagram of both gears. The force transmitted through the gears is given as f. In order to write the moment equations about the axis of rotation for each of the gears, the moment of inertia of each of the gears about the axis of rotation must be known. Using the results in Appendix I,

$$I_1 = \frac{1}{2}\left(\frac{28}{32.2}\right)(1)^2 = 0.435 \text{ lb-sec}^2\text{-ft}$$

$$I_2 = \frac{1}{2}\left(\frac{48}{32.2}\right)(2)^2 = 2.98 \text{ lb-sec}^2\text{-ft}$$

We shall first write the equation of motion of the second gear, since this equation contains our desired unknown, the angular acceleration of the gear:

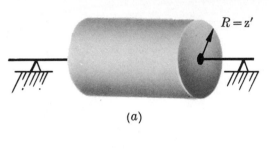

(a)

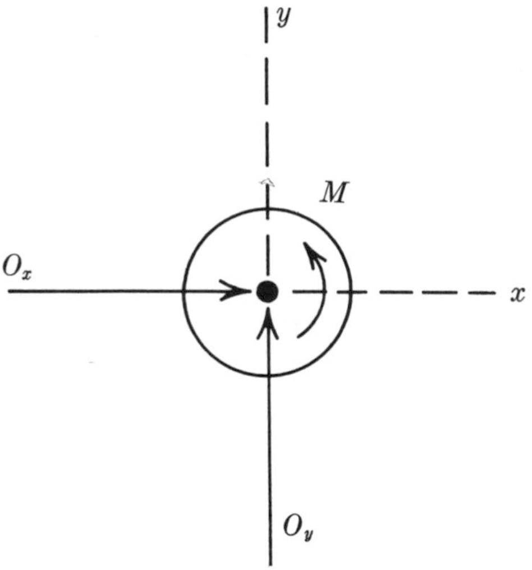

(b)

Figure 9-7

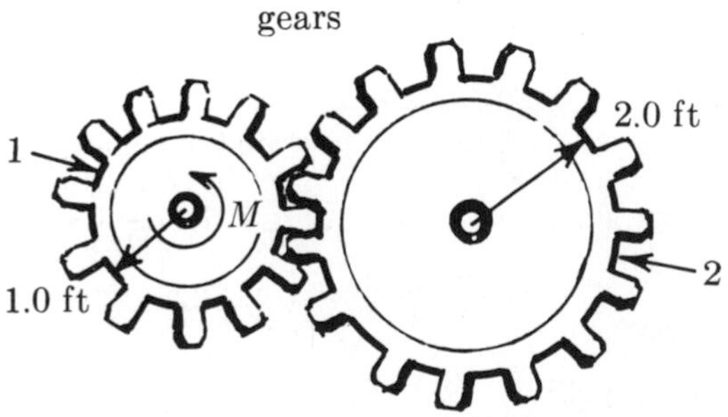

Figure 9-8

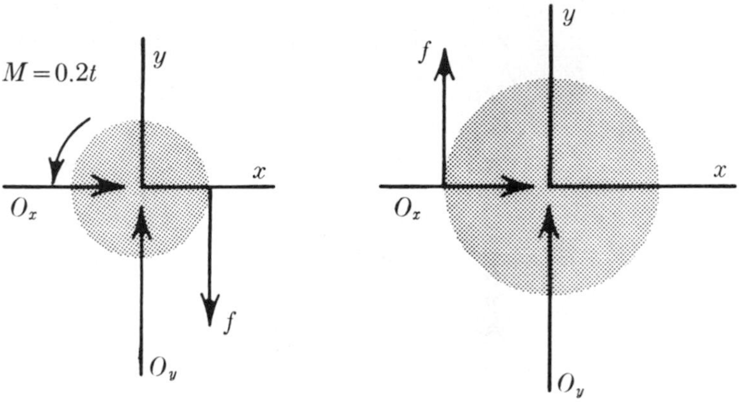

Figure 9-9

$$M_2 = I_2\dot{\omega}_2$$
$$-2f = 2.98\dot{\omega}_2$$

Note that counterclockwise moments are positive. In this one equation there are two unknown quantities, f and $\dot{\omega}_2$, so that we must seek another equation in which both terms appear. The logical choice would be the moment equation for the first gear. The force f will appear in this equation:

$$M_1 = I_1\dot{\omega}_1$$
$$0.2t - f = 0.435\dot{\omega}_1$$

By writing this equation, we have introduced another unknown, $\dot{\omega}_1$. However, the motions of the two gears are not independent; they are related by the following equation, based on the arc formula (Eq. 2.50):

$$\dot{\omega}_1 = -2\dot{\omega}_2$$

The minus sign indicates that when the first gear is moving counterclockwise (in a positive direction, as we have defined it by the right-hand rule), the second gear is moving clockwise, or in a negative direction. The two equations of motion along with this condition form a set of three simultaneous equations, which may be solved for $\dot{\omega}_2$:

$$\dot{\omega}_2 = -0.322t \quad \text{radians/sec}^2$$

The minus sign indicates that the second gear has an angular acceleration in the clockwise direction.

Example 9–6. The two weights shown in Fig. 9–10 are wrapped around the double pulley. If the system is released from rest, what will be the angular acceleration of the pulley? The moment of inertia of the pulley about the axis of rotation is equal to 3.0 lb-sec²-ft. The weights W_1 and W_2 are equal to 64.4 lb and 32.2 lb, respectively.

Solution: First draw a free-body diagram (Fig. 9–11) of each part of the system, noting that the forces in the cords are not known when the system is accelerating.

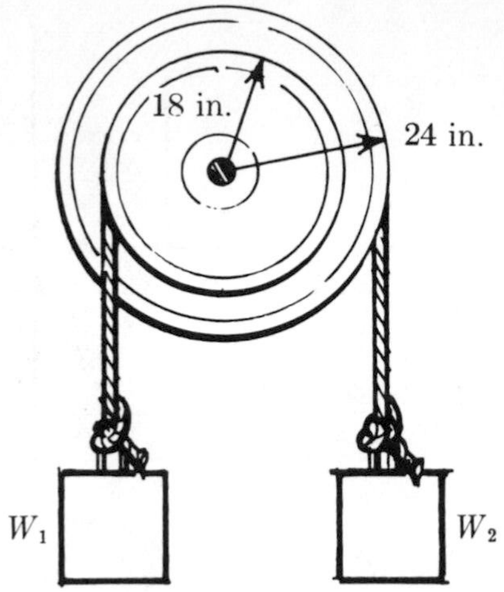

Figure 9-10

Next write an equation in which the desired unknown, the angular acceleration of the body, appears. This, of course, would be the moment equation, $M_O = I\dot{\omega}$. The moment equation becomes

$$T_1\left(\frac{18}{12}\right) - T_2\left(\frac{24}{12}\right) = 3.0\dot{\omega}$$

or

$$1.5T_1 - 2T_2 = 3.0\dot{\omega} \qquad \textbf{(9.9)}$$

It is important to note that the moment due to T_1 will be a positive moment because a vector representing this moment would be in the positive z direction.

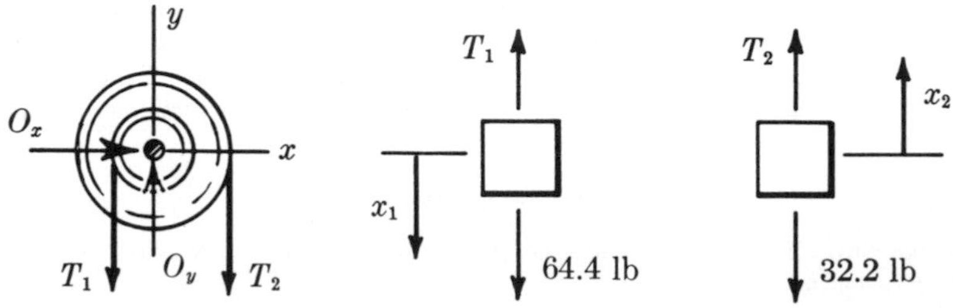

Figure 9-11

Similarly, the moment due to T_2 will be negative. Note now that Eq. 9.9 does indeed contain the desired angular acceleration, but it also contains two other terms, which are the unknown quantities T_1 and T_2. This means that at least two more equations must be found in which T_1 and T_2 appear. One might choose the first to be the force equation for the y direction for the wheel. Other possibilities would be the equation of motion for each of the two masses. The equations of motion for each of the two masses are:

$$\begin{aligned} F_{x1} &= M\ddot{x}_1 \\ 64.4 - T_1 &= 2\ddot{x}_1 \end{aligned} \tag{9.10}$$

$$\begin{aligned} F_{x2} &= M\ddot{x}_2 \\ T_2 - 32.2 &= \ddot{x}_2 \end{aligned} \tag{9.11}$$

The forces T_1 and T_2 appear in the two equations, but two other unknowns have been introduced. These are x_1 and x_2. Now there are three equations and five unknowns. Other equations are needed for a solution. These other two equations can be found from the arc formula by noting that the linear acceleration of the masses are related to the angular acceleration of the wheel:

$$\ddot{x}_1 = 1.5\dot{\omega} \tag{9.12}$$

$$\ddot{x}_2 = 2.0\dot{\omega} \tag{9.13}$$

Now we have five equations (Eqs. 9.9 through 9.13) and five unknowns (T_1, T_2, x_1, x_2, and $\dot{\omega}$). The equations may be solved for $\dot{\omega}$:

$$\dot{\omega} = 2.8 \text{ radians/sec}^2$$

This, of course, completely determines the motion of the system. By Eqs. 9.12 and 9.13, the motion of each of the masses may be determined, and the velocity or displacement of any part of the system may be subsequently determined by the appropriate integration.

Relationship between the motion of a body and the bearing reactions of the body. One of the very common problems in dealing with the motion of a rigid body rotating about a fixed axis is that of trying to determine the bearing reactions at the supports. Shown in Fig. 9–12 is a rigid body rotating about a fixed axis. This axis is supported

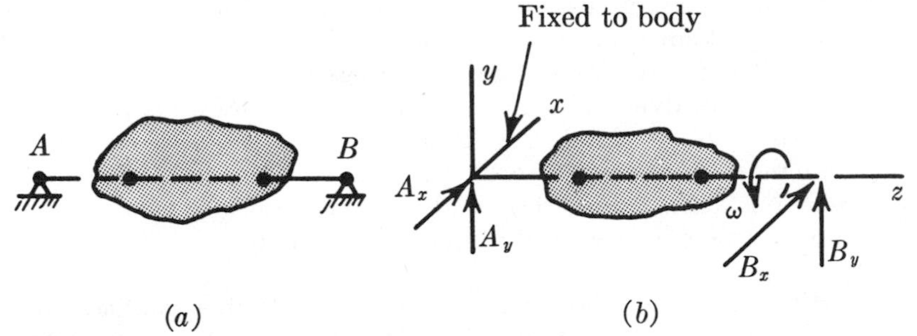

Figure 9-12

at two points, A and B. Figure 9–12 also shows a free-body diagram of the system. Given the motion of the body, we are interested in determining the values of the forces at the bearings; specifically, we should like to know A_x, A_y, B_x, B_y.

Upon examining the equations of motion for a body rotating about a fixed axis, Eqs. 9.7(a) and 9.7(b), we note that the unknown bearing reactions will appear in the first two of the moment equations only. They will also appear in the force equation but only in the x and y equations, assuming that the z axis is defined in the same direction as the axis of rotation, as shown in the figure. Thus, the equations of motion available for determining the four unknown bearing reactions are

$$\begin{aligned} M_x &= -I_{xz}\dot{\omega} + I_{yz}\omega^2 \\ M_y &= -I_{yz}\dot{\omega} - I_{xz}\omega^2 \\ F_x &= m\ddot{x}_c \\ F_y &= m\ddot{y}_c \end{aligned} \qquad \textbf{(9.14)}$$

The angular velocity ω is the angular velocity of the body about the z axis and is written previously in the text as ω_z.

The procedures to be followed in determining the bearing reactions of a rotating rigid body are as follows:

1. Draw a free-body diagram of the body.
2. Define a reference coordinate system. In general it is best to place the origin of the system at one of the bearings. Define the z axis colinear with the axis of rotation, and fix the system to the body. Draw the components of the bearing reactions in the same direction as the axes of the moving system, as shown in Fig. 9–12.
3. Determine the product of inertia of the body with respect to the xz axes and the yz axes.
4. Use the two moment equations and the two force equations to write four equations in which the four unknown bearing reactions appear. These, then, must subsequently be solved for the four unknowns.

For the following discussions, it is significant to note the difference between what is known as *static reactions* and *dynamic reactions*. Static reactions are the reactive forces at the bearings when the body is at rest. On the other hand, dynamic reactions refer to the forces induced at the bearings by the motion of the body. If the body is *balanced*, then there are no dynamic reactions; in other words, the motion of the body has no effect on the reactions. The body is then said to be dynamically balanced. This situation is discussed as a separate topic in this section.

Example 9–7. A uniform wheel (Fig. 9–13) weighing 240 lb is rotating about a fixed axis with an angular velocity of 3.5 radians/sec. Determine the reactions at the bearing points A and B. The moment of inertia of the body about the axis of rotation is 10 lb-sec²-ft. The rod is assumed to be weightless.

Solution: First, a free-body diagram of the system along with the reference axis is drawn in Fig. 9–13. Note that the reference axes are defined so that the z axis coincides with the axis of rotation. The origin of the axes is at the left bearing reaction. The axes are assumed to be fixed to the body so that they are rotating with the body. Before writing the equations of motion, the products of inertia with

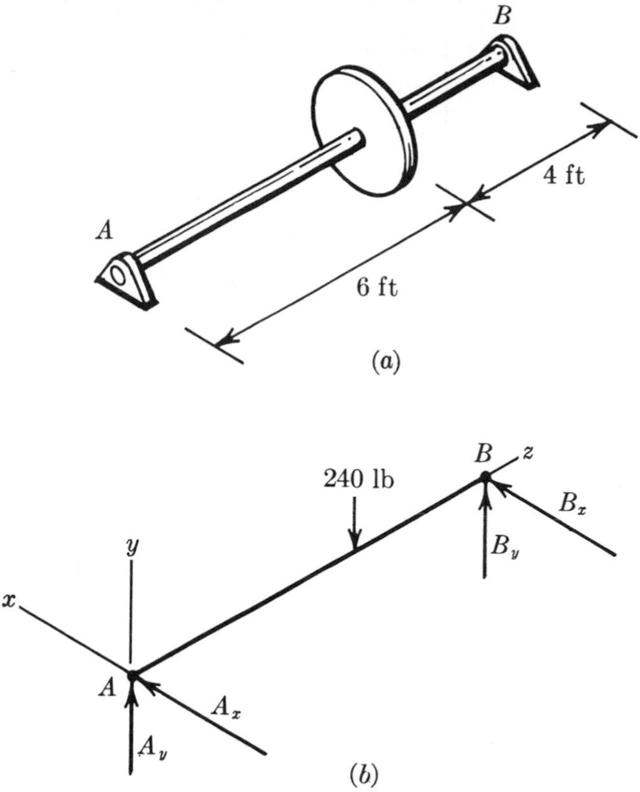

Figure 9-13

respect to the yz and zx axes must be determined. Figure 9–14 shows the body as seen in the yz and the xz planes.

Since in both cases, the z axis is an axis of symmetry, both I_{xz} and I_{zy} are equal to zero. It should also be noted that since the center of mass of the body lies on the axis of rotation, there is no motion of the center of mass, and therefore the acceleration of the center of mass is zero at all times. Finally, the equations of motion given by Eq. 9.14 reduce to the following:

$$\begin{aligned} F_x &= 0 \\ A_x + B_x &= 0 \\ F_y &= 0 \\ A_y + B_y - 240 &= 0 \\ M_x &= 0 \\ -10B_y + 6(240) &= 0 \\ M_y &= 0 \\ 10B_x &= 0 \end{aligned}$$

It is very important to note that the right-hand rule for determining the sign of the moment is employed. This rule must be adhered to strictly if the moment equation is to be written correctly, although in this case (since the products of inertia are equal to zero) it made no difference in the final equations.

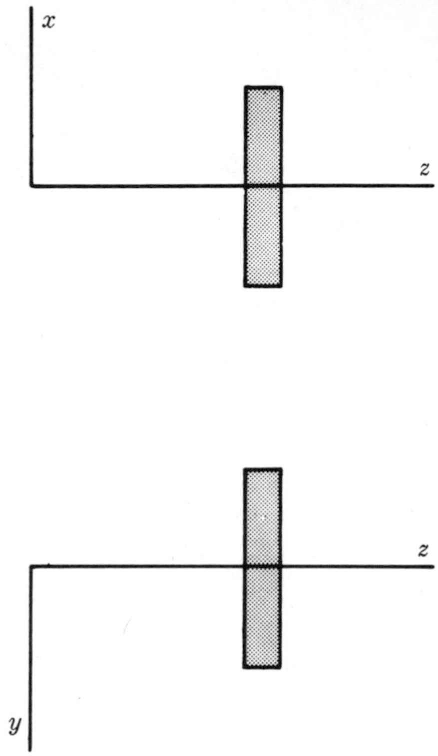

Figure 9-14

The set of four equations can then be solved simultaneously to show that

$$
\begin{aligned}
A_x &= 0 \\
A_y &= 96 \text{ lb} \\
B_x &= 0 \\
B_y &= 144 \text{ lb}
\end{aligned}
$$

But these reactions are nothing more than the static bearing reactions. That is to say, the reactions at the bearings when the body is in motion have the same value as the reactions at the bearings when the body is at rest. This is a very desirable condition because no dynamic or time-varying forces are transmitted to the supporting structures by this rotating body. This is why it is desirable for the reaction forces to be entirely static reaction forces.

Example 9-8. The system shown in Fig. 9-15 has a constant angular velocity of 10 radians/sec about the fixed axis. The first mass has a mass of 3 slugs and the second mass has a mass of 2 slugs. The bars are assumed to be weightless. Determine the dynamic bearing reactions as a function of time.

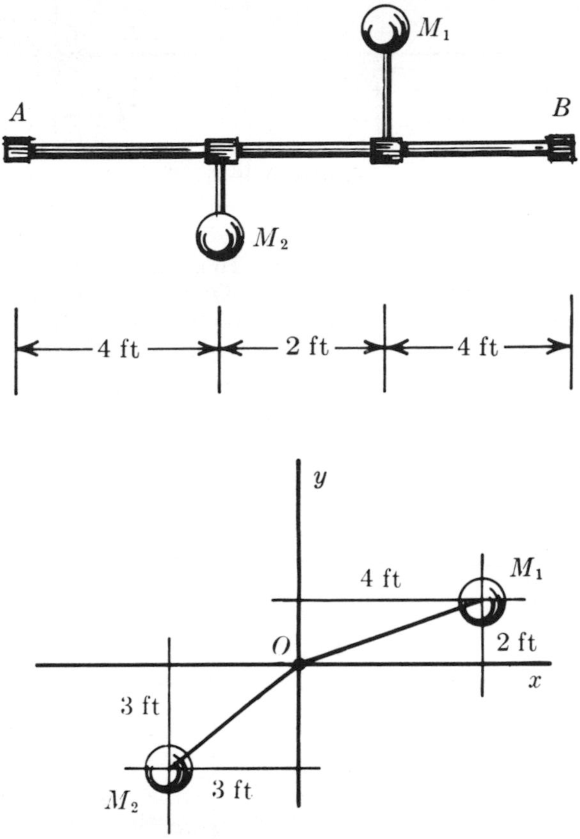

Figure 9-15

Solution: First a free-body diagram of the system (Fig. 9–15) will be drawn to define the unknown bearing reactions and the reference axes. Since we are interested only in the dynamic bearing reactions, the weight of the body is not shown in the free-body diagram. In order to use the force equations, the acceleration of the center of mass of the system must be determined, and in order to determine the acceleration of the center of mass, the position of the center of mass must be found. The position of the center of mass relative to the reference axes shown in Fig. 9–16 may be calculated as follows:

$$x_C = \frac{2(-3) + 3(4)}{5}$$

$$= 1.2 \text{ ft}$$

$$y_C = \frac{3(2) - 2(3)}{5}$$

$$= 0$$

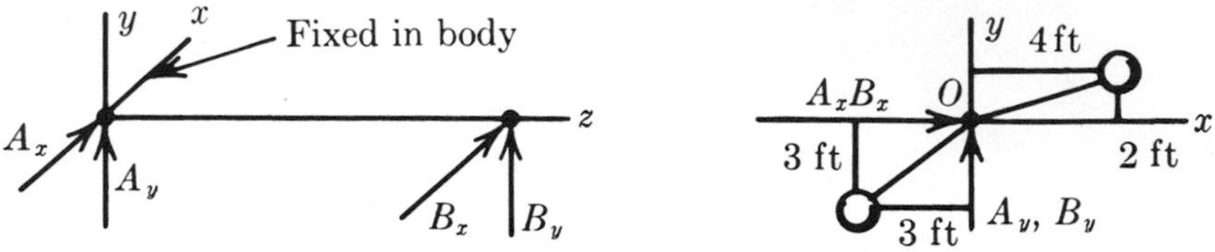

Figure 9-16

So, the center of mass lies right on the x axis. To use the force equations, we must know the acceleration of the center of mass. Since the system is moving with a constant angular velocity about the axis of rotation, the center of mass will be moving in a circular path. And since there is no angular acceleration, the acceleration of the center of mass will have a normal component only (Fig. 9–17). From Fig. 9–17 it is seen that

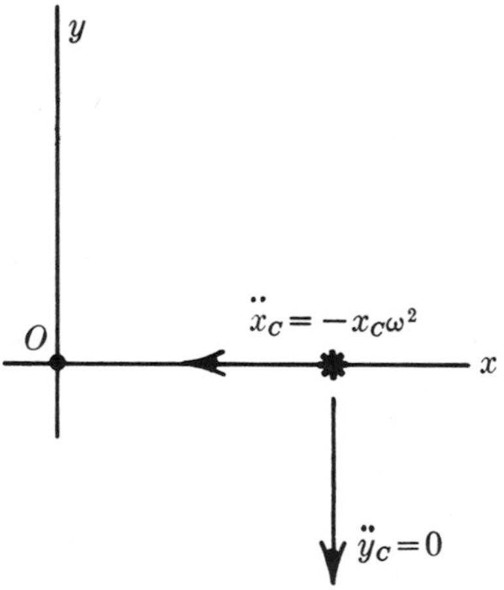

Figure 9-17

$$\begin{aligned}\ddot{y}_C &= 0\\ \ddot{x}_C &= -x_C\omega^2\\ &= -1.2(10)^2\\ &= -120\ \text{ft/sec}^2\end{aligned}$$

Now, in order to use the moment equations, we must know the product of inertia of the system with respect to the xz and the yz axes. Since the system is composed of point masses, we may perform a numerical integration to determine I_{xz} and I_{yz}:

$$\begin{aligned}I_{xz} &= \sum_i x_i z_i m_i\\ &= (4)(6)(3) + (-3)(4)(2)\\ &= 48\end{aligned}$$

and

$$\begin{aligned} I_{yz} &= \sum_i y_i z_i m_i \\ &= (2)(6)(3) + (-3)(4)(2) \\ &= 12 \end{aligned}$$

Now the four equations of motion may be written for the four unknowns (note that the angular velocity ω of the system is negative because its vector is in the negative z direction):

$$\begin{aligned} F_x &= m\ddot{x}_C \\ A_x + B_x &= -5(120) \\ &= -600 \\ F_y &= m\ddot{y}_C \\ A_y + B_y &= 0 \\ M_x &= -I_{xz}\dot{\omega}_z + I_{zy}\omega_z \\ -10B_y &= 12(10)^2 \\ B_y &= -120 \text{ lb} \\ M_y &= -I_{yz}\dot{\omega}_z - I_{xz}\omega \\ 10B_x &= -48(-10)^2 \\ B_x &= -480 \text{ lb} \end{aligned}$$

Then, from the force equations,

$$\begin{aligned} A_y &= 120 \text{ lb} \\ A_x &= -120 \text{ lb} \end{aligned}$$

What we have calculated here is the dynamic reaction components for the body at one particular position. But we are interested in writing the reactions as a function of time. We note that the reactions that we have determined here are rotating with the moving xy axes (Fig. 9–18). The magnitude of A is easily determined:

$$\begin{aligned} A &= \sqrt{120^2 + 120^2} \\ &= 170 \text{ lb} \end{aligned}$$

But since A is rotating with the moving coordinate system, as shown in Fig. 9–18,

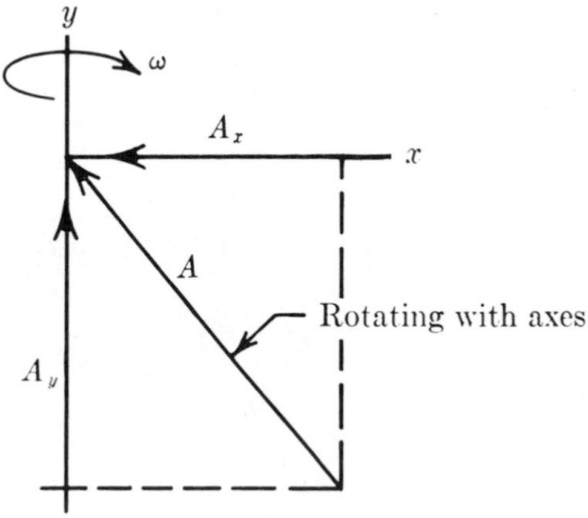

Figure 9-18

we must write the horizontal and vertical components of the bearing reactions at A (referred to inertial space) as

$$\begin{aligned} A_V &= 170 \cos(\omega t + \phi) \\ A_H &= 170 \sin(\omega t + \phi) \end{aligned}$$

The phase angle ϕ simply indicates that the starting position of the system may vary. By a similar argument, the magnitude of the reaction at B is

$$\begin{aligned} B &= \sqrt{480^2 + 120^2} \\ &= 494 \text{ lb} \end{aligned}$$

and the horizontal and vertical components of the reaction at B are

$$\begin{aligned} B_V &= 494 \cos(\omega t + \alpha) \\ B_H &= 494 \sin(\omega t + \alpha) \end{aligned}$$

The phase angle α indicates not only that the starting position of the system may vary, but also that the reaction at B is out of phase with the reaction at A; that is, they do not attain their maximum values at the same time. We have also shown that the horizontal and vertical components of the bearing reactions at A and B vary with time and have the same frequency as the rotational speed of the system.

Dynamic balancing. Example 9–8 demonstrates that, in general, a body rotating about a fixed axis will have horizontal and vertical components of the bearing reactions that are harmonic functions of time. By Newton's third law, the force of the support on the system is equal to the force of the system on the support.

Shown in Fig. 9–19 is a body rotating with both an angular velocity and angular acceleration at a given instant of time. The reference axes are defined so that the origin of the system coincides with point O on the axis of rotation and the y axis is aligned so that it is in the same direction as the line joining the axis of rotation and the center of mass of the body. Thus, the equations of motion become

$$\begin{aligned} F_x &= m\ddot{x}_C \\ A_x + B_x &= mr\dot{\omega} \\ F_y &= m\ddot{y}_C \\ A_y + B_y - W &= -mr\dot{\omega}^2 \\ M_x &= -I_{xz}\dot{\omega} + I_{zy}\omega^2 \\ A_yl_1 - B_yl_2 &= -I_{zx}\dot{\omega} + I_{zy}\omega^2 \\ M_y &= -I_{yz}\dot{\omega} - I_{xz}\omega^2 \\ B_xl_2 - A_xl_1 &= -I_{yz}\dot{\omega} - I_{xz}\omega^2 \end{aligned} \qquad (9.15)$$

Now, if the body is not rotating and is in static equilibrium, the equations of equilibrium are

$$\begin{aligned} F_x &= 0 \\ A_x + B_x &= 0 \\ F_y &= 0 \\ A_y + B_y - W &= 0 \\ M_x &= 0 \\ A_yl_1 - B_yl_2 &= 0 \\ M_y &= 0 \\ -A_xl_1 + B_xl_2 &= 0 \end{aligned} \qquad (9.16)$$

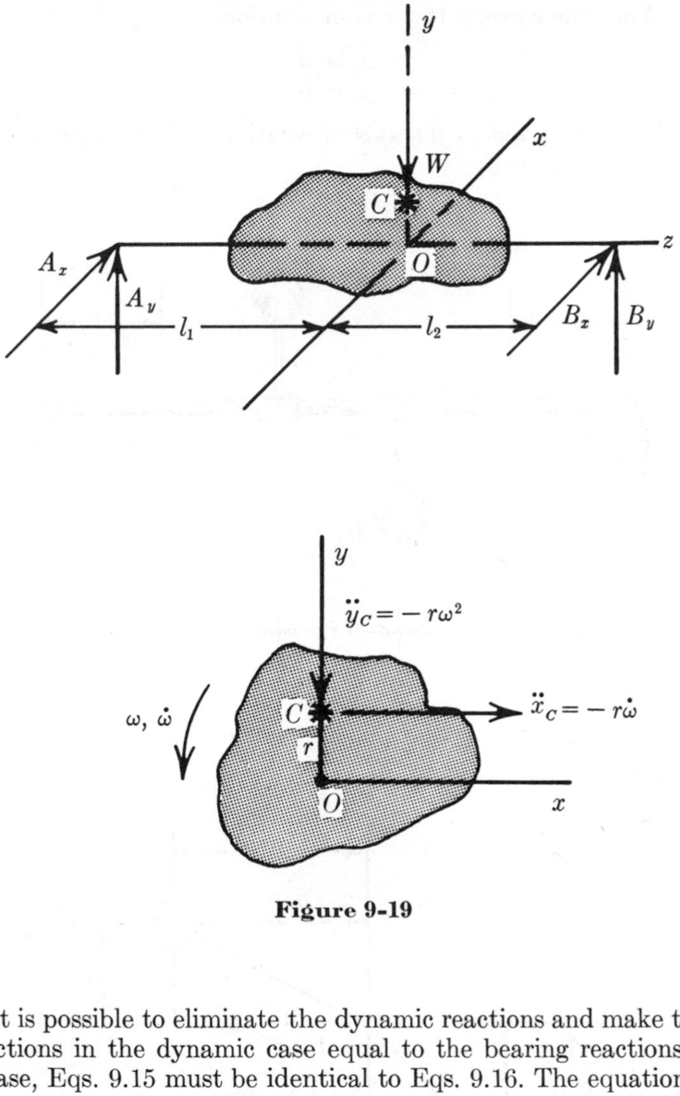

Figure 9-19

If it is possible to eliminate the dynamic reactions and make the bearing reactions in the dynamic case equal to the bearing reactions for the static case, Eqs. 9.15 must be identical to Eqs. 9.16. The equations of the dynamic system reduce to the equations for the static system if the following conditions exist:

1. The center of mass of the body lies on the axis of rotation (so that the distance r is equal to zero).
2. The products of inertia about the xz and yz axes are equal to zero.

Thus these two conditions must be fulfilled if the rotating body is to have no dynamic reactions. A rotating body that fulfills these two conditions is said to be *dynamically balanced.* The two conditions stated above actually imply four mathematical conditions concerning the geometry of a balanced body. They are:

1. When the z axis is the axis of rotation,

$$x_c = 0$$
$$y_c = 0$$

2. When the z axis is the axis of rotation and the reference axes are fixed in the body,

$$I_{xz} = 0$$
$$I_{yz} = 0$$

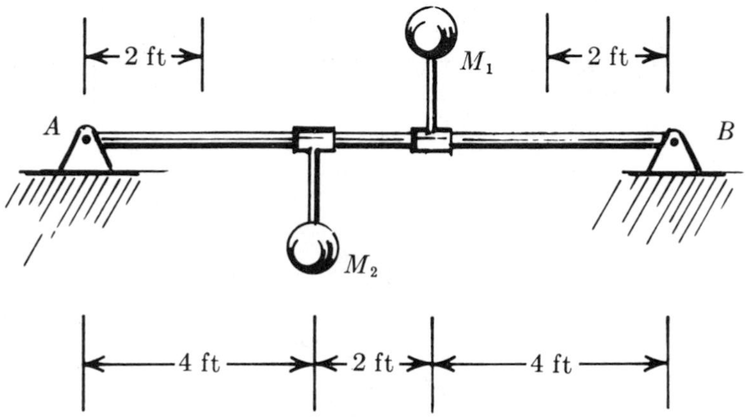

(a)

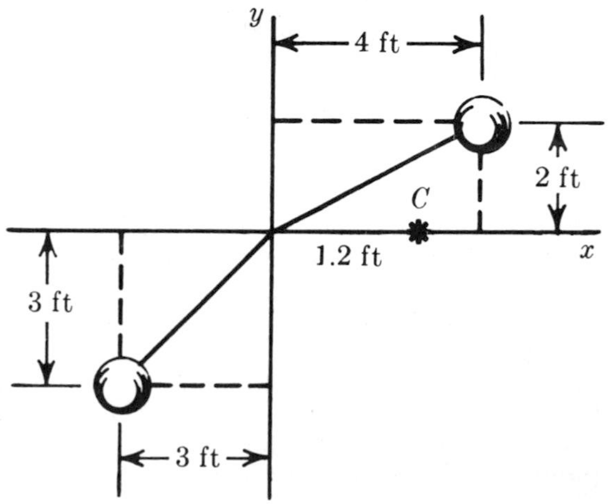

(b)

Figure 9-20

It must be, then, that these four equations are satisfied simultaneously if the body is to be dynamically balanced.

Example 9–9. The system of Example 9–8 is to be dynamically balanced by adding two 32.2-lb weights in correction planes, each 2 ft from each bearing, as shown in Fig. 9–20. The first mass is equal to 3 slugs and the second mass is equal to 2 slugs.

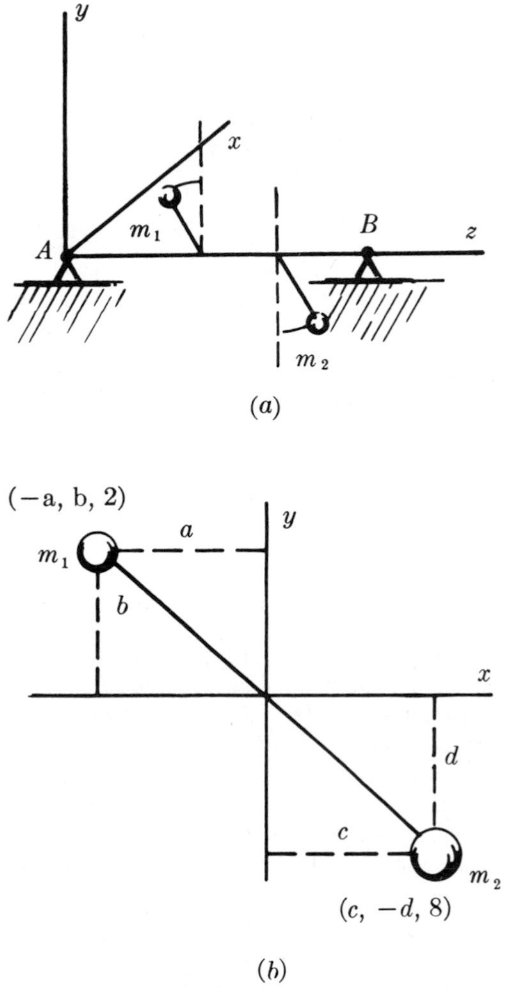

Figure 9-21

Solution: The position of the center of mass was determined in Example 9–8, and here we assume that its position is given as shown in Fig. 9–20. The moving reference axes are as shown in Fig. 9–20, and in Fig. 9–21 the position of the two balancing masses are assumed. The distances a, b, c, and d must be determined from the conditions for balance. Direct evaluation of the four equations gives

$$y_c = 0$$
$$m_1 b + m_2(-d) = 0$$
$$b - d = 0$$

$$x_c = 0$$
$$5(1.2) + m_1(-a) + m_2(c) = 0$$
$$-a + c = 6$$

$$I_{xz} = 0$$
$$4(3)(6) + (-3)(4)(2)$$
$$+ (-a)(2)(m_1) + (c)(8)m_2 = 0$$
$$-2a + 8c = -48$$

$$I_{yz} = 0$$
$$(b)(2)m_1 + (-d)(8)m_2$$
$$+ 2(6)(3) + (-3)(4)(2) = 0$$
$$2b - 8d = -12$$

Solving for a, b, c, and d,

$$a = -16$$
$$b = 2$$
$$c = -10$$
$$d = 2$$

The significance of the minus sign is that the direction of a and c were chosen incorrectly. So, presumably, by taking 32-lb weights and planning them in the positions indicated by Fig. 9–21, with the appropriate values of a, b, c, and d, the system may spin about the axis of rotation, free from dynamic reactions.

The center of percussion. Figure 9–22 shows a rigid body rotating in a horizontal plane about a fixed point O. It is possible to apply a force, in the plane of motion, at some point on the body so that there will be no reaction at the fixed point O. A baseball player knows that if he hits the ball at a certain point on the bat, the force of the bat on his hands will be relatively small. This point on the body, where the force may be applied without any reaction, is called the *center of percussion* of the body.

In an attempt to determine the distance L from the axis of rotation to the center of percussion of the body, we shall draw a free-body diagram of the body, define a set of reference axes, and then apply the equations of motion. The origin of the moving reference axes is taken at the fixed point of rotation. To determine the distance L, we shall first try to write an equation in which L appears. The first choice would be the moment equation:

$$M_O = I_O\dot{\omega}$$
$$-FL = I_O\dot{\omega} \qquad \textbf{(9.17)}$$

Hoping that we should be able to find that the center of percussion is a point independent of the applied force F, we shall write the force equation in an attempt to eliminate F:

$$F_x = m\ddot{x}_c$$
$$F + O_x = m\ddot{x}_c \qquad \textbf{(9.18)}$$

We shall stipulate now that there will be no reactions at O. Thus, O_x will be equal to zero. Also note that, for the position shown, $\ddot{x}_c = d\dot{\omega}$ by the arc formula. Dividing the moment equation by the force equation,

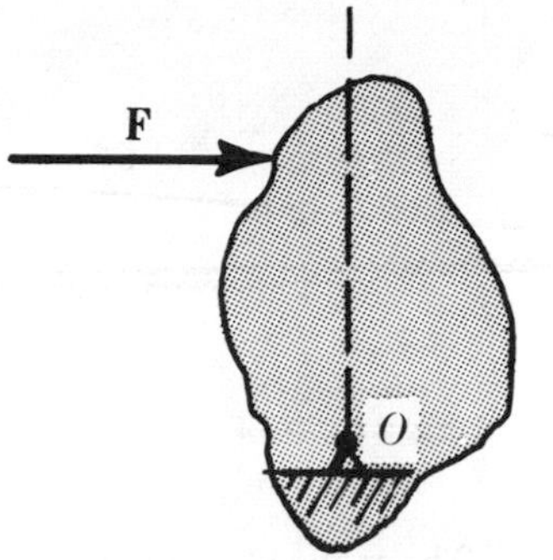

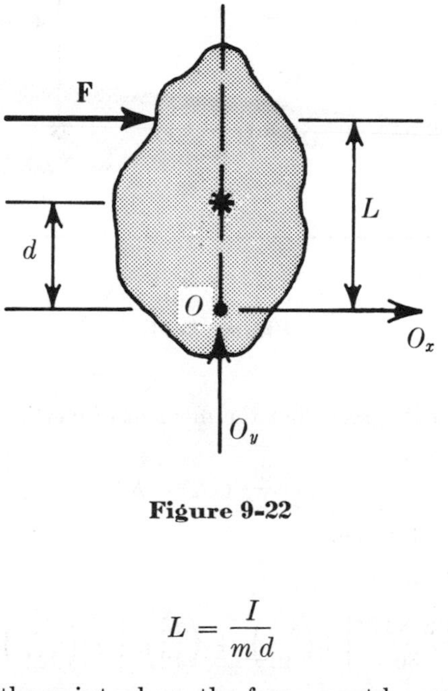

Figure 9-22

$$L = \frac{I}{m\,d} \tag{9.19}$$

This, then, defines the point where the force must be applied so that there will be no reaction at point O. No matter how large F is, or in what manner it is applied, there will be no force whatsoever experienced by point O.

Example 9–10. Determine the center of percussion for the baseball bat shown in Fig. 9–23. The bat weighs 2 lb and it is 36 in. long. It is assumed to be swung at a point in the middle of the grip, 4 in. from the end, as shown.

Solution: The distance from point O to the center of percussion of the bat is given by Eq. 9.19. Before we can use this equation, however, we must determine the moment of inertia of the bat about the point O. To do this, we shall assume

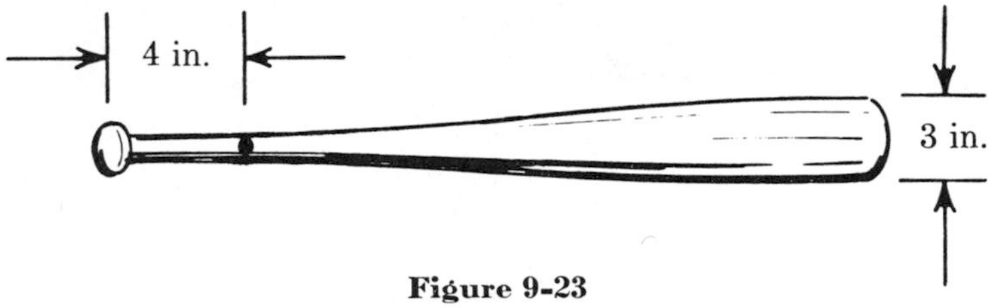

Figure 9-23

that the bat has a conical shape. The moment of inertia of a cone may be determined from Appendix I. The assumed cone is shown in Fig. 9–24.

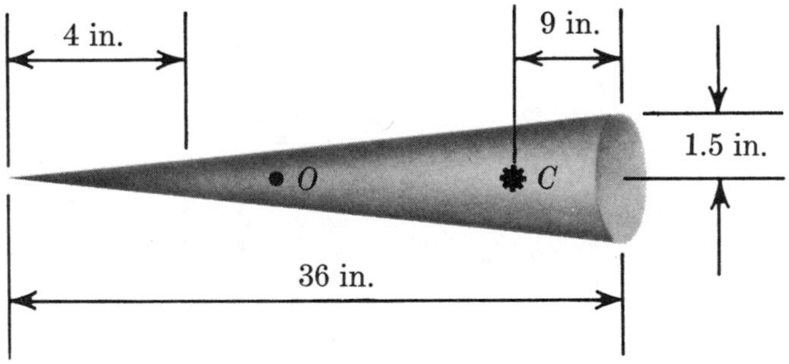

Figure 9-24

From Appendix I it is seen that the moment of inertia of the cone about the point C is

$$I_c = \frac{3m}{80}(4R^2 + h^2)$$

Using the parallel axis theorem,

$$I_O = I_c + md^2$$

$$= \frac{3(2/32.2)}{80}\left[4\left(\frac{1.5}{12}\right)^2 + \left(\frac{23}{12}\right)^2\right] + \left(\frac{12}{32.2}\right)\left(\frac{23}{12}\right)^2$$

$$I_O = 0.238 \text{ lb-sec}^2\text{-ft}$$

Therefore the distance from the axis of rotation to the center of percussion of the bat is

$$L = \frac{I_O}{md}$$

$$= \frac{0.238}{(2/32.2)(23/12)}$$

$$= 2.00 \text{ ft}$$
$$= 24 \text{ in.}$$

Thus, the center of percussion for the bat is at a distance of 1 in. to the right of the center of mass, so that by hitting the ball with the bat at that particular point on the bat, theoretically the ballplayer should experience no force from the bat. One should realize, however, that the assumption that the bat was pinned at the point O was not quite correct, since obviously a bat cannot be gripped at a point.

PROBLEMS

9-13. If the system shown in Fig. P.9-13 is released from rest, what is the angular velocity of the disk after 6 sec? The weight W_1 is equal to 64.4 lb, the weight W_2 is equal to 32.2 lb, the weight of the disk is equal to 192 lb, and the radius of the disk is equal to 1 ft.

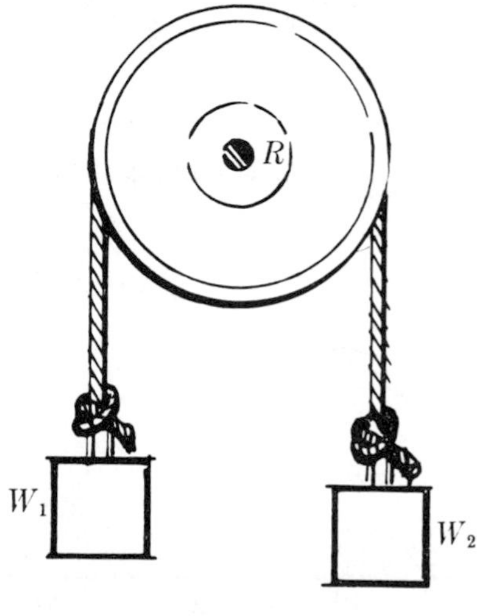

Figure Prob. 9-13

9-14. Consider the system of Example 9-4. Suppose that instead of applying a constant 40 ft-lb moment to the body, a 40 ft-lb moment is applied to the body at rest by means of a 20-lb weight that is attached to a rope, which in turn is wrapped around the body. Determine the angular velocity of the body as a function of time and compare your results with those obtained in Example 9-4. Indicate the reason for the differences in the angular velocity between the two cases.

9-15. If the system shown in Fig. P.9-15 is released from rest, determine the angular velocity as a function of time. The moment of inertia of the body about its axis of rotation is 2.0 lb-sec²-ft. The weights W_1 and W_2 are equal to 32.2 and 48.3 lb, respectively.

9-16. The moment driving the wheel shown in Fig. P.9-16 is given as a function of time in the graph. If the body is initially at rest, draw a sketch of the angular velocity of the body as a function of time. The weight of the wheel is 96.6 lb and its radius is equal to 18 in.

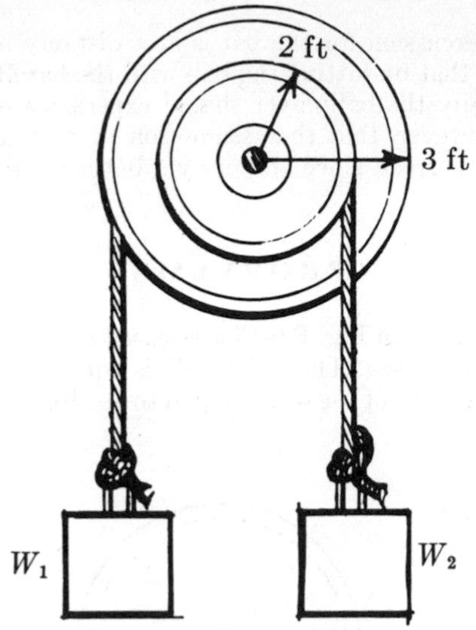

Figure Prob. 9-15

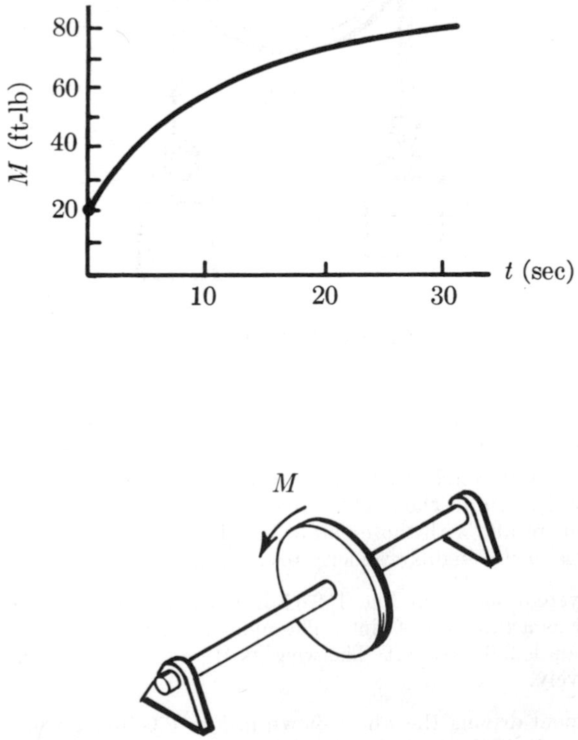

Figure Prob. 9-16

9-17. A rotating system consists of a wheel weighing 60 lb and four concentrated weights, each weighing 10 lb each and mounted on the periphery of the wheel. What constant moment must be applied to this system to make it accelerate from an angular velocity of 20 radians/sec to an angular velocity of 40 radians/sec in 30 sec? The radius of the wheel is 15 inches.

9-18. The 100-lb wheel shown in Fig. P.9-18 is spinning with an angular velocity of 500 radians/sec. It is desired to bring the wheel to rest by applying the hand brake. If the coefficient of dynamic friction between the brake and the wheel is 0.30, what force F must be applied to the brake so that the wheel will come to rest in 20 sec with a constant deceleration?

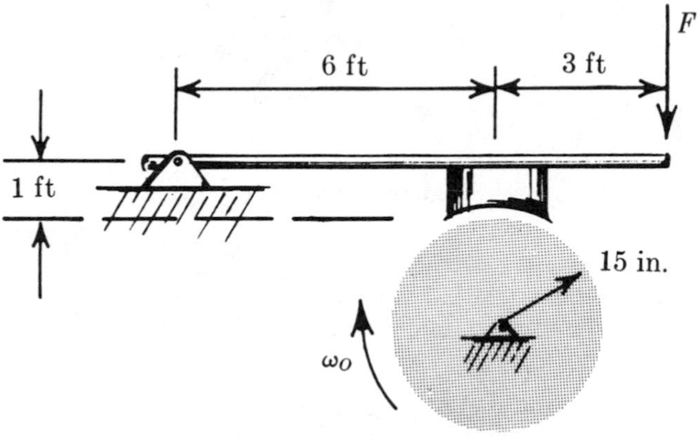

Figure Prob. 9-18

9-19. A uniform rod of mass m and length l is pinned at one end. At rest, it will hang in a vertical position, but with small disturbances, it will oscillate about the vertical with harmonic motion. Show that the differential equation of motion of the rod is

$$\ddot{\theta} + \frac{3g}{2l}\,\theta = 0$$

where θ is measured from the vertical to the rod.

9-20. An armature of an electric motor having a moment of inertia about its axis of rotation of 0.04 lb-sec^2-ft is observed to accelerate from rest to 2000 rpm in 10 sec when the motor is energized under no-load conditions. Observations show that the angular acceleration of the armature is not uniform, but in an attempt to estimate the magnitude of the moment or torque of the armature, assume a constant angular acceleration. Then calculate the constant torque on the armature.

9-21. The pendulum shown in Fig. P.9-21 is falling under the action of gravity. If, at the position shown, the clockwise angular velocity of the pendulum is 2.0 radians/sec, what are the horizontal and vertical reactions at the pin? The disk weighs 16 lb and the rod weighs 4 lb.

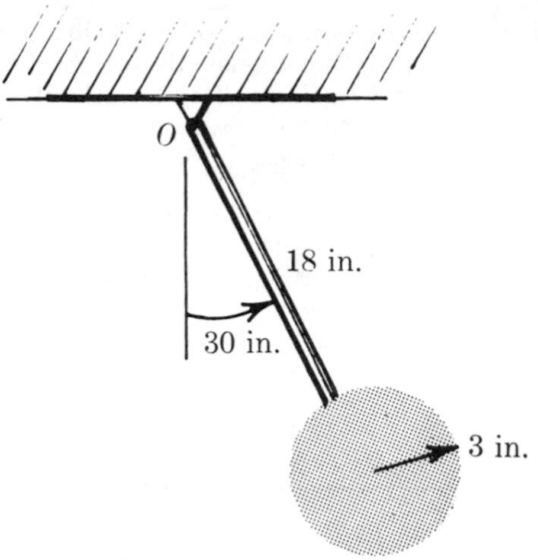

Figure Prob. 9-21

9-22. Suppose that the system of Problem 9-21 is released from rest in a horizontal position. What are the reaction components at O at the instant that the system is released?

9-23. The single, concentrated 2.0-slug mass in Fig. P.9-23 is rotating about the fixed axis with an angular velocity of 2.0 radians/sec and an angular acceleration of 3.0 radians/sec^2 in the position shown. What are the components of the dynamic reactions at A and B at this instant?

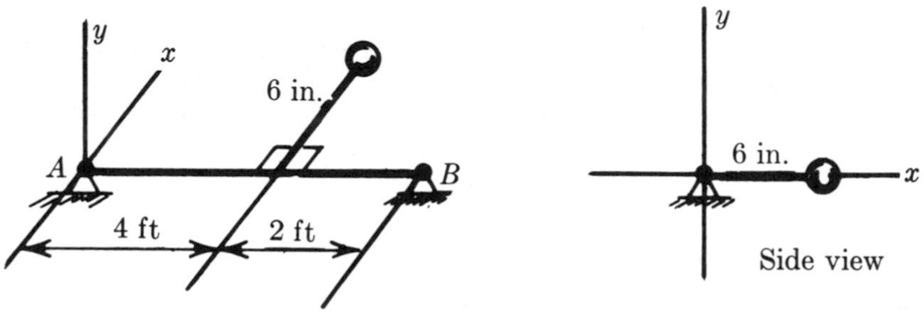

Figure Prob. 9-23

9-24. The system of the preceding problem may be balanced by adding a single 32.2-lb weight in the xz plane. What are the coordinates of the point where the weight must be placed for dynamic balancing?

9-25. Consider the system shown in Fig. P.9-25. What must be the constant moment required to accelerate the system from an angular velocity of 4 radians/sec

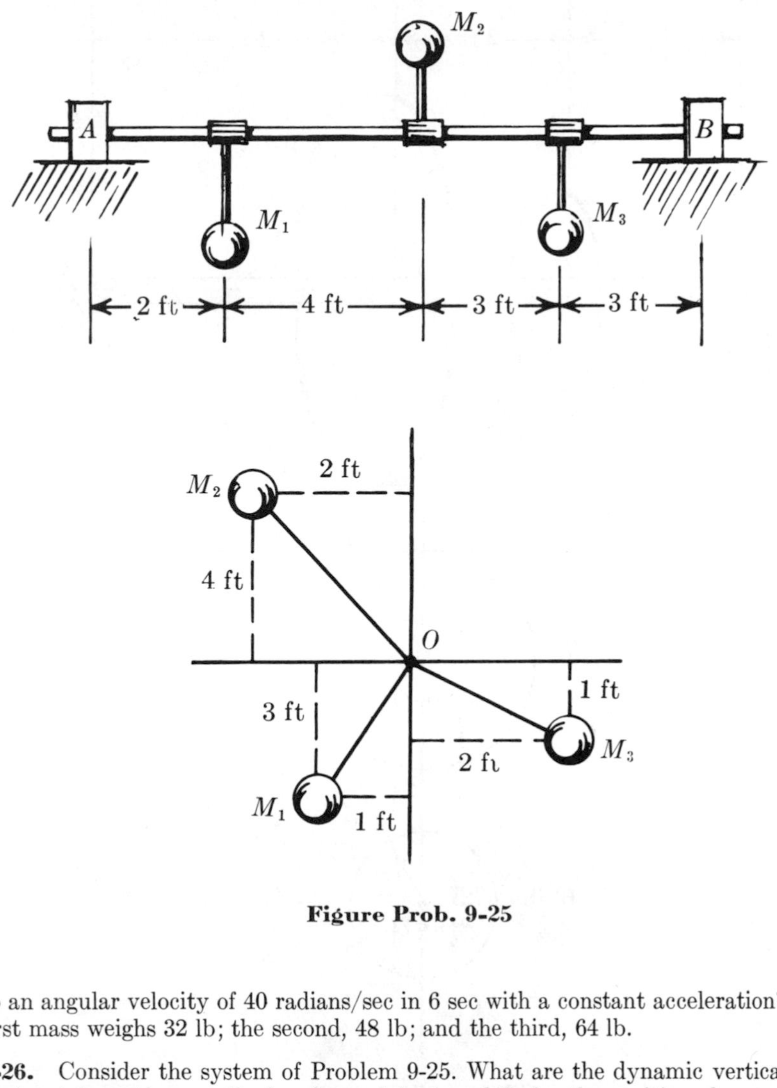

Figure Prob. 9-25

to an angular velocity of 40 radians/sec in 6 sec with a constant acceleration? The first mass weighs 32 lb; the second, 48 lb; and the third, 64 lb.

9-26. Consider the system of Problem 9-25. What are the dynamic vertical and horizontal reactions at the bearing points A and B, for the position shown, if the system is rotating with a constant angular velocity of 4 radians/sec?

9-27. Consider the system of Problem 9-25. Determine the position in which to hang two 16-lb weights so that the system is dynamically balanced. The corrections planes are located 1 ft from each of the reactions.

9-28. Consider the system shown in Fig. P.9-28, where m_1 is 0.5 slug and m_2 is 2.0 slugs. Each of the two disks is symmetrical, but neither of the two is mounted on the axis of rotation so that the center of mass of the body coincides with the axis of rotation. The eccentricity, or the distance from the axis of rotation to the center of mass of each wheel, is given in the figure. Determine the moment required to accelerate the body from rest to 5000 rpm in 10 sec with a constant acceleration.

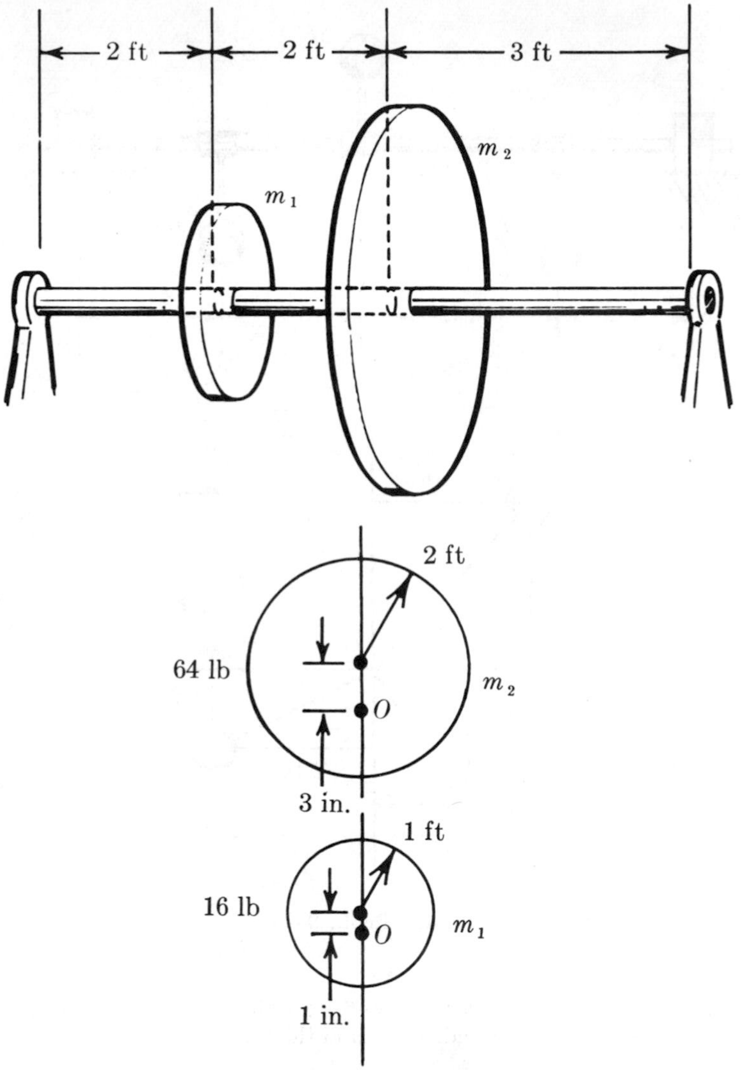

Figure Prob. 9-28

9-29. Determine the vertical reactions of Problem 9-28 when the system is rotating at a constant velocity of 5000 rpm for the instant shown.

9-30. Two 4-lb weights are available for balancing the system of Problem 9-28. Determine the positions at which these weights should be placed on the two wheels so that the system will be dynamically balanced. Note that it may not be possible to fix the weights to the wheels to balance the system because the distances are too large.

9-31. It is desired to balance dynamically the system in Fig. P.9-31. Two 5-lb weights are used and are placed in the correction plane shown. Determine the distances to the axis of rotation for each mass.

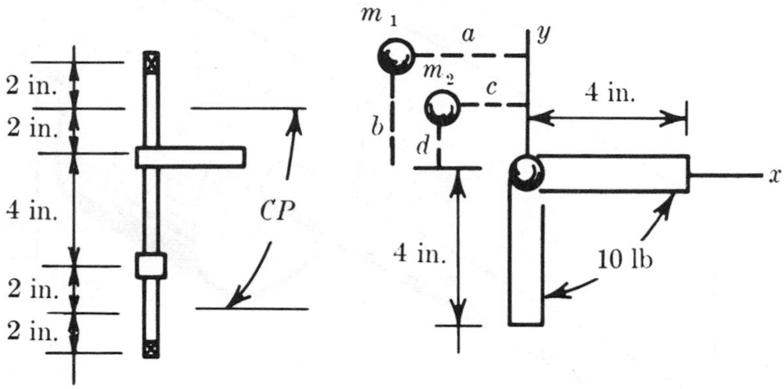

Figure Prob. 9-31

9-32. Determine the center of percussion for the system shown in Fig. P.9-32. The bar weighs 4 lb and the ball on the end weighs 16 lb.

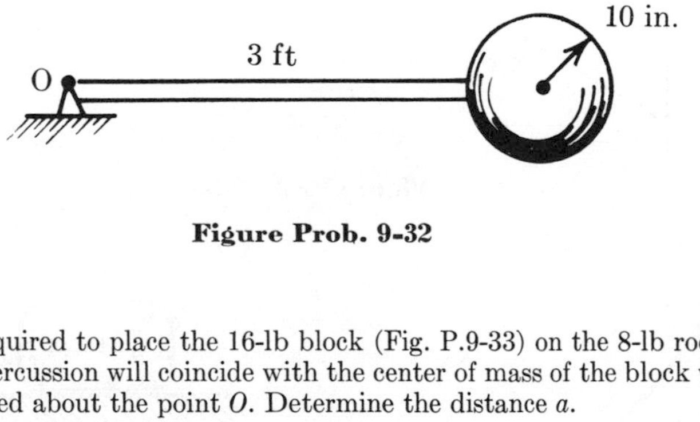

Figure Prob. 9-32

9-33. It is required to place the 16-lb block (Fig. P.9-33) on the 8-lb rod so that the center of percussion will coincide with the center of mass of the block when the system is rotated about the point *O*. Determine the distance *a*.

9-34. The torque of an electric motor can be expressed as a function of its angular velocity. Suppose that this motor is driving the wheel shown in Fig. P.9-34. The wheel weighs 96 lb and has a radius of 2 ft. If the system starts from rest, determine the angular velocity of the wheel 5 sec later.

9-35. A device for lifting weights is constructed by placing three spur gears in series, as shown in Fig. P.9-35. A motor drives the first gear. If it is desired to lift the 48-lb weight with a constant acceleration of 2.0 ft/sec², what must be the magnitude M of the moment required by the motor? The moments of inertia of gears one, two, and three, respectively, are 0.2, 0.6, and 1.2 lb-sec²-ft.

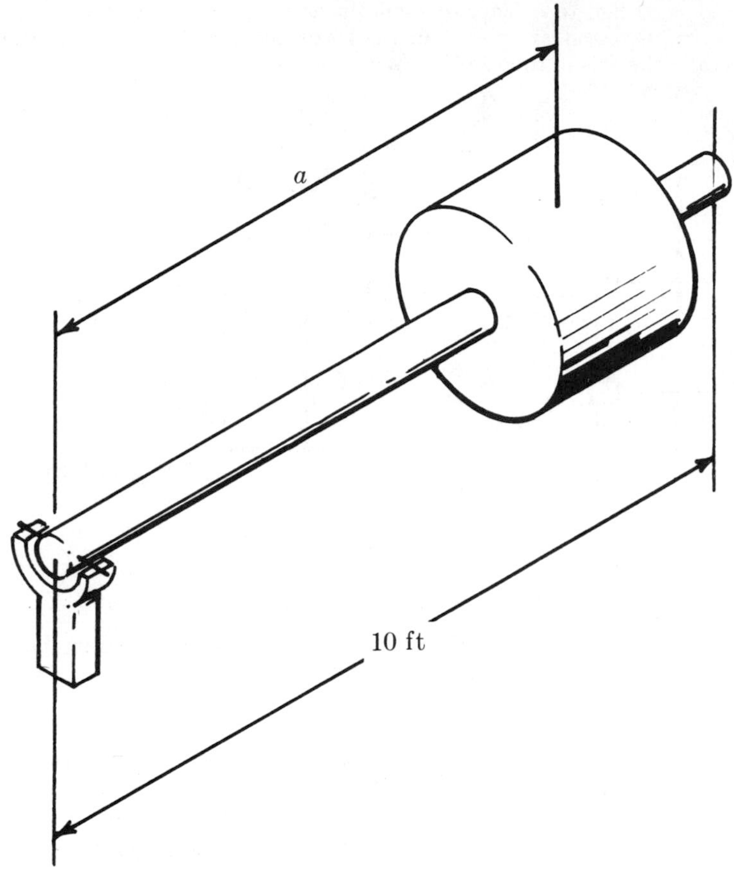

Figure Prob. 9-33

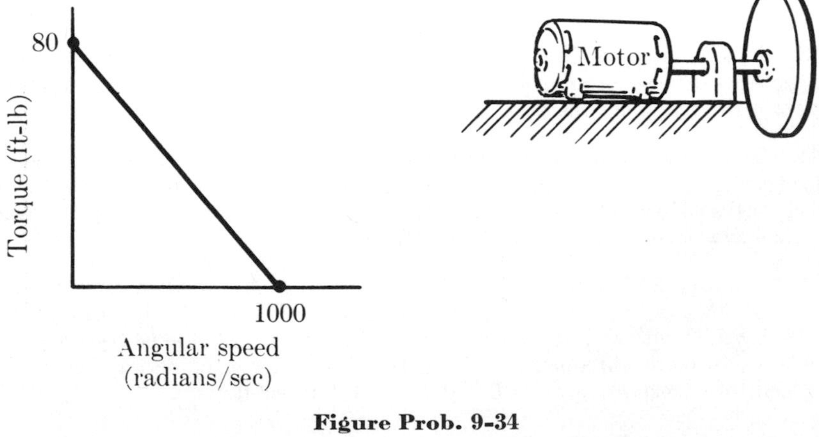

Figure Prob. 9-34

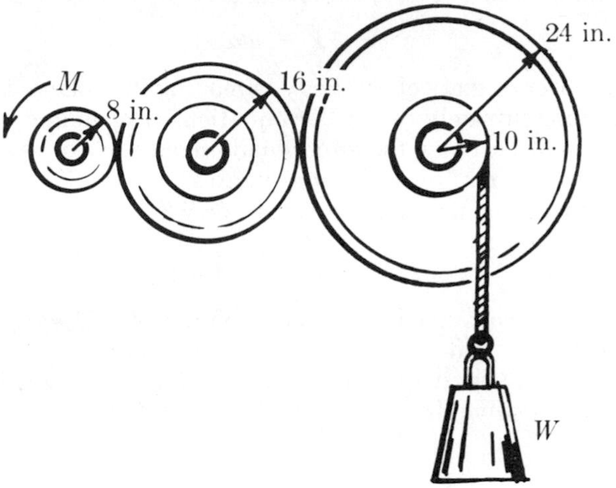

Figure Prob. 9-35

9-36. The wheel shown in Fig. P.9-36 is driven by a motor at a constant angular velocity of 800 rpm. The clutch connecting the two is disengaged, and it is observed that the wheel slows down and comes to rest in $3\frac{1}{2}$ min. The moment responsible for the angular deceleration is the moment caused by friction in the bearings. What is the average frictional moment in the bearings? The weight of the rim is 10 lb and the weight of each of the four spokes is 4 lb.

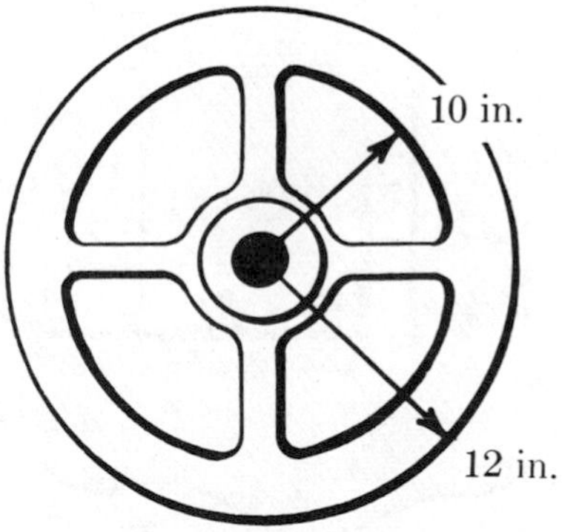

Figure Prob. 9-36

9-3. PLANE MOTION OF A RIGID BODY

There are three coordinates required to describe the general motion of a rigid body that is moving in a plane. Generally, two translation coordinates representing the translation of the center of mass are taken, along with one rotation coordinate representing the rotation of the body.

The force equation for the motion of a rigid body in a plane is

$$\boldsymbol{F} = m\boldsymbol{a}_c \tag{9.20}$$

Since the center of mass of the body is moving in a plane, the vector-force equation represents only two scalar equations. Depending upon the nature of the motion of the body, the force equation may be expressed in Cartesian, polar, or normal and tangential coordinates.

The general moment equation may be written (see Eq. 8.18 and associated derivation) as

$$M_P = I_P\dot{\omega} - d(ma_P) \tag{9.21}$$

where P is any convenient reference point. Both M_P and ω are positive counterclockwise, and if an x axis is taken through P in the direction of $\boldsymbol{a}_P$, then d is positive in the direction of positive y axis. Figure 9–25 indicates the positive directions for M, ω, and d.

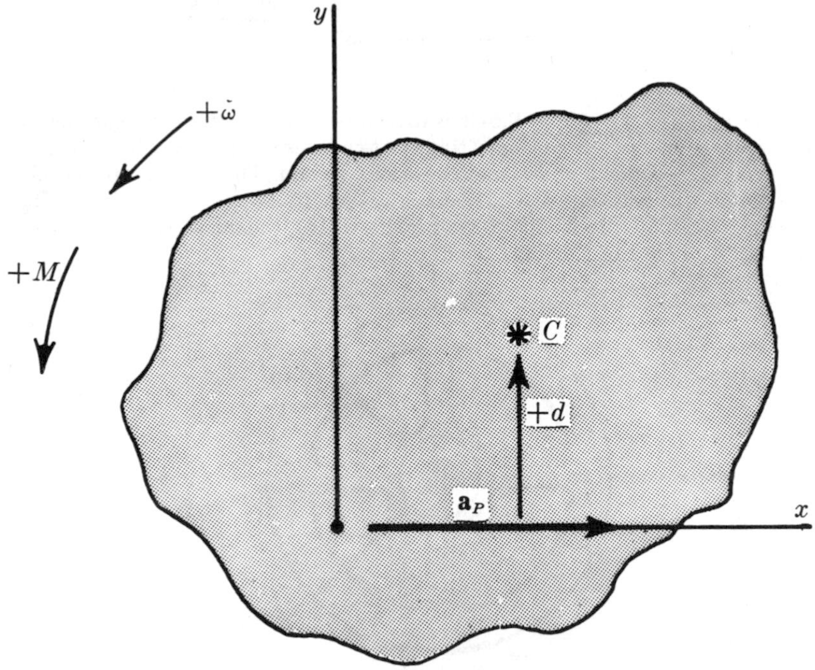

Figure 9-25

Generally, the center of mass is taken as the reference point; in this case, Eq. 9.21 reduces to

$$M_c = I_c\dot{\omega} \tag{9.22}$$

The procedure for solving these types of problems is as follows:

1. Define the reference system fixed to the body with the origin at the center of mass of the body. If the body is moving in a straight-line direction, it is helpful (but not necessary) to define the x axis as the direction of motion of the body.

2. Draw a free-body diagram of the rigid body.

3. From the free-body diagram, tabulate the force and the moments acting on the body, and then write the three equations indicated by Eqs. 9.20 and 9.21. Then, if the problem is not indeterminate, these three equations may be solved simultaneously for the motion of the system in terms of the forces or of the forces in terms of the moment.

Example 9–11. Determine the acceleration of the center of mass of the cylinder of weight W and radius R (Fig. 9–26) as it rolls down an incline that is tilted at ad angle of θ with the horizontal.

Solution: The moving axes are fixed in the body in the position shown. At this instant, the x axis is defined in the direction of motion of the center of mass so that

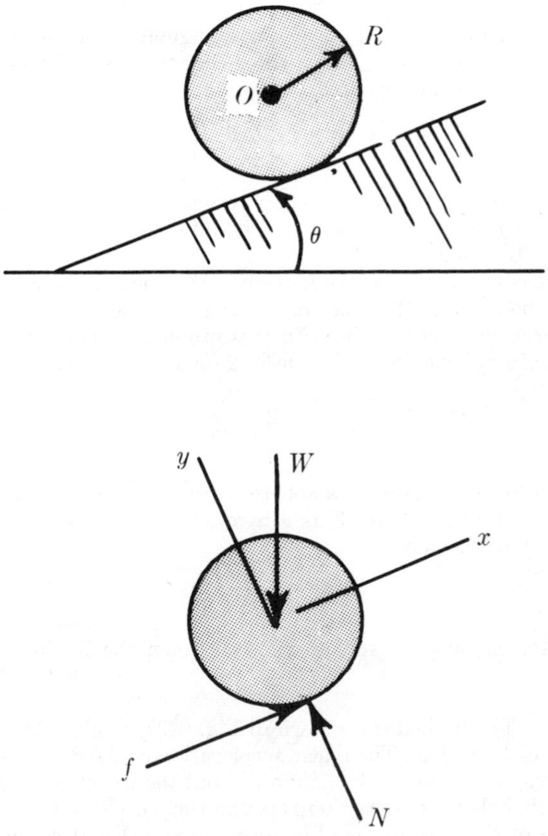

Figure 9-26

the equations of motion may be simplified. If the reference axes were defined horizontally, then components of motion in both the x and the y directions would have to be considered. Since it is desired to determine the acceleration of the body along the incline, first write an equation in which this acceleration term appears. This, of course, would be the force equation for the x direction:

$$F_x = m\ddot{x}_c$$
$$-W \sin\theta + f = m\ddot{x}_c$$

But the acceleration cannot be determined because f is not known. Therefore at least one other equation is required. Since the moment equation contains f, this will be written as

$$M_O = I_O\dot{\omega}$$
$$fR = I_O\dot{\omega}$$

Now another unknown, $\dot{\omega}$, is introduced, and so still another equation is needed. But it is noted that the angular acceleration of the body and the linear acceleration of the center of mass are related by the arc formula. This, then, completes the set of equations required for the solution:

$$\ddot{x}_c = -R\dot{\omega}$$

The minus sign is included because a positive angular acceleration corresponds to a negative linear acceleration. Now the three equations may be solved simultaneously for the linear acceleration:

$$\ddot{x}_c = -\frac{W \sin\theta}{m + I_O/R^2}$$

This equation for the linear acceleration represents the linear acceleration of any circular body as it rolls down an incline. The minus sign indicates that the body is accelerating in the minus x direction.

It should be pointed out that the motion of the body depends a good deal upon geometry of the body, since the acceleration is a function of the moment of inertia about the center of mass of the body. In this problem, it is required to determine the acceleration of a cylinder. Since $I = mR^2/2$ for a cylinder, the linear acceleration becomes

$$\ddot{x}_c = -\frac{2}{3}\, g \sin\theta$$

Now compare this to the motion of a sphere. From Appendix I it is found that the moment of inertia of a sphere about its centroidal axis is $I = 2mR^2/5$, so that the linear acceleration of the sphere is

$$\ddot{x}_c = -\frac{5}{7}\, g \sin\theta$$

This, then, indicates that the sphere will roll down the incline faster than the cylinder.

Example 9–12. The flatbed cart shown in Fig. 9–27 weighs 128.8 lb, and each of its two wheels weighs 16.1 lb. The linear acceleration of the car under the action of the 10-lb force may be estimated by assuming that the wheels are rigidly connected to the cart and that there is no friction between the wheels and the road. Calculate the acceleration of the cart (using this approximation) and compare it with the *exact* acceleration of the cart, taking into account the rotary motion of the wheels. The center of mass of the system lies on the axle.

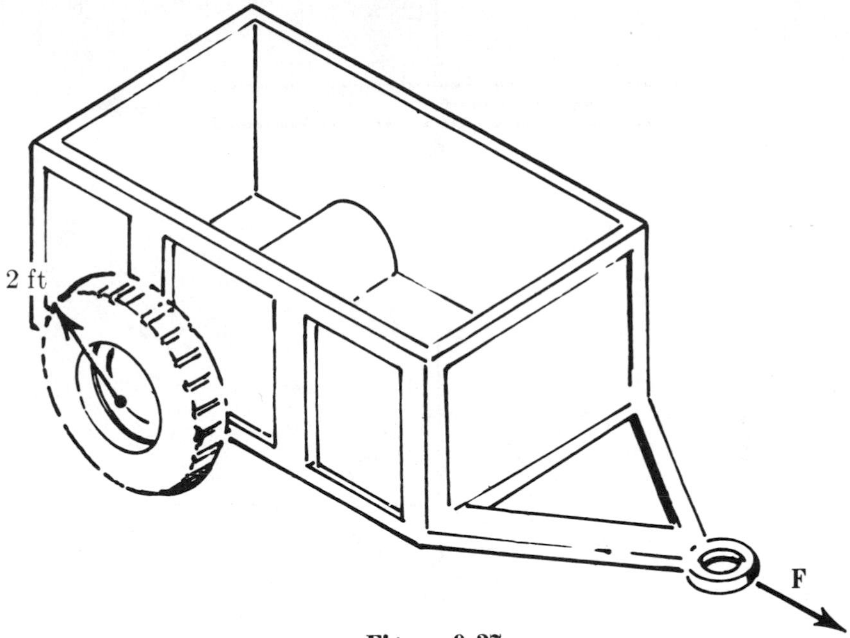

Figure 9-27

Solution: By assuming that the wheels are connected to the cart, the acceleration of the cart is easily calculated by using the force equation for the x direction:

$$F_x = m\ddot{x}_C$$

$$10 = \left(\frac{128 + 2(16)}{32.2}\right)\ddot{x}_C$$

$$\ddot{x}_c = 2.0 \text{ ft/sec}^2$$

Taking into account the angular motion of the wheels, first draw a free-body diagram of both the cart and the wheels (Fig. 9–28). The equation of motion for the cart in the x direction becomes

$$F_x = m\ddot{x}_c$$
$$10 - A_x = 4\ddot{x}_c$$

and to eliminate A_x, we write the force equation for the wheels:

$$F_x = m\ddot{x}_c$$
$$A_x - f = \ddot{x}_c$$

Now we must eliminate f by seeking another equation. The moment equation may be introduced:

$$M_z = I_{zz}\dot{\omega}$$

$$-2f = \frac{1}{2}\left(\frac{32.2}{32.2}\right)(2)^2\dot{\omega}$$

$$-2f = 2\dot{\omega}$$

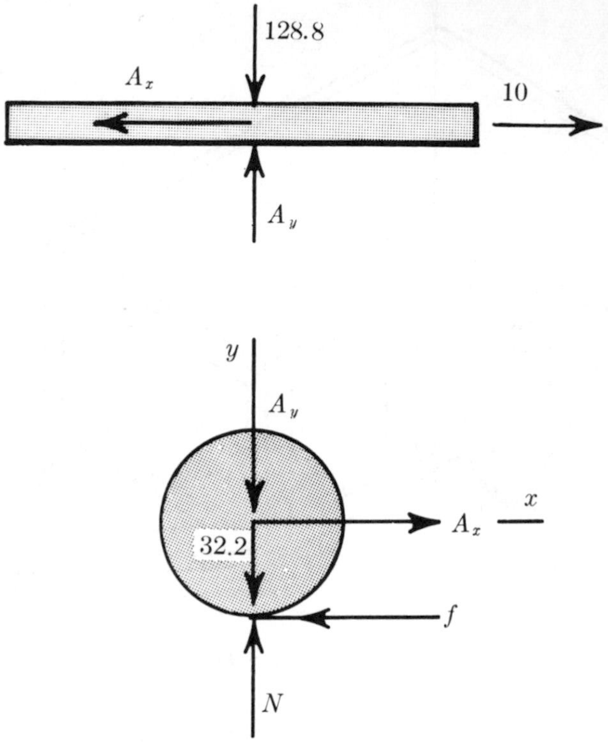

Figure 9-28

Solve the preceding three equations simultaneously for the linear acceleration of the center of mass of the cart by noting that $\ddot{x}_c = -2\dot{\omega}$:

$$\ddot{x}_c = 1.82 \text{ ft/sec}^2$$

Thus, it is seen that by ignoring the rotary motion of the wheels, the linear acceleration of the cart can be calculated to within roughly 10 percent of the true value. This approximation becomes better when the weight of the cart becomes much larger than the weight of the wheels and vice versa. Calculation of the percentage error in terms of the parameters of the system is given as an exercise.

Example 9–13. An open car door of mass m is swinging on its hinges. The automobile, in turn, is accelerating with a constant acceleration a, as shown in Fig. 9–29. Determine the angular acceleration of the door as a function of the acceleration of the automobile.

Solution: First draw a free-body diagram of the door. It is apparent that point A would make a good reference point for the moment equation, since the two unknown forces passing through point A would not appear in the moment equation. Then the reference axes are defined with the x axis in the direction of the moment of the body and the origin of the system at the point A. Since it is desired to de-

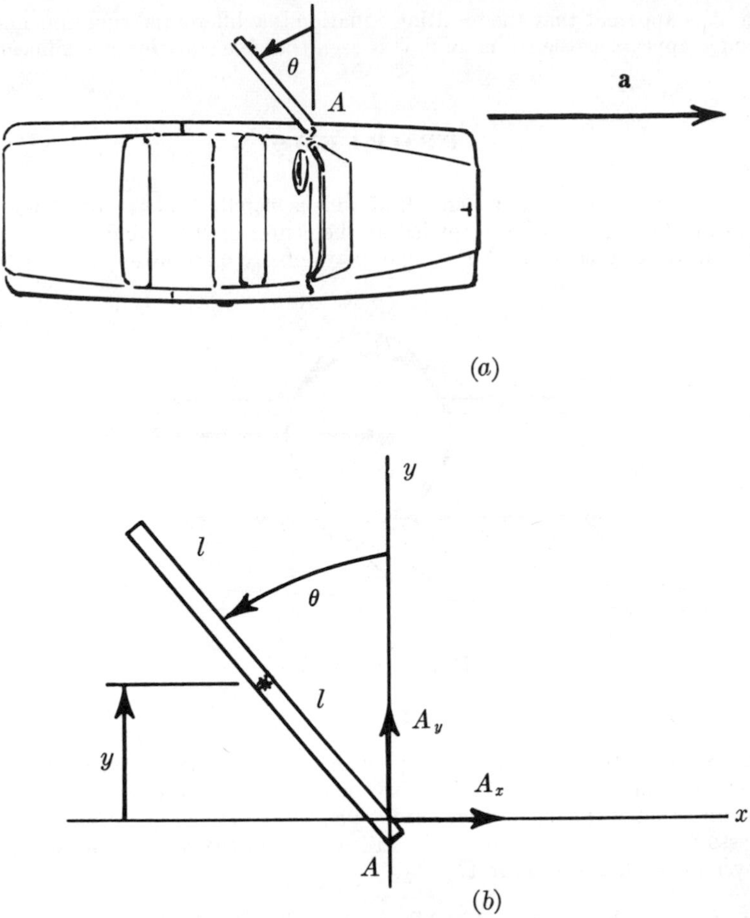

Figure 9-29

termine the angular acceleration of the door, the moment equation will be written first, since the angular acceleration appears in the moment equation:

$$M_A + ma_A y = I_A \dot{\omega}$$

The moment of all forces acting on the door about point A is equal to zero, so the moment equation becomes

$$ma_A(l \cos \theta) = I_A \dot{\omega}$$

Solving for the angular acceleration of the door,

$$\dot{\omega} \equiv \ddot{\theta} = \frac{ma_A(l \cos \theta)}{I_A}$$

Since the angular displacement θ appears in the equation for the angular acceleration, it is apparent that the resulting equation is a differential equation, and since the angle appears as the cosine of θ, it is seen that the equation is nonlinear.

PROBLEMS

9-37. The cylinder shown in Fig. P.9-37 weighs 96.6 lb and has a diameter of 3 ft. A constant force ***F*** of 20 lb is applied at the center of the cylinder. What will be the linear velocity of the center of mass of the body 6 sec after the system starts from rest?

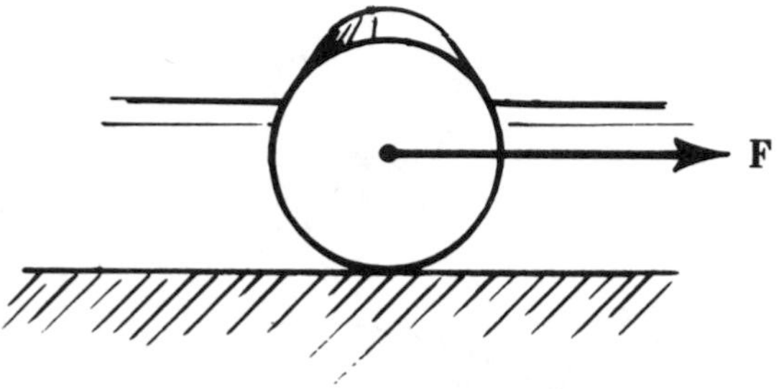

Figure Prob. 9-37

9-38. Suppose the cylinder of the preceding problem is placed on an inclined plane that makes an angle of 15 deg with the horizontal. If the same force is applied in the direction of the plane downward, what will be the acceleration of the center of mass of the body, and what will be the velocity of the center of mass 3 sec after the system is released from rest?

9-39. Suppose that the force ***F*** of 5 lb is applied 3 in. below the center of the wheels as shown in Fig. P.9-39. Determine the acceleration of the center of mass and the minimum coefficient of friction between the wheel and the ground so that the cylinder will not slip. The cylinder weighs 48.3 lb.

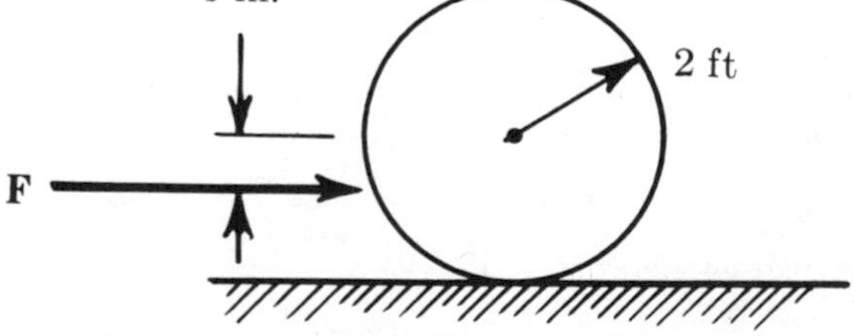

Figure Prob. 9-39

9-40. Consider a body moving in a plane. The x and y components of force and the moment about the z axis are all given as a function of time in a graphical fashion in Fig. P. 9-40. What is the angular acceleration and the linear acceleration of the body at $t = 3$ sec if the body weighs 36 lb and has a moment of inertia about its axis of rotation of 2.0 lb-sec²-ft?

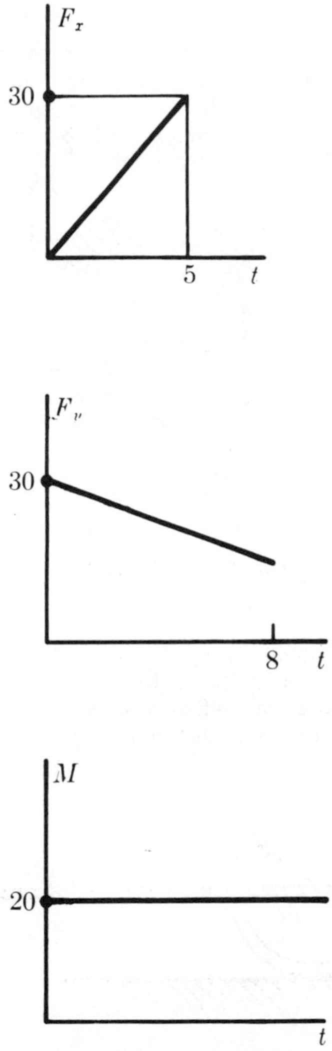

Figure Prob. 9-40

9-41. For Problem 9-40, sketch the velocity in the x and the y directions, assuming that the system starts from rest. Also sketch the angular velocity of the body as a function of time.

9-42. It is desired to determine the moment of inertia of a 32.2-lb object with circular symmetry about its axis of rotation. To do this, the body is allowed to roll down an inclined plane. The motion of the center of mass is a function of the moment of inertia. If the body is released from rest on a plane that makes an angle of 30 deg with the horizontal and is observed to have a velocity of 44 fps 4 sec after it is released, what is the moment of inertia of the body? The radius of the body is 3 ft.

9-43. It is desired to determine the moment of inertia of a body weighing 40 lb and having circular symmetry about its axis of rotation. To do this, a cord is wrapped around the body and attached to a rigid support. When the body is released, it is observed to have an acceleration of 18 ft/sec². What is the moment of inertia of the body about its axis of rotation?

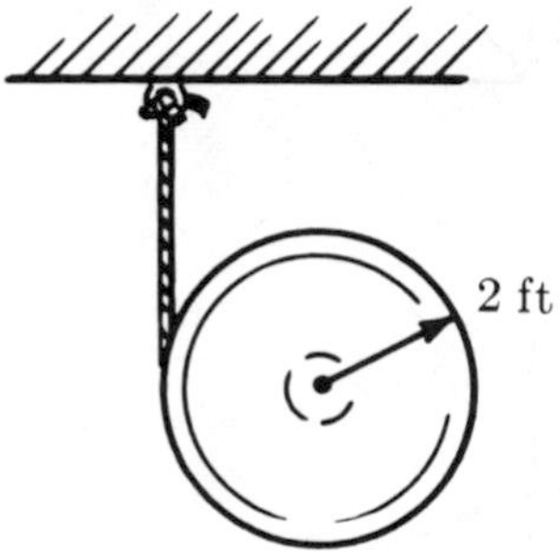

Figure Prob. 9-43

9-44. If the mass of the cylinder in Fig. P.9-44 is M and the mass of the block is m, show that the acceleration of the center of mass of the cylinder is equal to $g/(1.5M/m + 1)$. Assume that the coefficient of friction is large enough so that the cylinder does not slip with respect to the plane.

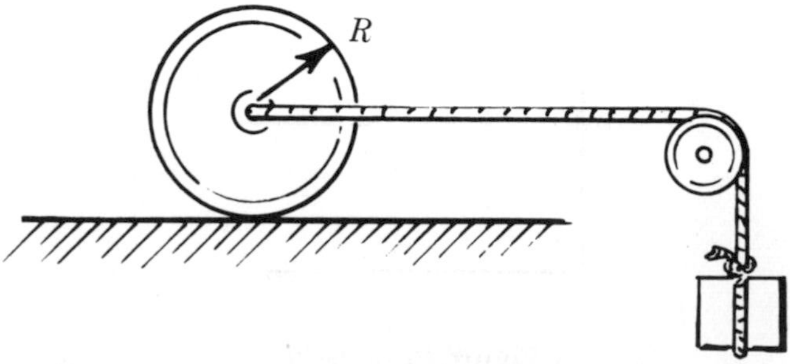

Figure Prob. 9-44

9-45. Using the results of Problem 9-44, determine the minimum coefficient of friction required between the cylinder and the surface so that the cylinder does not slide. The cylinder has a weight of 80 lb and a radius of 4.0 ft. The weight is equal to 24 lb.

9-46. A cord is wound upon a spool of weight 48.3 lb and radius 3 ft, as shown in Fig. P.9-46. If a constant force F of 10 lb is applied to the rope, what will the acceleration of the spool be? Will the spool move to the right or to the left? The moment of inertia of the spool about its axis of rotation is 6.0 lb-sec²/ft. Assume that the spool does not slip.

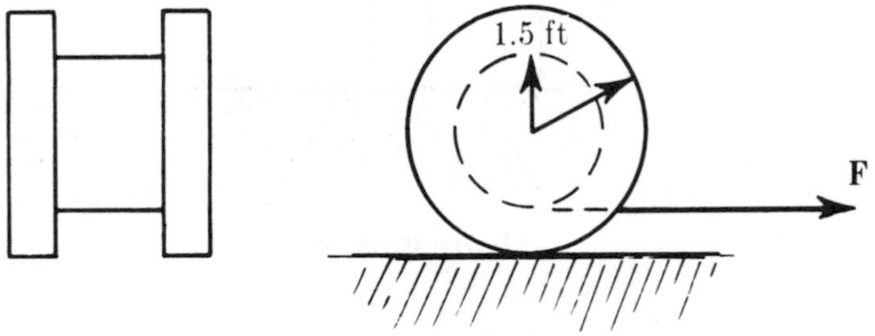

Figure Prob. 9-46

9-47. Consider Problem 9-46. What is the maximum force F that can be applied to the spool if the spool is not to slip? The coefficient of friction between the surfaces is 0.20.

9-48. Write the equation of motion of the beam shown in Fig. P.9-48. Assume that the system is constrained so that the center of mass of the beam is allowed to translate only in the vertical direction. This implies that the force equation for the x direction is redundant, so that there are only two equations of motion. Measure the vertical displacement from the equilibrium position of the bar, and note that the force in the springs at this point is not zero.

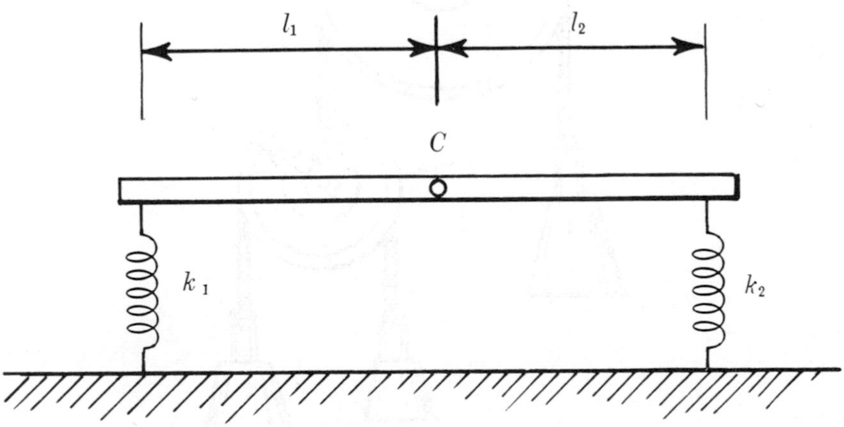

Figure Prob. 9-48

9-49. Consider an 8000-lb, 30-ft missile, which is traveling free from any gravitation force and is accelerating under the action of the thrust force T of the engines.

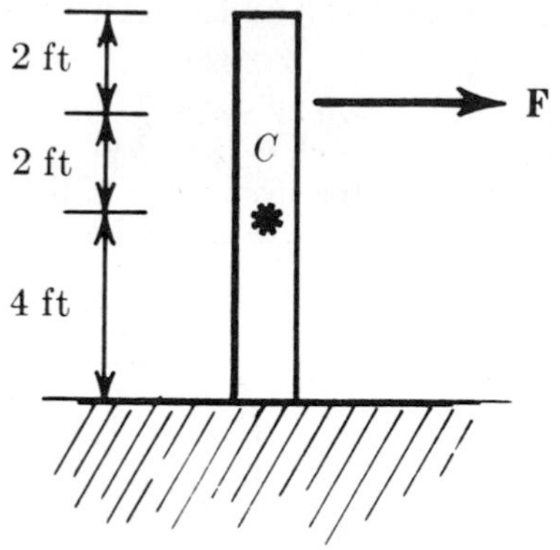

Figure Prob. 9-50

Determine the response of the missile due to a thrust misalignment, that is, what is the angular acceleration of the rocket as a function of θ (degrees) if θ is the angle between $\boldsymbol{T}$ and the longitudinal axis of the missile? In calculating the moment inertia of the missile, consider the missile as a long slender rod.

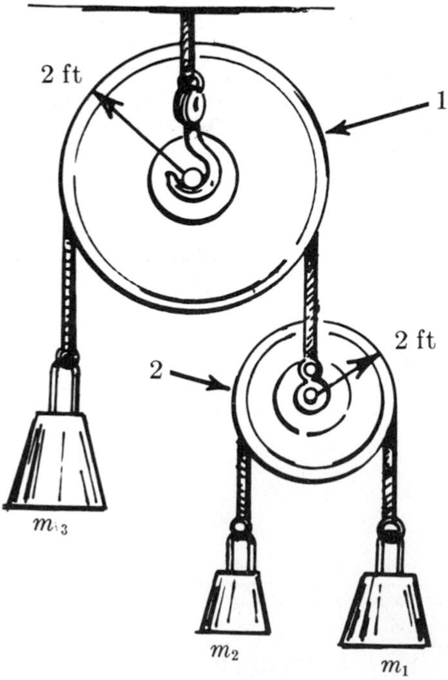

Figure Prob. 9-51

9-50. The 60-lb rod is resting in an upright position on a smooth surface. At $t = 0$, a force $\boldsymbol{F}$ of 10 lb is applied as shown in Fig. P.9-50. What is the acceleration of the center of mass of the body and the angular acceleration of the body at this instant of time? Assume that μ_k is large enough so that the body does not slip at contact.

9-51. If the system shown in Fig. P.9-51 is released from rest, what will be the acceleration of each mass? Each pulley weighs 64.4 lb; block 1 weighs 48.3 lb, and blocks 2 and 3 each weigh 32.2 lb.

9-52. Examine the stability of the two systems shown in Fig. P.9-52. This can be done by first writing the equations of motion for each, then assuming a small displacement so that the differential equations of motion become linear ($\sin\theta = \theta$), and then solving the equations. The solutions show when the system is stable. The applied forces $\boldsymbol{F}$ are always horizontal. This problem should not be attempted by anyone lacking knowledge of the solution of differential equations.

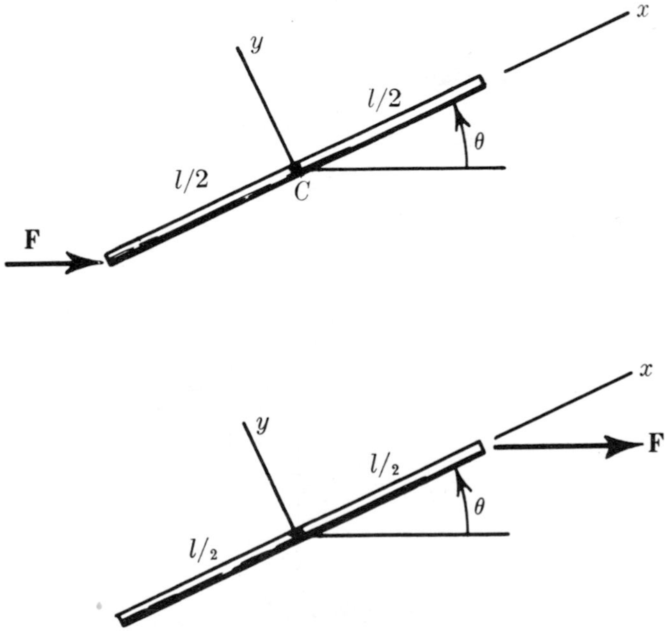

Figure Prob. 9-52

9-53. Shown in Fig. P.9-53 is a schematic diagram of a cart. Each of the wheels has a mass of $m/2$, and the mass of the bed of the cart is M. The acceleration of the cart under the action of the force $\boldsymbol{F}$ may be approximated by assuming that the system moves as a unit and by using the force equation only for the whole system. This approach does not take into account the dynamical effects caused by inertia of the wheels. Show that the error introduced in assuming that the system moves as a unit is $m/2(M + m)$.

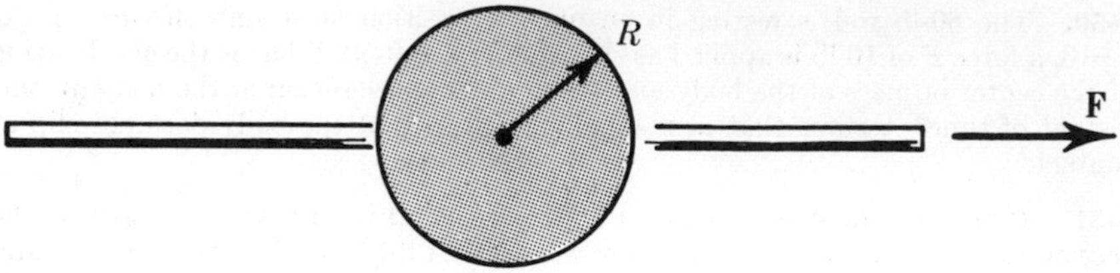

Figure Prob. 9-53

9-54. Shown in Fig. P.9-54 is a schematic diagram of a small motorized cart. The cart weighs 250 lb, and each of the wheels weighs 30 lb. What moment is required for the back wheels to make the cart accelerate with an acceleration of 4.0 ft/sec^2?

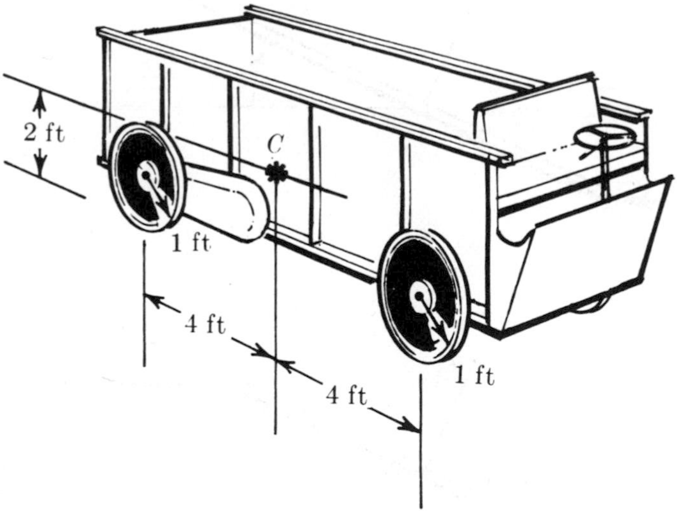

Figure Prob. 9-54

9-4. THE IMPULSE-MOMENTUM AND WORK-ENERGY EQUATIONS FOR A RIGID BODY

The impulse-momentum equations. Consider first the moment equation of motion for a rigid body:

$$M = \dot{H} \tag{9.23}$$

Integrating this equation with respect to time,

$$\int_A^B \mathbf{M}\,dt = \int_A^B \left(\frac{d}{dt}\right) \mathbf{H}\,dt \tag{9.24}$$

Then

$$\boxed{\int_A^B \mathbf{M}\,dt = \mathbf{H}_B - \mathbf{H}_A} \tag{9.25}$$

This, then, is the impulse-momentum equation for the moment equation for a rigid body. The impulse-momentum equation derived from the force equation was established in Chapter 6. From Eq. 6.13,

$$\int_A^B \mathbf{F}\,dt = m\mathbf{v}_{c_B} - m\mathbf{v}_{c_A} \tag{9.26}$$

These two equations may then be employed to advantage in analyzing the motion of rigid bodies in the cases where it is desired to determine the angular velocity and the force is given as a function of time.

If the body is restricted to move in the xy plane, only the z component of the moment equation contains the terms describing the motion of the body. Then, Eq. 9.25 reduces to

$$\int_A^B M_z\,dt = H_{z_B} - H_{z_A} \tag{9.27}$$

Since the angular velocity of the body about the x and y axes is equal to zero, the moment of momentum is simply equal to $I\omega$, so that

$$\int_A^B M\,dt = I\omega_B - I\omega_A \tag{9.28}$$

Here it must be understood that both the moment and the moment of inertia must be referred to a point that is fixed either in space or in the moving center of mass of the body. This was the assumption that was required in order to write Eq. 9.23 in the first place.

Example 9–14. The large flywheel shown in Fig. 9-30 weighs 1000 lb and is rotating in a horizontal plane. Its angular velocity is controlled by a rocket attached to the wheel. At $t = 0$, the rocket is fired and the thrust force exerted by the engine is a function of time, as shown in Fig. 9-30. What will be the angular velocity (rpm) of the wheel at $t = 10$ sec if the angular velocity of the wheel at $t = 0$ is 40 rpm?

Solution: Since the force (and thus the moment) is given as a function of time, and since it is desired to determine the change in the angular velocity of a rigid body, it appears that the impulse-momentum equation may be the best approach:

$$\int_A^B M_O\,dt = I_O\omega_B - I_O\omega_A$$

The equation is referred to the fixed point in the system, that is, the axis of rotation, which, incidentally, coincides with the center of mass of the disk in this case.

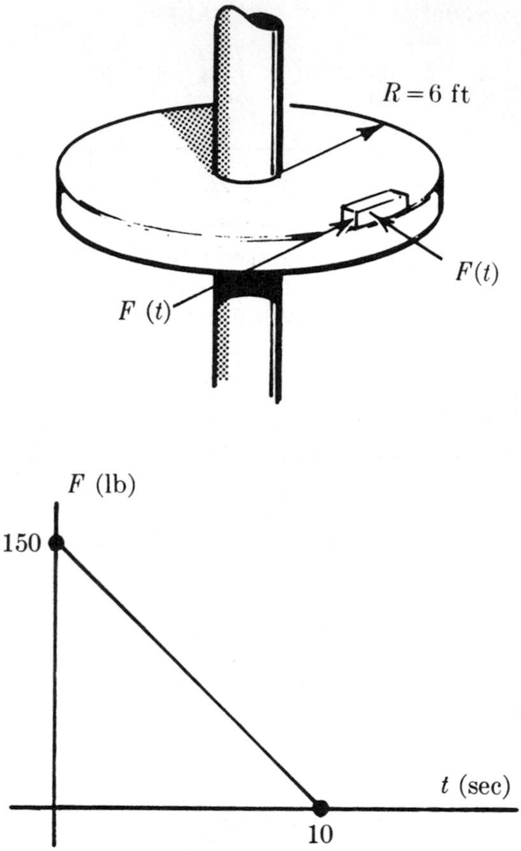

Figure 9-30

First of all, the moment of inertia of the body must be evaluated. The moment of inertia of the flywheel about its axis is equal to $\frac{1}{2}mR^2$. Thus,

$$I_O = \frac{1}{2}\left(\frac{1000}{32.2}\right)(6)^2$$
$$= 558 \text{ lb-sec}^2\text{-ft}$$

The impulse moment may be written as

$$\int_0^{10} M\,dt = \int F(t)R\,dt$$
$$= (6)[\tfrac{1}{2}(150)(10)]$$
$$= 4500 \text{ lb-ft-sec}$$

Hence the impulse-momentum equation for the moment equation becomes

$$4500 = (558)\omega_B - (558)\left(\frac{2\pi}{60}\right)(40)$$

Solving for the angular velocity of the body after 10 sec,

$$\omega_B = 12.6 \text{ radians/sec}$$

or

$$\omega_B = 120 \text{ rpm}$$

The work-energy equation. The work-energy equation for a system of particles was discussed in Chapter 6, where it was pointed out that the work done by all forces acting on the system of particles as the system moves from one configuration to another is equal to the change in kinetic energy of the system:

$$W_{AB} = T_B - T_A \tag{9.29}$$

It was emphasized at the time that the work done on the system is equal to the work done by both external and internal forces. In the case of a rigid body, there will be no work done by any of the internal forces in the body because none of the particles moves relative to another. We shall, however, be interested in the work done by the external forces on the system in moving the center of mass of the body, which is equal to

$$W_{AB} = \int_a^B \boldsymbol{F} \cdot d\boldsymbol{r}_c \tag{9.30}$$

We shall also be interested in the work done on a rigid body by a couple. If the moment of a couple is equal to $\boldsymbol{M}$, it is shown that

$$W_{AB} = \int_A^B \boldsymbol{M} \cdot d\boldsymbol{\theta} \tag{9.31}$$

Since the internal forces in a rigid body do no work, and all external forces on a rigid body may be replaced by a force and couple at the center of mass of the moving body, the general form of the work for a rigid body may be expressed as

$$\boxed{W_{AB} = \int_A^B \boldsymbol{F} \cdot d\boldsymbol{r}_c + \int_A^B \boldsymbol{M} \cdot d\boldsymbol{\theta}} \tag{9.32}$$

We shall now attempt to obtain a convenient form for the kinetic energy of a rigid body. The approach we take will be similar to that used extensively in the discussion of the motions of systems of particles. That is, we shall write the kinetic energy for a single particle (or in this case, an increment of mass of the body) and then perform a summation of the kinetic energy over the body.

The kinetic energy dT for the element of mass dm, shown in Fig. 9–31, is given as

$$dT = \tfrac{1}{2}v^2\, dm \tag{9.33}$$

The total kinetic energy of the body may be obtained by summing over the body. The summation may be performed by an integration:

$$T = \int \tfrac{1}{2}v^2\, dm \tag{9.34}$$

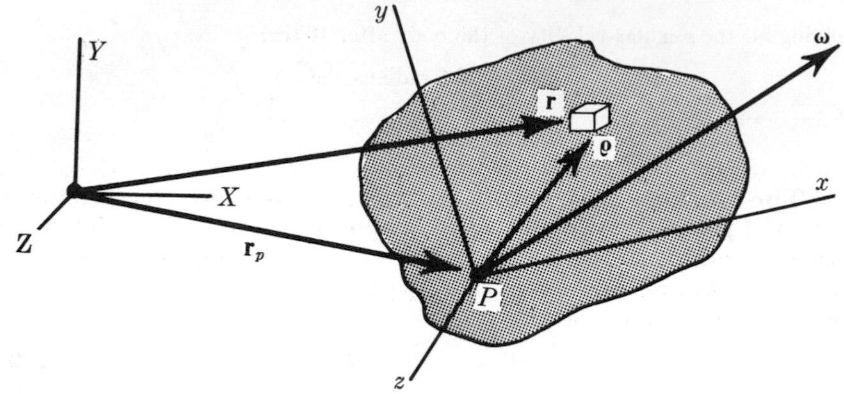

Figure 9-31

But

$$v^2 = \boldsymbol{v}\cdot\boldsymbol{v} \tag{9.35}$$

and since

$$\boldsymbol{r} = \boldsymbol{r}_P + \boldsymbol{\rho} \tag{9.36}$$

it follows that

$$\boldsymbol{v} = \boldsymbol{v}_P + \dot{\boldsymbol{\rho}} \tag{9.37}$$

so that the kinetic energy may be written as

$$T = \int \tfrac{1}{2}(\boldsymbol{v}_P\cdot\boldsymbol{v}_P)\,dm + \int (\boldsymbol{v}_P\cdot\dot{\boldsymbol{\rho}})\,dm + \int \tfrac{1}{2}(\dot{\boldsymbol{\rho}}\cdot\dot{\boldsymbol{\rho}})\,dm \tag{9.38}$$

or

$$T = \tfrac{1}{2}mv_P^2 + \tfrac{1}{2}\int \dot{\rho}^2\,dm + \int (\boldsymbol{v}_P\cdot\dot{\boldsymbol{\rho}})\,dm \tag{9.39}$$

Note that the last term of Eq. 9.39 is equal to zero in the case that:

1. The reference point P is chosen as a fixed point in the system, in which case $\boldsymbol{v}_P$ would be equal to zero.
2. The reference point P is chosen as the center of mass of the body, so that the integral of $\boldsymbol{v}_c \cdot \dfrac{d}{dt}\displaystyle\int \boldsymbol{\rho}\,dm$ would be equal to zero.

For the general motion of the body, there is no fixed point in the body; therefore the reference axes should be taken at the center of mass of the body, in which case the kinetic energy of the body becomes

$$T = \tfrac{1}{2}mv_C^2 + \tfrac{1}{2}\int \dot{\rho}^2\,dm \tag{9.40}$$

where ρ is measured from the center of mass of the body.

If there is one point in the body that is fixed, then the kinetic energy of the body may be written as

$$T = \int \tfrac{1}{2}\dot{\rho}^2\,dm \tag{9.41}$$

where now the vector $\boldsymbol{\rho}$ is measured from the fixed point.

If the angular velocity of the body were given, it is obvious that the velocity $\dot{\boldsymbol{\rho}}$ of any of the elemental particles of the body may be written as a function of the angular velocity. Since the vector $\boldsymbol{\rho}$ to the particle is not changing its length, it has a time derivative only by virtue of the fact that it is changing direction, and it is changing direction because the body has an angular velocity.

We shall now attempt to write the expression $\int \frac{1}{2}\dot{\rho}^2\, dm$ in terms of the angular velocity of the body. First note that

$$\dot{\rho}^2 = \dot{\boldsymbol{\rho}} \cdot \dot{\boldsymbol{\rho}} \tag{9.42}$$

Since $\boldsymbol{\rho}$ is a vector of constant length, which is rotating with an angular velocity of $\boldsymbol{\omega}$, the first time derivative of $\boldsymbol{\rho}$ may be evaluated by taking the indicated cross-product:

$$\dot{\boldsymbol{\rho}} = \boldsymbol{\omega} \times \boldsymbol{\rho} \tag{9.43}$$

Thus,

$$\dot{\rho}^2 = (\boldsymbol{\omega} \times \boldsymbol{\rho}) \cdot (\boldsymbol{\omega} \times \boldsymbol{\rho}) \tag{9.44}$$

Both $\boldsymbol{\rho}$ and $\boldsymbol{\omega}$ may be expressed in terms of their Cartesian components. Then, upon substitution into Eq. 9.41,

$$\begin{aligned} \dot{\rho}^2 = {} & z^2\omega_y^2 - 2yz\omega_y\omega_z + y^2\omega_z^2 + x^2\omega_z^2 - 2xz\omega_x\omega_z \\ & + z^2\omega_x^2 + y^2\omega_x^2 - 2xy\omega_y\omega_x + x^2\omega_y^2 \end{aligned} \tag{9.45}$$

Upon substituting the value of $\dot{\rho}^2$ into the expression for the kinetic energy (Eq. 9.44), the kinetic energy of the body relative to the center of mass of the body may be written as

$$\begin{aligned} \int \tfrac{1}{2}\dot{\rho}^2\, dm = {} & \tfrac{1}{2}[I_{xx}\omega_x^2 + I_{yy}\omega_y^2 + I_{zz}\omega_z^2 \\ & - 2I_{xy}\omega_x\omega_y - 2I_{xz}\omega_x\omega_z - 2I_{yz}\omega_y\omega_z] \end{aligned} \tag{9.46}$$

The term on the right-hand side may be written simply as

$$\tfrac{1}{2}\boldsymbol{H} \cdot \boldsymbol{\omega}$$

This relationship may be verified by expanding the dot product. Thus, the total kinetic energy of the system may be written as

$$\boxed{T = \tfrac{1}{2}mv_c^2 + \tfrac{1}{2}\boldsymbol{H} \cdot \boldsymbol{\omega}} \tag{9.47}$$

If the rigid body is constrained to move in the xy plane, then the angular velocity of the body about the x and y axes will be zero. Also, the velocity of the body in the z direction will be zero. Then the kinetic energy of the body may be written as

$$T = \tfrac{1}{2}m\dot{x}_c^2 + \tfrac{1}{2}m\dot{y}_c^2 + \tfrac{1}{2}I\omega^2 \tag{9.48}$$

where it is understood that the moment of inertia, I, is the moment of inertia of the body about a z axis passing through the center of mass of the body.

If the body is rotating in a plane about a fixed point (that is, the body is rotating about a fixed axis, which is in the z direction), then the kinetic energy of the body is simply

$$T = \tfrac{1}{2}I\omega^2 \tag{9.49}$$

where now it is understood that the moment of inertia, I, is the moment of inertia of the body about the fixed point or axis of rotation.

Example 9–15. The 20-lb ball shown in Fig. 9-32 is rolled with a velocity of 5.0 fps into the 30-lb bar that is pinned at its upper end. The rebound velocity of

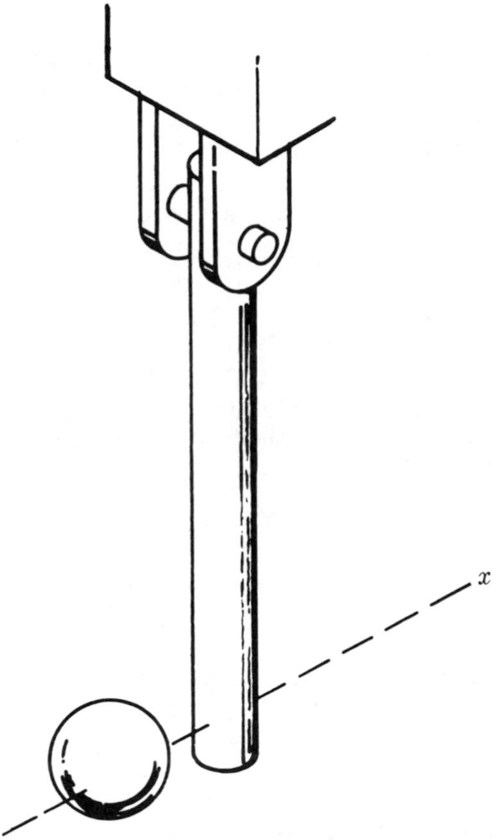

Figure 9-32

the ball is observed to be 4.0 fps. Through what angle will the bar swing after the impact? The bar is four feet long.

Solution: Using the impulse-momentum equation for a single particle, the impulse of the bar on the ball may be evaluated:

$$\int_A^B F\,dt = m\dot{x}_B - m\dot{x}_A$$

$$= \frac{20}{32.2}[-5.0 - (4.0)]$$

$$= -5.58 \text{ lb-sec.}$$

The minus sign indicates that the impulse of the bar on the ball is in the negative x direction. By Newton's third law, it follows that the impulse of the ball on the bar is equal to 5.58 lb-sec. By using the impulse-momentum equation for the moment equation, the angular velocity of the bar directly after the impact may be determined as

$$\int_B^C M\,dt = I_O\omega_c - I_O\omega_B$$

This impulse-momentum equation is referred to the fixed point O. Since the bar is at rest before the impulse, the angular velocity ω_B will be zero. The impulse moment is equal to

$$\int M\,dt = 5.58(4)$$
$$= 22.3 \text{ lb-sec-ft}$$

From Appendix I it is seen that the moment of inertia of a long slender bar about a point at the end of the bar is equal to $\frac{1}{3}mL^2$. Thus,

$$I_O = \frac{1}{3}\left(\frac{30}{32.2}\right)(4)^2$$

$$= 4.97 \text{ lb-sec}^2\text{-ft}$$

and it follows that

$$22.3 = 4.97\omega_c$$

Solving for the angular velocity of the bar after the impact,

$$\omega = 4.48 \text{ radians/sec}$$

The angle through which the bar will rotate may be determined by use of the work-energy equation for a rigid body:

$$W_{CD} = T_D - T_C$$

The only force on the bar as the bar swings upward is the gravitational force acting through the center of mass of the bar. The motion of the center of mass of the bar is described in Fig. 9-33. The work done by the gravitational force as the bar moves from its vertical position to some angle θ is

$$W_{CD} = -W\left(\frac{l}{2}\right)(l - \cos\theta)$$

so that the work-energy equation becomes

$$\frac{-30(4)}{2}(l - \cos\theta) = \frac{-1}{2}(4.97)(4.48)^2$$

and, solving for the cosine of θ,

$$\cos\theta = 0.165$$

Then, solving for θ, it is seen that θ is equal to roughly 80 deg.

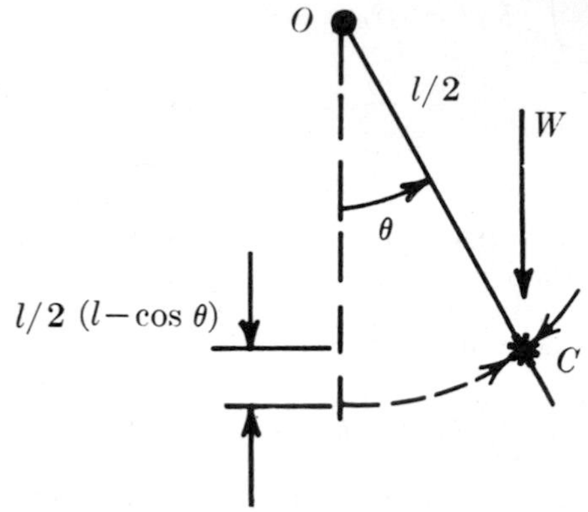

Figure 9-33

Example 9–16. A large flywheel weighs 1200 lb and has a radius of 8 ft. What constant moment must be applied to the wheel about its axis of rotation so that the angular velocity of the flywheel is equal to 30 rpm in six revolutions after the wheel starts from rest?

Solution: The work-energy equation may be employed in this case, since the desired angular velocity is contained in the expression for the kinetic energy, and the work done on the body is easily calculated:

$$W_{AB} = T_B - T_A$$
$$= \int_A^B M\, d\theta$$
$$= M\theta$$
$$M[2\pi(6)]$$

The only work done on the system is that done by the moment. The kinetic energy at the beginning of the process, point A, is equal to zero, since the system started from rest. The kinetic energy at B is equal to

$$T_B = \tfrac{1}{2}I\omega^2$$

The moment of inertia of the wheel about its axis of rotation is equal to $\frac{1}{2}mR^2$, or

$$I = \frac{1}{2}\left(\frac{1200}{32.2}\right)(8)^2$$
$$= 1190 \text{ lb-sec}^2\text{-ft}$$

Therefore the work-energy equation becomes

$$12\pi M = 1190\left[\left(\frac{2\pi}{60}\right)(30)\right]^2$$

and, solving for the moment,

$$M = 312 \text{ ft-lb}$$

PROBLEMS

9-55. For a given rigid body, the xyz axes are given as the principal axes. The moment of inertia about the x, y, and z axes, respectively, is equal to 6, 4, and 3. If at $t = 0$, a moment given as $M(t) = 3t\bar{i} - 4\bar{j} + 3t^2\bar{k}$ is applied to the body, what is the angular velocity of the body at $t = 2$ sec? The angular velocity of the body at $t = 0$ is $\boldsymbol{\omega}_0 = 2\bar{i} + 4\bar{j} - 6\bar{k}$.

9-56. The armature of a large electric motor is shown schematically in Fig. P.9-56. The 100-lb armature is spinning with an angular velocity of 200 rpm when an impulse moment tending to decrease the speed of the armature is applied. The moment as a function of time is given in the figure. What is the angular velocity (in rpm) of the armature after the impulse has been applied? The radius of the armature is 1.2 ft.

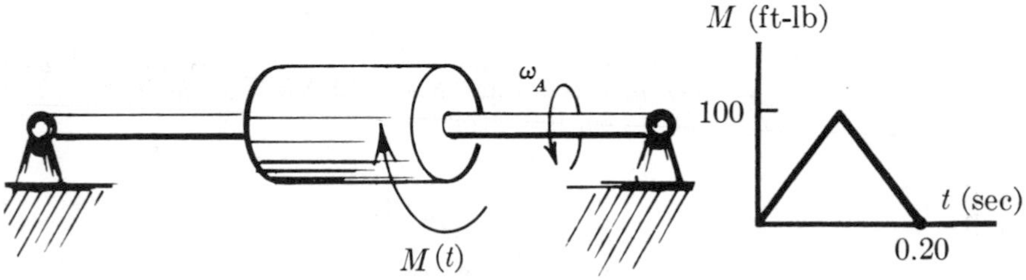

Figure Prob. 9-56

9-57. The body shown in Fig. P.9-57 has the xyz axes oriented as the principal axes of the body. At the instant shown, the angular velocity of the body is equal to $\boldsymbol{\omega} = -3\bar{i} + 4\bar{j}$, and this is the instant that an impulse force $F(t)$ is applied. The force acts only for one-hundredth of a second, but has a constant magnitude during that time of 1000 lb. What is the angular velocity of the body immediately after the impact? The moments of inertia about the x, y, and z axes, respectively, are 2, 7, and 5 lb-sec^2-ft.

9-58. A ballistic pendulum is made of a 10-ft 4×4 beam weighing 20 lb. The pendulum is pinned at one end and allowed to hang in a vertical position. If a shell weighing 0.20 lb is fired into the pendulum 2 ft from the bottom, and the pendulum is observed to rotate through an angle of 15 deg, what is the velocity of the shell?

9-59. The propeller shown in Fig. P.9-59 can be thought of as composed of four long, thin bars, each weighing 10 lb. What is the magnitude of the constant moment that must be applied to the system so that the angular velocity of the propeller is 500 rpm after 20 revolutions?

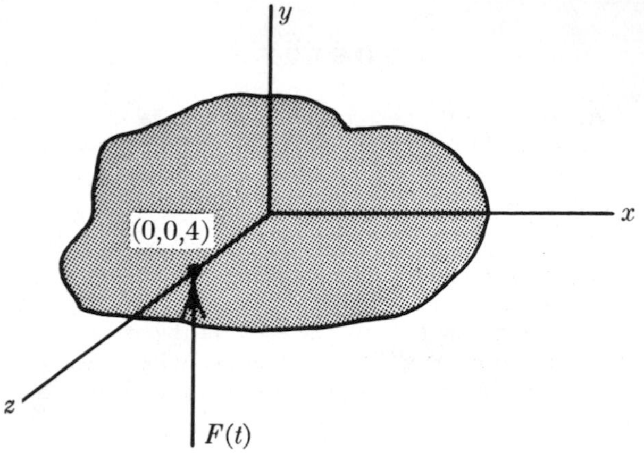

Figure Prob. 9-57

9-60. Consider the system of the preceding problem. What constant moment must be applied to the body about its axis of rotation so that it will accelerate from rest to an angular velocity of 50 rpm in 100 revolutions?

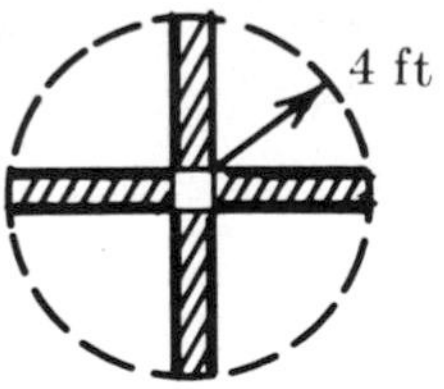

Figure Prob. 9-59

9-61. A constant moment of 20 ft-lb is applied to the system shown in Fig. P.9-61. What will be the angular velocity of the system after it moves through 100 revolutions? Each block on the ends weighs 20 lb, and the bar weighs 10 lb.

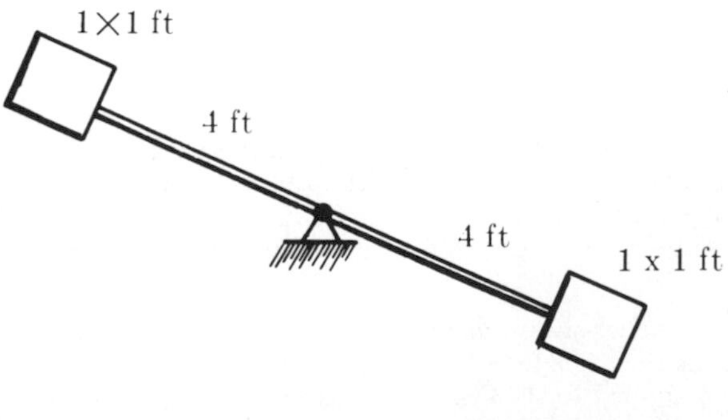

Figure Prob. 9-61

9-62. The moment that is applied to the system shown in Fig. P.9-62 is given as a function of the angular displacement. If the system starts from rest, what will be the angular velocity of the system after it makes a total of 100 revolutions? The weight of the body is 80 lb.

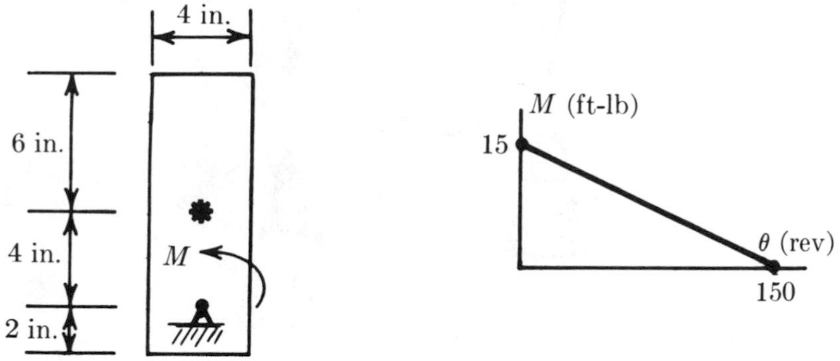

Figure Prob. 9-62

9-63. The system shown in Fig. P.9-63 is released from rest. The weight of the flywheel is equal to 26 lb, and the weight of the mass is 90 lb. What is the velocity of the 90-lb block after it falls through a distance of 4 ft?

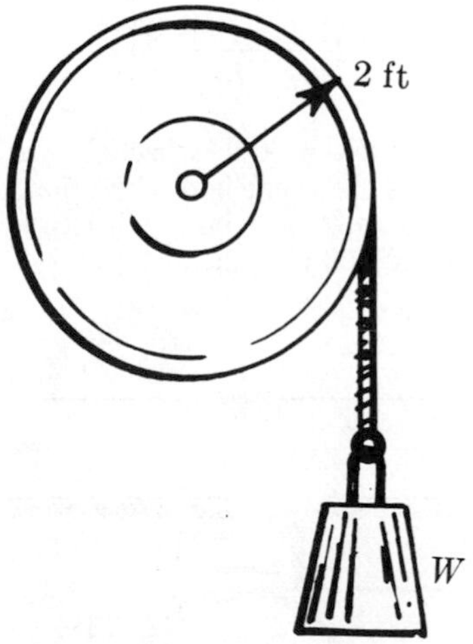

Figure Prob. 9-63

9-64. The system shown in Fig. P.9-64 is released from rest. What is the velocity of W_1 after it falls through a distance of 5.0 ft? The weight of the flywheel is equal to 60 lb, and W_1 and W_2 are respectively equal to 55 and 40 lb.

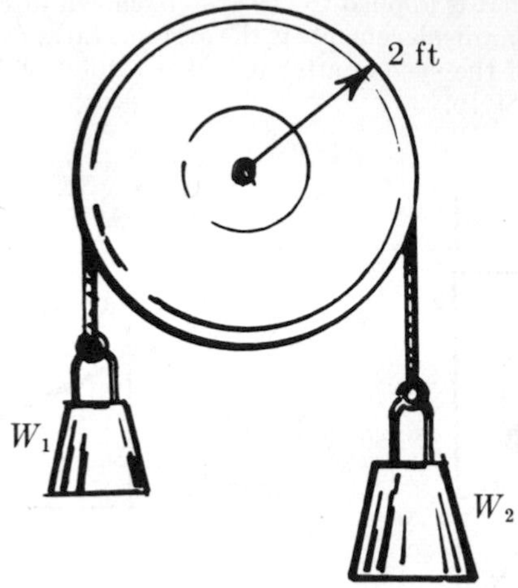

Figure Prob. 9-64

9-65. A long, slender bar of mass m and length L, is placed in an upright position. Since the body is unstable, it will tend to fall over, owing to gravitational force. Assuming that the frictional force between the bar and the surface is large enough so that no slipping occurs, show that the angular velocity of the bar as a function of the angle from the measured vertical is equal to

$$\left\{\frac{3g(1-\cos\theta)}{L}\right\}^{1/2}$$

9-66. The angular velocity of the 50-lb wheel shown in Fig. P.9-66 is 500 rpm before the brake is applied. If the coefficient of friction between the brake and the wheel is 0.30, how much pressure must be applied to the brake if the wheel is to come to rest after making only 20 revolutions?

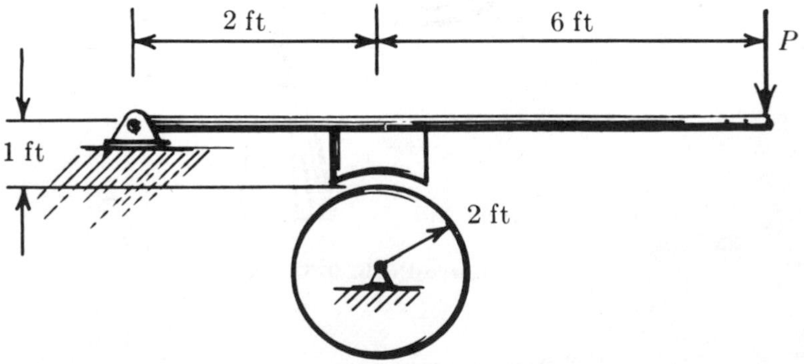

Figure Prob. 9-66

9-67. Using the work-energy theorem, determine the angular velocity of the body shown in Fig. P.9-67 as it passes position B. The body was released from rest in position A and falls under the action of the gravitational force. The weight of the block is 20 lb and the weight of the bar is 10 lb.

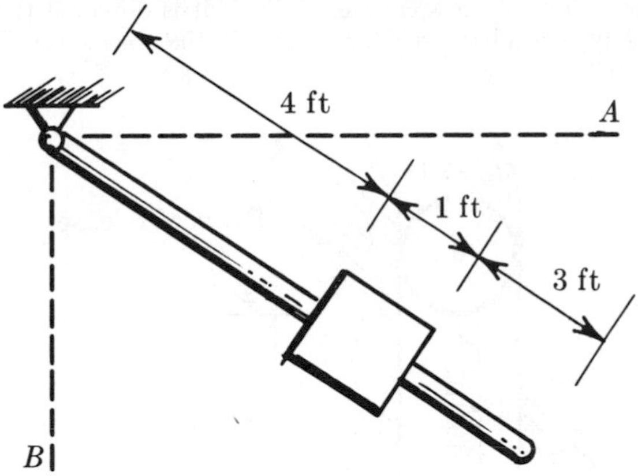

Figure Prob. 9-67

9-68. A flywheel weighing 100 lb and having a radius of 4 ft is rotating with an angular velocity of 200 rpm when it is suddenly engaged by means of a clutch to a mechanism that lifts a block weighing 50 lb. How far will the flywheel lift the block before it has expended its energy and comes to a rest? The pulley lifting the weight may be assumed to be weightless.

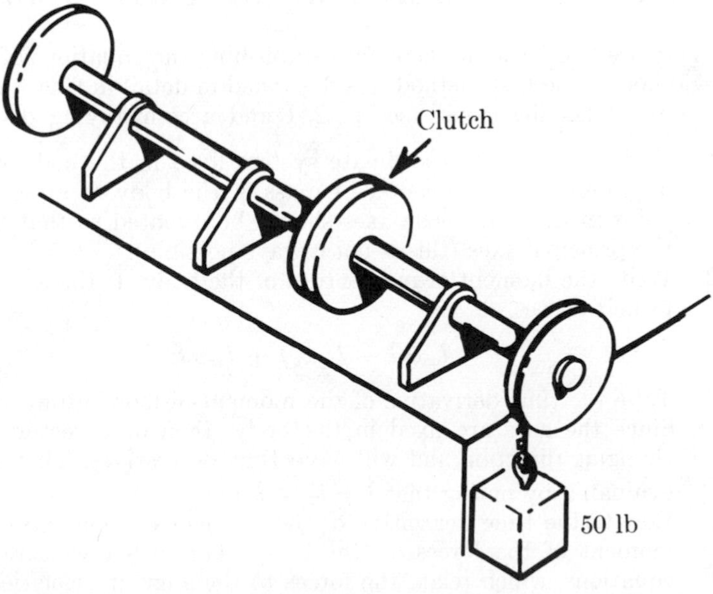

Figure Prob. 9-68

9-69. A spring-loaded mechanism fires a spherical object upward. The line of action of the spring force does not pass exactly through the center of mass of the body; as a result, the body has an angular velocity as it moves upward. The system is fired in the position shown in Fig. P.9-69. The unstretched length of the spring is 20 in., and the weight of the sphere is 10 lb. If it is observed that the angular velocity of the body is 6 radians/sec, how high will the object rise? The spring has a stiffness of 80 lb/ft.

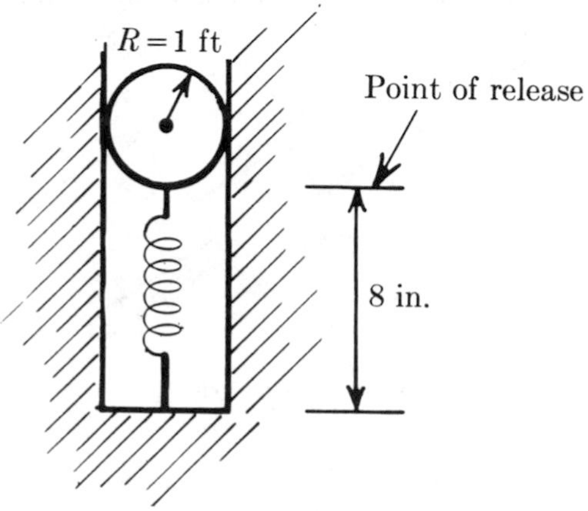

Figure Prob. 9-69

9-5. THE GENERAL MOTION OF A RIGID BODY

There are two basic methods for establishing the equations of motion of a rigid body. The first method was described in detail in Chapter 8, and involves the following steps: (see p. 231 and accompanying discussion)

1. Define a reference coordinate system fixed in the body with the origin either at the center of mass of the body or at some fixed point in the body. The axes should be oriented so that they are the principal axes (this is not always possible).
2. Write the moment of momentum of the body. If the axes are the principal axes,

$$\boldsymbol{H} = I_{xx}\omega_x\bar{\boldsymbol{i}} + I_{yy}\omega_y\bar{\boldsymbol{j}} + I_{zz}\omega_z\bar{\boldsymbol{k}} \tag{9.50}$$

3. Take the time derivative of the moment-of-momentum equation. Since the axes are fixed in the body, then unit vectors will be changing direction and will have time derivatives. They may be evaluated by noting that $\dot{\bar{\boldsymbol{i}}} = \boldsymbol{\omega} \times \bar{\boldsymbol{i}}$, etc.
4. Equate the time derivative of the moment of momentum to the moment of the forces on the body. This will give three scalar equations, which relate the forces to the angular velocities of the body.

The second method that can be used is just a direct application of the results of the method outlined above. If the procedure indicated is carried out for a body whose reference axes are the principal axes, then the resulting equations will be

$$\boxed{\begin{aligned} M_x &= I_{xx}\dot{\omega}_x + (I_{zz} - I_{yy})\omega_y\omega_z \\ M_y &= I_{yy}\dot{\omega}_y + (I_{xx} - I_{zz})\omega_x\omega_z \\ M_z &= I_{zz}\dot{\omega}_z + (I_{yy} - I_{xx})\omega_x\omega_y \end{aligned}} \tag{9.51}$$

These equations are called *Euler's equations for the motion of a rigid body.*

Both approaches will be employed in the subsequent examples.

Example 9–17. The large turntable shown in Fig. 9-34 is rotating with a constant angular velocity of $\dot{\psi}$ in the direction shown. In turn, the small disk is spinning on its axis, AB, with a constant angular velocity of $\dot{\phi}$. If the system is moving in this

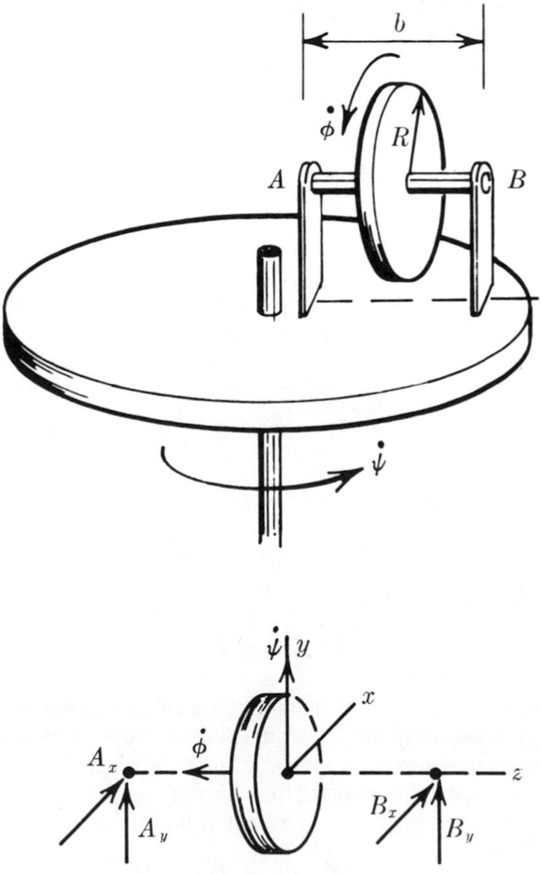

Figure 9-34

direction, what is the force that the bearings A and B must exert on the spinning disk?

Solution: A free-body diagram of the spinning disk is shown in Fig. 9-34. The axes shown are fixed in the body and have the orientation shown at this instant of time. They are the principal axes. The total angular velocity of the disk is a combination of the angular velocity due to the spin of the disk and the angular velocity due to the spin of the turntable. The moment of momentum of the body is

$$\boldsymbol{H} = I_{xx}\omega_x\bar{\boldsymbol{i}} + I_{yy}\omega_y\bar{\boldsymbol{j}} + I_{zz}\omega_z\bar{\boldsymbol{k}}$$

At this instant, the angular velocity of spin about the x, y, and z axes are zero, $\dot{\psi}$ and $-\dot{\phi}$, respectively. Thus, the moment of momentum of the body becomes

$$\boldsymbol{H} = I_{yy}\dot{\psi}\bar{\boldsymbol{j}} - I_{zz}\dot{\phi}\bar{\boldsymbol{k}}$$

The time derivative of the moment of momentum is

$$\dot{\boldsymbol{H}} = I_{yy}\dot{\psi}\dot{\bar{\boldsymbol{j}}} - I_{zz}\dot{\phi}\dot{\bar{\boldsymbol{k}}}$$

The angular velocities $\dot{\psi}$ and $\dot{\phi}$ are constant.

The time derivatives of the unit vectors $\bar{\boldsymbol{j}}$ and $\bar{\boldsymbol{k}}$ may be determined by taking the following cross-products:

$$\dot{\bar{\boldsymbol{j}}} = \boldsymbol{\omega} \times \bar{\boldsymbol{j}}$$
$$\dot{\bar{\boldsymbol{k}}} = \boldsymbol{\omega} \times \bar{\boldsymbol{k}}$$

The angular velocity of the body is

$$\boldsymbol{\omega} = \dot{\psi}\bar{\boldsymbol{j}} - \dot{\phi}\bar{\boldsymbol{k}}$$

so that

$$\dot{\bar{\boldsymbol{j}}} = \begin{vmatrix} \bar{\boldsymbol{i}} & \bar{\boldsymbol{j}} & \bar{\boldsymbol{k}} \\ 0 & \dot{\psi} & -\dot{\phi} \\ 0 & 1 & 0 \end{vmatrix} = \dot{\phi}\bar{\boldsymbol{i}}$$

and

$$\dot{\bar{\boldsymbol{k}}} = \begin{vmatrix} \bar{\boldsymbol{i}} & \bar{\boldsymbol{j}} & \bar{\boldsymbol{k}} \\ 0 & \dot{\psi} & -\dot{\phi} \\ 0 & 0 & 1 \end{vmatrix} = \dot{\psi}\bar{\boldsymbol{i}}$$

Finally, the time derivative of the moment of momentum becomes

$$\dot{\boldsymbol{H}} = (I_{yy}\dot{\psi}\dot{\phi} - I_{zz}\dot{\phi}\dot{\psi})\bar{\boldsymbol{i}}$$

and since $\boldsymbol{M} = \dot{\boldsymbol{H}}$, it follows that

$$M_x = (I_{yy} - I_{zz})\dot{\phi}\dot{\psi}$$

Now, since the body is not accelerating in the direction of the motion of the center of mass (the center of mass does have a radial acceleration, since it is moving in a circular path), it must be that A_y and B_y are equal in magnitude and opposite in direction (ignoring the weight). Thus, they form a couple of magnitude A_yb. Then it follows that

$$A_y = \frac{I_{yy} - I_{zz}}{b}\,\dot{\phi}\dot{\psi}$$

But, since I_{yy} is equal to $\frac{1}{4}mR^2$, it follows that

$$A_y = \frac{-mR^2\dot{\phi}\dot{\psi}}{4b}$$

Since the moment of the forces about the y axis is equal to zero, then the forces A_x and B_x are equal to zero.

Alternate method of determining the moment on the body. The moment of the bearing forces on the body may be determined directly from Euler's equations (Eq. 9.51). It is noted from Fig. 9–34 that

$$\omega_x = 0 \qquad \dot{\omega}_x = 0$$

$$\omega_y = \dot{\psi} \qquad \dot{\omega}_y = 0$$
$$\omega_z = -\dot{\phi} \qquad \dot{\omega}_z = 0$$

and that

$$I_{xx} = I_{yy}$$

Therefore Eq. 9.51 becomes,

$$M_x = (I_{yy} - I_{zz})\dot{\psi}\dot{\phi}$$
$$M_y = 0$$
$$M_z = 0$$

which is the same result that was obtained by writing $\boldsymbol{M} = \dot{\boldsymbol{H}}$ directly. It goes without saying that it is much easier to obtain the moment equations by writing Euler's equations in this case, but the previous method is basic and does not involve the memorization of a set of complicated equations.

Example 9–18. Shown in Fig. 9-35 is a schematic diagram of an armature that has been misaligned, that is, the axis of symmetry of the armature does not coincide with the axis of rotation of the body. The angle between the axis of symmetry and the axis of rotation is given as ϕ, as shown in the figure. If the armature is rotating with an angular velocity of $\dot{\theta}$, what are the reactions at the bearings A and B?

Solution: The reference axes for the body are chosen as defined in Fig. 9-35. The axes shown are the principal axes for the body. First write the moment of momentum for the body:

$$H = I_{xx}\omega_x\bar{\boldsymbol{i}} + I_{yy}\omega_y\bar{\boldsymbol{j}} + I_{zz}\omega_z\bar{\boldsymbol{k}}$$

The angular velocity of the body is

$$\boldsymbol{\omega} = -\dot{\theta}\sin\phi\bar{\boldsymbol{j}} + \dot{\theta}\cos\phi\bar{\boldsymbol{k}}$$

and, from Appendix I, the moments of inertia of the body about the x, y, and z axes are

$$I_{xx} = I_{yy} = \frac{mR^2}{4}$$

$$I_{zz} = \frac{mR^2}{2}$$

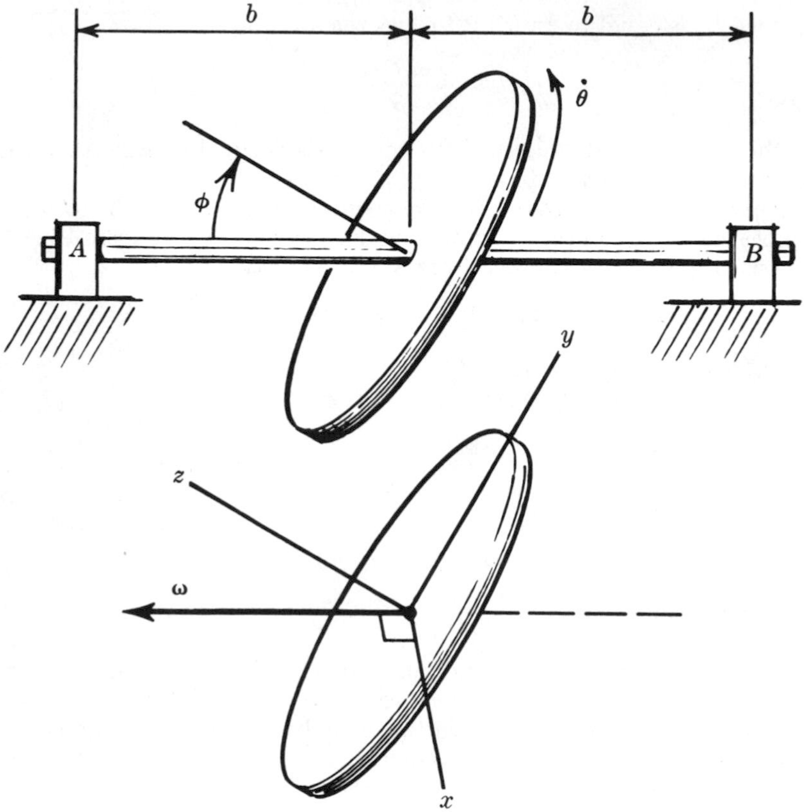

Figure 9-35

so that the moment of momentum may be written as

$$\boldsymbol{H} = -\frac{mR^2\dot{\theta}}{4}\sin\phi\bar{\boldsymbol{j}} + \frac{mR^2\dot{\theta}}{2}\cos\phi\bar{\boldsymbol{k}}$$

Since the angular velocity of rotation of the body about the axis of rotation is a constant, and since the angle ϕ does not change, the time derivative of the moment of momentum becomes

$$\dot{\boldsymbol{H}} = -\frac{mR^2\dot{\theta}}{4}\sin\phi\dot{\bar{\boldsymbol{j}}} + \frac{mR^2\dot{\theta}}{2}\cos\phi\dot{\bar{\boldsymbol{k}}}$$

Evaluating the time derivatives of the unit vectors $\bar{\boldsymbol{j}}$ and $\bar{\boldsymbol{k}}$,

$$\dot{\bar{\boldsymbol{j}}} = \boldsymbol{\omega} \times \bar{\boldsymbol{j}} = \begin{vmatrix} \bar{\boldsymbol{i}} & \bar{\boldsymbol{j}} & \bar{\boldsymbol{k}} \\ 0 & -\dot{\theta}\sin\phi & \dot{\theta}\cos\phi \\ 0 & 1 & 0 \end{vmatrix} = \dot{\theta}\cos\phi\bar{\boldsymbol{i}}$$

$$\dot{\bar{\boldsymbol{k}}} = \boldsymbol{\omega} \times \bar{\boldsymbol{k}} = \begin{vmatrix} \bar{\boldsymbol{i}} & \bar{\boldsymbol{j}} & \bar{\boldsymbol{k}} \\ 0 & -\dot{\theta}\sin\phi & \dot{\theta}\cos\phi \\ 0 & 0 & 1 \end{vmatrix} = -\dot{\theta}\sin\phi\bar{\boldsymbol{i}}$$

The time derivative of the moment of momentum becomes

$$\dot{\boldsymbol{H}} = -\frac{mR^2\dot{\theta}^2}{8} \sin 2\phi \bar{\boldsymbol{i}}$$

and then from the equation of motion, $\boldsymbol{M} = \dot{\boldsymbol{H}}$, it follows that

$$M_x = -\frac{mR^2\dot{\theta}^2}{8} \sin 2\theta$$

$$M_y = 0$$
$$M_z = 0$$

This says that there will be a moment about the x axis only. But note that the x axis is fixed to the wheel. Thus, the moment of the body and the forces at the reactions depend upon the position of the x axis. When the x axis is in the position shown, the vertical reactions at A and B will be a maximum; when the x axis is vertical, the vertical reactions at A and B will be equal to zero and the horizontal reactions will be a maximum. Thus the vertical reactions are harmonic functions of time.

The magnitude of the reactions may be evaluated by noting that the moment about the x axis in the position shown will be equal to $2A_Vb$. (The forces A_V and B_V are equal in magnitude and opposite in direction. The two must add to zero, since there is no motion of the center of mass of the system in that direction.) The magnitude of the vertical reaction at A is

$$A_V = \frac{mR^2\dot{\theta}^2}{16b} \sin 2\phi$$

and since the line of action of the reactive forces rotates with the body, it follows that

$$A_V(t) = \left[\frac{mR^2\dot{\theta}^2}{16b} \sin 2\phi\right] \cos \dot{\theta}t$$

PROBLEMS

9-70. Derive Euler's equations by using the first method indicated in Sec. 9-5. Equation 9-50 is written, assuming the axes are the principal axes. Then continue with the remainder of the procedure.

9-71. Determine the moment of the body in Example 9-18, using Euler's equations.

9-72. The bar, of length L and mass m, is attached to the axis AB in Fig. P.9-72. The system is spinning about the axis AB with an angular velocity of $\dot{\theta}$. The turntable is also rotating; it has an angular velocity of $\dot{\psi}$ in the direction shown. Determine the bearing reactions at A and B for the position shown (the bar and the axis AB are in a vertical plane). The axes defined in the figure are the principal axes of the body. $\dot{\theta}$ and $\dot{\psi}$ are constant.

9-73. A rigid body has a weight of 322 lb, and moments of inertia about its principal reference axes in slugs of $I_{xx} = 20$, $I_{yy} = 16$, $I_{zz} = 12$. The force on the body is $\boldsymbol{F}(t) = -30t\bar{\boldsymbol{i}} + 12t^2\bar{\boldsymbol{j}} - 40\bar{\boldsymbol{k}}$, and the moment about the center of mass of the body is $\boldsymbol{M}(t) = 8t\bar{\boldsymbol{i}} + 4\bar{\boldsymbol{j}} - t^2\bar{\boldsymbol{k}}$. Write the six equations of motion of the body.

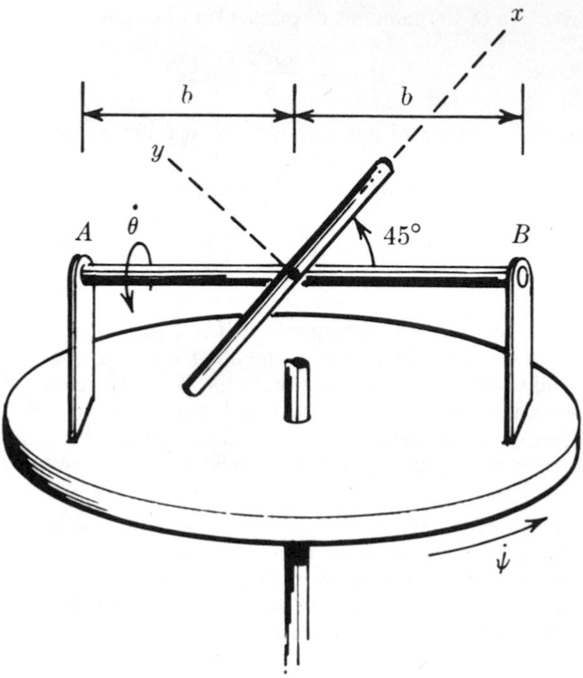

Figure Prob. 9-72

9-74. The 18-in. rod in Fig. P.9-74 is welded to the axis of rotation. If the rod weighs 3 lb and is rotating with an angular velocity of 40 radians/sec, what is the magnitude of the total horizontal reaction at the bearings A and B? The moment equation may be referred to the point O. Define one of the reference axes so that it is colinear with the longitudinal axis of the rod. For convenience when using the force equation, define another set of reference axes with the y axis colinear with AB.

9-75. Work Example 9-18, assuming that $\ddot{\psi}$ is not zero and is in the same direction as $\dot{\psi}$.

9-76. The bar OA shown in Fig. P.9-76 is rotating with a constant angular velocity of $\dot{\psi}$ as shown. Attached to the bar is a pendulum of mass m and length l. The plane of oscillation of the pendulum rotates with the bar OA by virtue of the attachment at O, as shown. Taking the axis shown in the figure, develop the moment equations of motion of the body, using the first method indicated in Sec. 9-5.

9-77. Work Problem 9-76, using Euler's equations.

9-78. Shown in Fig. P.9-78 is a disk with no external moment acting on it. It is assumed, however, that the body does have an angular velocity, $\boldsymbol{\omega}$. Show that the angular velocity of the body about the z axis is a constant. Also show from the equations of motions that $\sqrt{\omega_x^2 + \omega_y^2} = \text{constant}$.

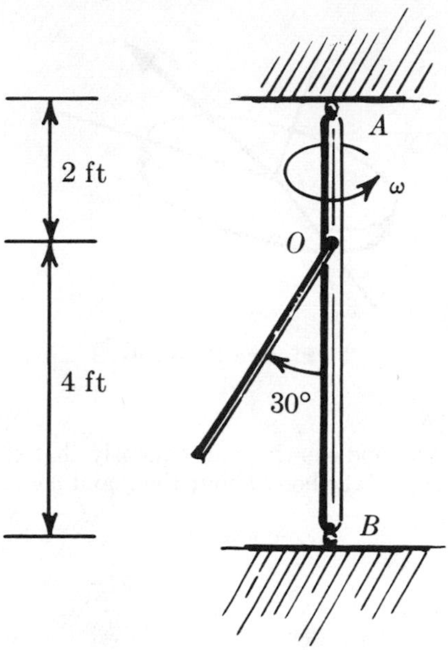

Figure Prob. 9-74

9-79. The attitude of a spinning rocket may be controlled by pulse rockets attached to the nose, which create a force in the direction shown in Fig. P.9-79. The xyz axes shown in the figure are fixed to the body, and since the pulse rocket is also fixed to the missile, it will always be creating a moment about the x axis. The rocket, however, will not be able to control the motion of the rocket about the x axis, but it will affect the motion of the missile about the y axis. Demonstrate this by writing

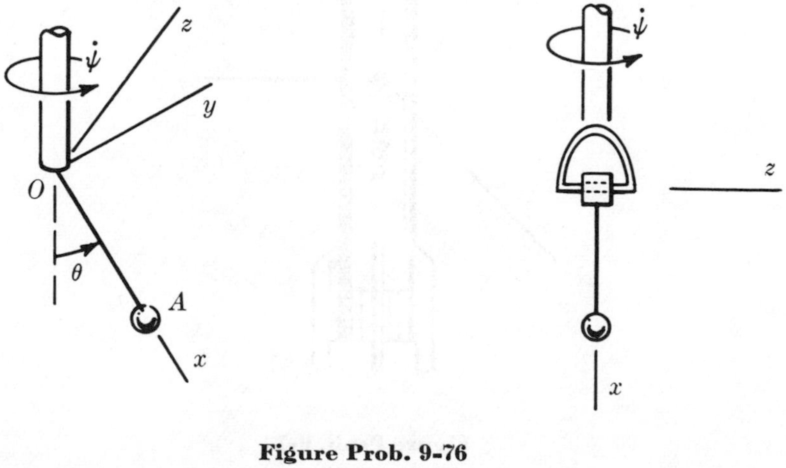

Figure Prob. 9-76

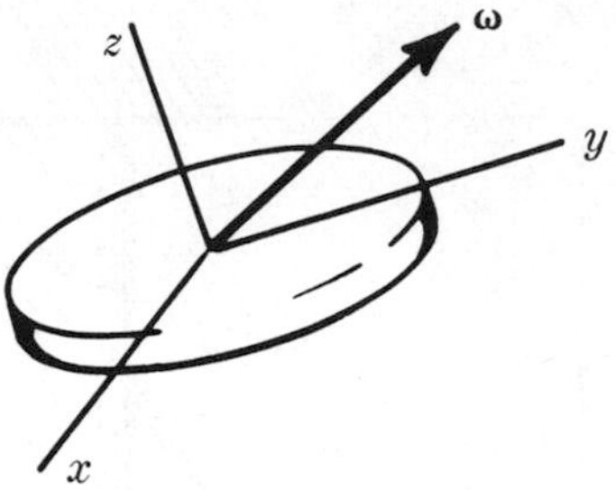

Figure Prob. 9-78

the equations of motion and showing subsequently that the differential equations for the angular velocity of the body about the x and y axes are

$$\ddot{\omega}_x + \dot{\phi}^2\omega_x = 0$$

$$\ddot{\omega}_y + \dot{\phi}^2\omega_y = -\frac{FL\dot{\phi}}{I}$$

where $\dot{\phi}$ is the angular velocity of the body about the z axis. Show that this is a constant. Assume that the moment of inertia about the z axis is insignificant with respect to the moment of inertia about the x and y axes. Let the latter moments of

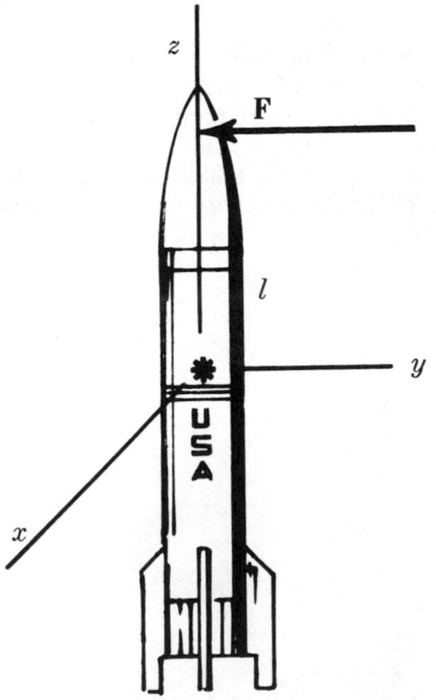

Figure Prob. 9-79

inertia be equal to I. Assume that the force of the pulse rocket is a constant and equal to F.

9-6. THE GYROSCOPIC EFFECT

The principle of the gyroscope. A *gyroscope* is nothing more than a rigid body, usually with circular symmetry such as a flywheel, that has a comparatively large angular velocity about one of its axes. This large angular velocity is known as the *angular velocity of spin*, and is designated by the vector $\dot{\boldsymbol{\phi}}$ (Fig. 9–36); the axis of rotation is known as the *axis of spin*.

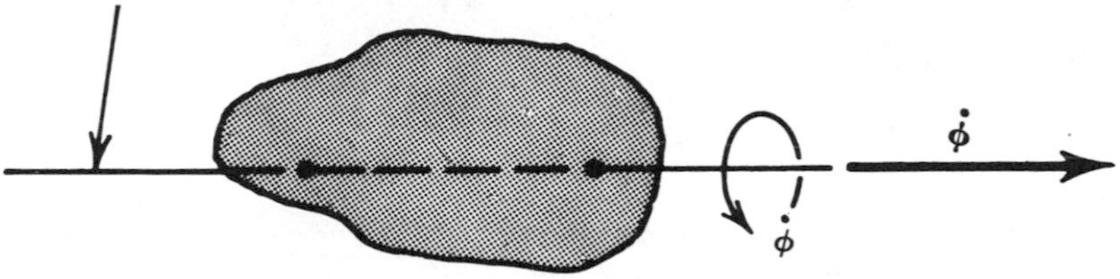

Figure 9-36

The gyroscope may be supported at one or two points along its axis of spin. A toy top, for instance, can be thought of as one form of a gyroscope.

As it rotates about the axis of spin, the gyroscope is basically stable. The direction of the axis of spin remains the same in space and resists any externally applied force that would tend to change its direction. A high angular velocity of spin is imparted to cylindrical satellites for the sole reason of maintaining the same orientation of the longitudinal axis of the body as the satellite moves on its trajectory; And as one should suspect, the stability of the gyroscope depends upon the magnitude of the angular spin of velocity; the higher the velocity of spin, the larger the moment required to change the direction of the spin axis. The exact relationship will be discussed later.

The gyroscope possesses a peculiar dynamical property. When an external moment is applied to the spinning body, the body will not rotate about the same axis as that when the moment was applied, but rather an axis that is mutually perpendicular to both the axis of spin and the axis about which the moment was applied. Thus, if a moment were applied to the spinning body shown in Fig. 9–37, the body would not rotate about the y' axis, but rather it would rotate about the x' axis in a counterclockwise sense as referred to in the figure. The angular velocity with which the body will rotate about the x' axis is known as the angular velocity of *precession*, and is designated by the vector $\dot{\boldsymbol{\psi}}$ (Fig. 9–37). It is said that the body *precesses* about the x' axis.

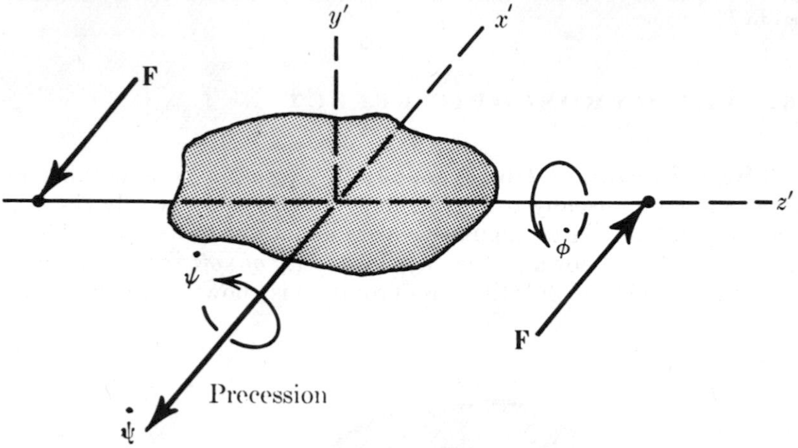

Figure 9-37

This phenomenon can be demonstrated very simply by actually performing this test on a spinning body, but one can show that this will happen analytically with no foreknowledge of the results. For simplicity, consider a body that possesses circular symmetry, say, a cylinder, about its longitudinal axis; suppose that this body has a high angular velocity of spin about this longitudinal axis.

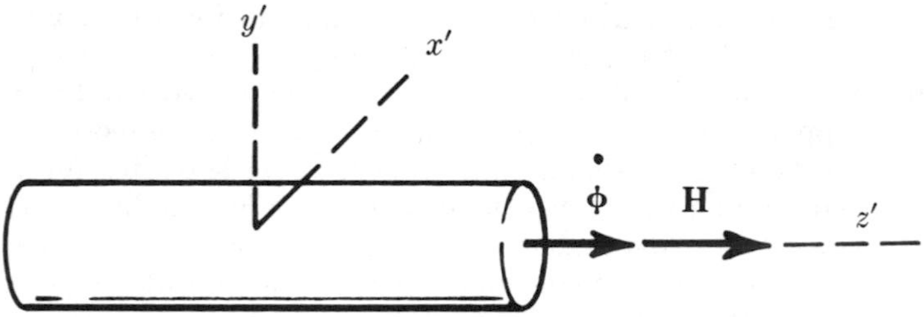

Figure 9-38

The vector $\boldsymbol{H}$, which represents the moment of momentum of the cylinder, will coincide with the axis of spin and will be equal to $I\dot{\phi}\bar{\boldsymbol{k}}$. Now suppose a moment is applied to the body by the two forces shown in Fig. 9–39. This moment can be represented by the vector $\boldsymbol{M}$ (which is equal to $M\bar{\boldsymbol{j}}$). Now the question: How will the body move under the action of this external moment? Recall that the moment equation, in vector form, for a rigid body is

$$\boldsymbol{M} = \frac{d\boldsymbol{H}}{dt} \tag{9.52}$$

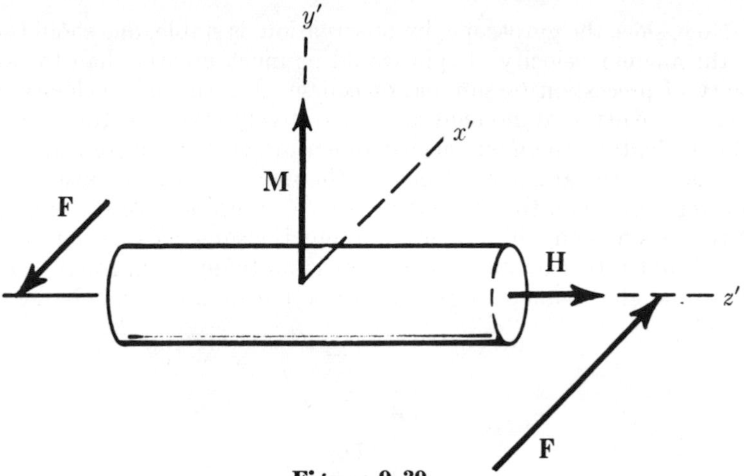

Figure 9-39

If this is true, then the vector $d\boldsymbol{H}$, representing the change in moment of momentum, must be in the same direction as the moment $\boldsymbol{M}$. The vector $d\boldsymbol{H}$ must be vertical (Fig. 9–40).

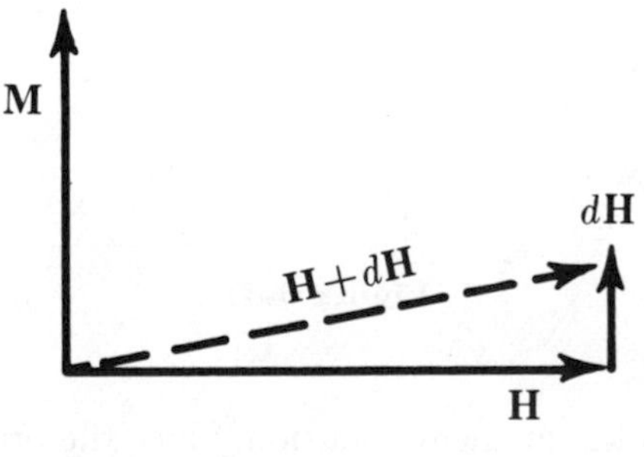

Figure 9-40

Since $d\boldsymbol{H}$ is in the same direction as the vector $\boldsymbol{M}$, this implies that the moment-of-momentum vector is rotating about an axis that is mutually perpendicular to $\boldsymbol{H}$ and $\boldsymbol{M}$. If the vector $\dot{\boldsymbol{\psi}}$ represents the angular velocity of the moment-of-momentum vector, the vector $\dot{\boldsymbol{\psi}}$ would be in the direction shown in Fig. 9–41, since $\boldsymbol{H}$ is rotating counterclockwise. The time derivative of $\boldsymbol{H}$ is obtained by taking the cross-product of the angular velocity vector and the moment-of-momentum vector:

$$\dot{\boldsymbol{H}} = \dot{\boldsymbol{\psi}} \times \boldsymbol{H} \tag{9.53}$$

so that the moment equation becomes

$$\boldsymbol{M} = \dot{\boldsymbol{\psi}} \times \boldsymbol{H} \tag{9.54}$$

Now, since the gyroscope, by observation, is stable, one should suspect that the angular velocity of spin would be much greater than the angular velocity of precession (assuming, of course, that the spin velocity is very large and the external moment is comparatively small). If this assumption can be made, then the moment-of-momentum vector will coincide with the spin axis, and the angular velocity of the moment-of-momentum vector $\dot{\psi}$ is nothing more than the angular velocity of precession of the spin axis, so that the axis of spin will not rotate about the same axis as the moment is directed, but rather about an axis that is mutually orthogonal to the axis of spin and the moment axis. The direction of precession is defined by Fig. 9–41.

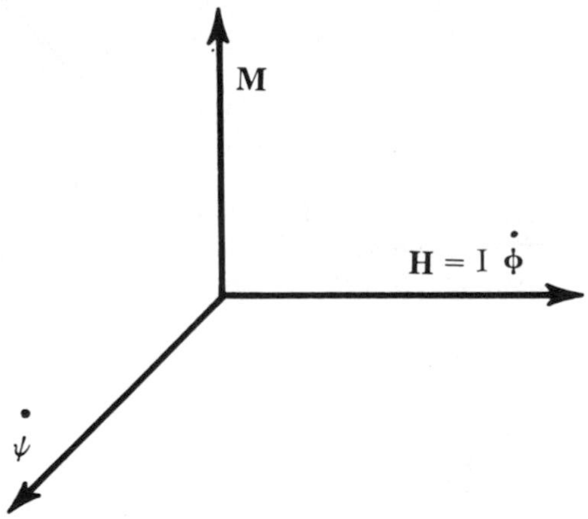

Figure 9-41

Consider again the moment equation. Since the precession vector and the moment-of-momentum vector are perpendicular, then the moment equation may be put into scalar form:

$$M = \dot{\psi}H \tag{9.55}$$

and since the moment of momentum about the spin axis is equal to $I\dot{\phi}$, where I is the moment of inertia of the gyroscope about the spin axis, then the moment equation becomes

$$M = \dot{\psi}I\dot{\phi} \tag{9.56}$$

The direction of these quantities is defined by Fig. 9–41. The angular velocity of precession is then equal to

$$\boxed{\dot{\psi} = \frac{M}{I\dot{\phi}}} \tag{9.57}$$

This shows, then, that the precession of the gyroscope depends, as one should suspect, upon the magnitude of the moment applied; the larger the moment, the larger the precession. Equation 9.57 also shows that the stability of the gyroscope depends not only upon the moment of inertia of the body about the spin axis, but also upon the angular velocity of spin itself. As each of these quantities becomes larger, the moment required to make the gyro precess becomes larger.

The dynamical properties of the gyroscope can be used to great advantage in several physical situations. A high angular velocity of spin is imparted to a cylindrical satellite so that the direction of its longitudinal axis will remain constant as the satellite moves through space; if the angular velocity of spin is large, then it will require a large moment (owing to the forces of the atmosphere) in order to change the direction of spin. Gyroscopes are used in guidance systems by utilization of the stability property of the spinning body. A gyroscopic compass uses the property that the precession of the gyroscope is proportional to the external moment applied. Each of these cases will be discussed separately.

Applications of the gyroscope. Two examples of gyroscope applications are discussed below.

The heavy symmetrical top. Consider a rigid body with a circular symmetry that is spinning with a comparatively large angular velocity of $\dot{\phi}$ and is supported at two points, A and B (Fig. 9–42). Now suppose that

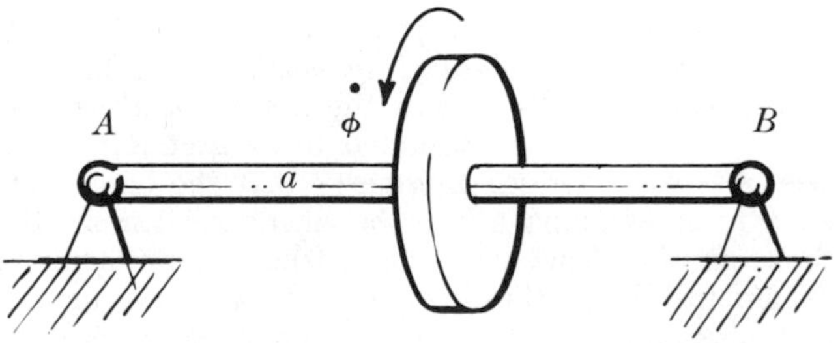

Figure 9-42

the reaction at point B is suddenly removed. One would suspect that the top would fall to the ground. But no! The body will actually move in the horizontal plane and precess about the vertical axis. This happens because the weight of the body causes a moment, as shown in Fig. 9–43. The response of the gyroscope to the moment would be to rotate about the vertical axis with an angular velocity of $\dot{\psi}$. The direction of this angular velocity is given in Fig. 9–43, and it is determined by the gyroscopic rule.

The angular velocity of rotation of the body in the horizontal plane will be the angular velocity of precession:

$$\dot{\psi} = \frac{Wa}{I\dot{\phi}} \tag{9.58}$$

It is curious to note that the angular velocity of precession will become smaller if the angular velocity of spin is very large. It would be possible, then, to have a top with such a high velocity of spin that the body would appear not to be moving when the support is removed.

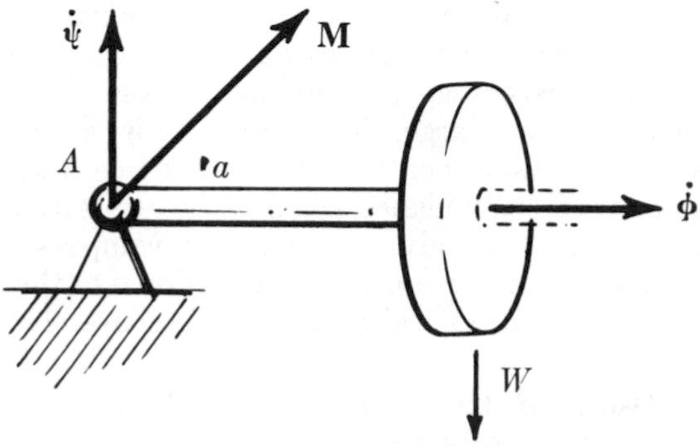

Figure 9-43

The gyroscope used in the control system. Shown in Fig. 9–44 is a gyroscope mounted in a frame called a *gimbal.* The figure defines the axes known as the *outer gimbal axis* and the *inner gimbal axis.* Each of the connections of the system are assumed to be frictionless bearings. This system possesses the interesting property that the base may be rotated about either the outer gimbal axis or the inner gimbal axis without disturbing the direction of the spin axis. This is true because it takes an external moment in order to change the direction of the spin axis, and if the bearings are all frictionless, there will be no external moment applied to the system as the base moves about either the outer or the inner gimbal axis.

Now suppose that a rheostat is mounted on the base with a moving contact on the gimbals as shown in Fig. 9–45. As the base rotates about the outer gimbal axis, the angle of rotation of the base may be measured simply by measuring the electrical resistance in the rheostat. A similar device may be used to determine the rotation about the inner gimbal axis.

If this type of system were mounted in an airplane or space vehicle, the device could be used not only to determine the orientation of the body, but also to act as a brain center for the control system for the vehicle. An electric signal due to the change in resistance of the potentiometer could be relayed to the control rockets or any other device that controls the vehicle.

It is important to note that the one gyroscope will define only two angles of orientation. In order to describe the three angles of orientation

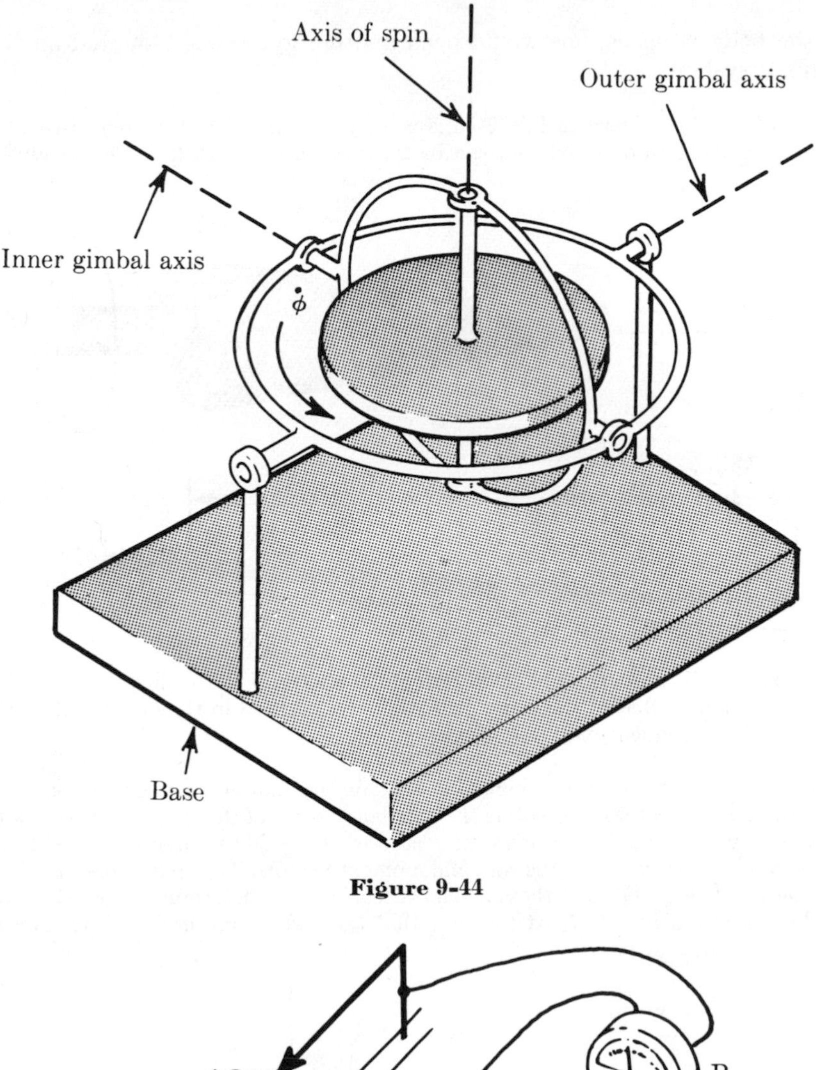

Figure 9-44

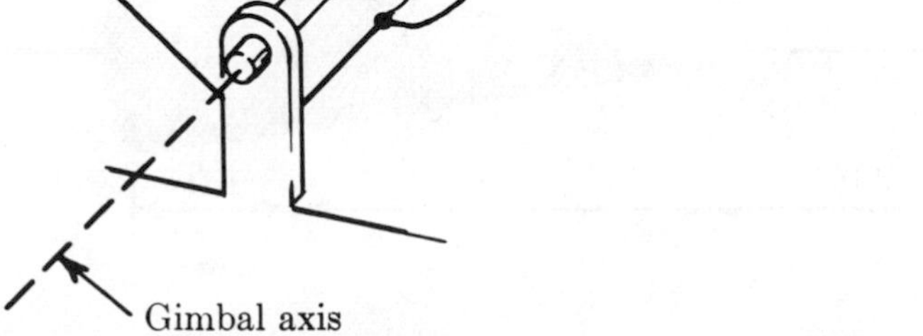

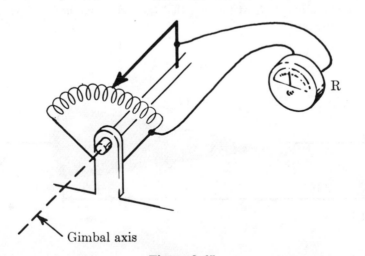

Figure 9-45

of the body in space, one would need another gyroscope mounted on the gimbals system.

Example 9–19. Shown in Fig. 9-46 is a heavy symmetrical top comprised of a solid cone mounted on a rod that can be assumed to be weightless. The weight of

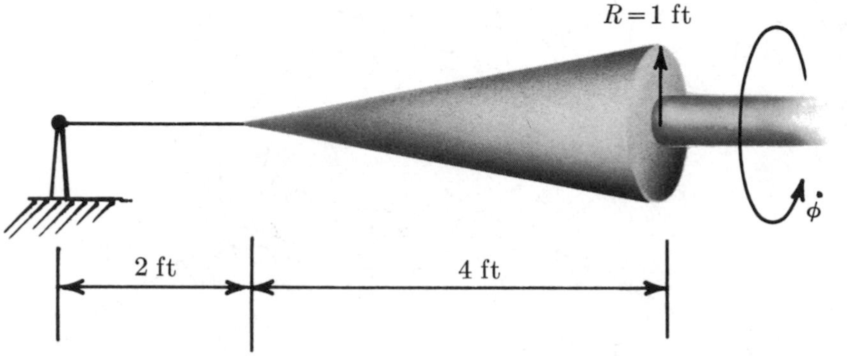

Figure 9-46

the cone is 64 lb, and angular velocity of spin of 8000 rpm in the direction shown in the figure is imparted to the body. If the body is released in the horizontal plane, discuss the subsequent motion of the body.

Solution: From the preceding discussion of the motion of a gyroscope, it is known that the vector representing the angular velocity of the spin axis (precession) is mutually orthogonal to the moment vector and the spin vector. So, the first thing to do would be to establish the spin and moment vectors. The spin, represented by the vector $\dot{\boldsymbol{\phi}}$, is given, and the moment vector may be determined from the free-body diagram in Fig. 9-47. At the time that the body is released, the reaction at

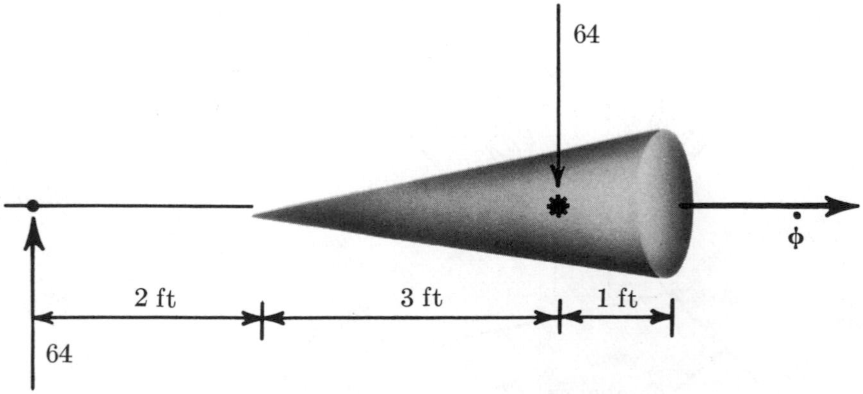

Figure 9-47

the support will be equal to the weight of the body, and the two forces will create a couple; the moment of the couple is equal to

$$M = 64 \times 5$$
$$= 320 \text{ ft-lb}$$

and the vector representing the moment is in a direction shown in Fig. 9-48. Of course that implies that the vector representing the angular velocity of precession ($\dot{\psi}$) would be in the direction shown in Fig. 9-48 (recall the rule for determining this direction).

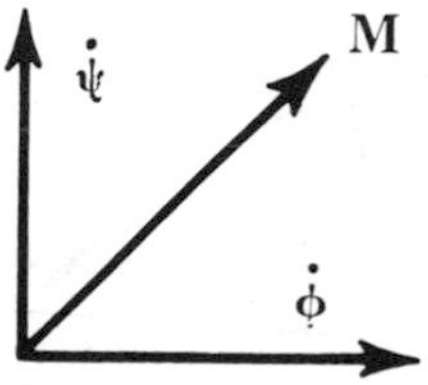

Figure 9-48

The angular velocity of precession may be determined from Eq. 9.57:

$$\dot{\psi} = \frac{M}{I\dot{\phi}}$$

First the moment of inertia of the body about its axis of spin must be found. From Appendix I, it is found that the moment of inertia of a cone about its longitudinal axis is $\frac{3}{10}mR^2$, so that

$$I = \frac{3}{10}\left(\frac{64}{32.2}\right)(l)^2$$
$$= 0.6 \text{ lb-sec}^2\text{-ft}$$

The angular velocity of precession becomes

$$\dot{\psi} = \frac{320}{0.6[2\pi(800b)/60]}$$

$$\dot{\psi} = 0.64 \text{ radian/sec}$$

Therefore this top will rotate about the vertical axis (and not a horizontal axis as one might have suspected) with an angular velocity of 0.64 radian/sec.

The general motion of a symmetrical gyro. Consider the gimbal-mounted gyroscope shown in Fig. 9–49. We shall develop in this section the general equations of motion of this gyroscope in terms of the

Euler angles. First the reference axes are defined so that the origin of the system coincides with the center of mass of the gyro. The axes are aligned so that the z axis coincides at all times with the spin axis of the gyro, and the x axis coincides with the inner gimbal axis. This means that the body

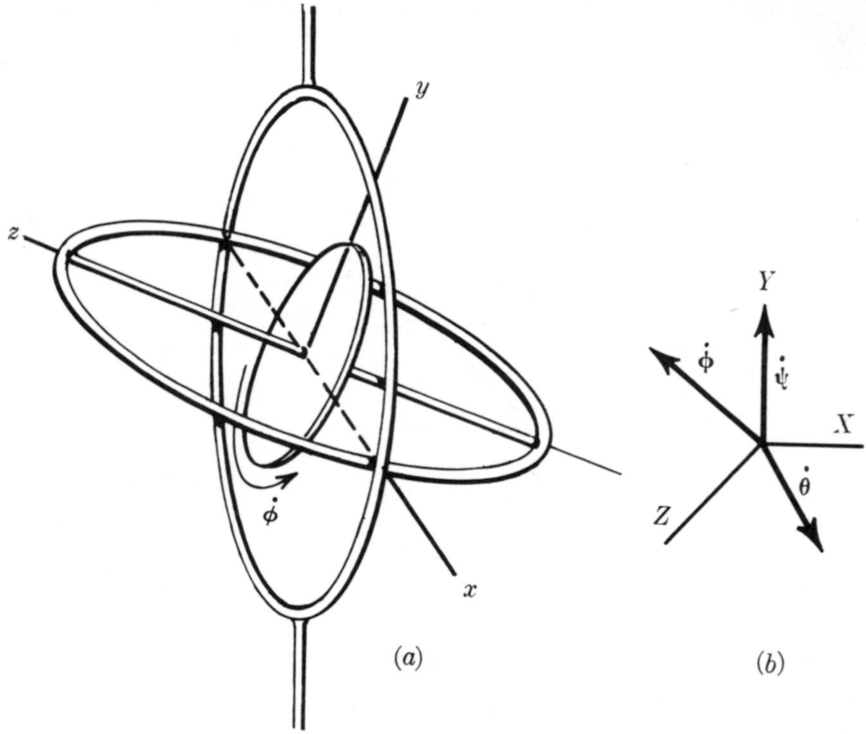

Figure 9-49

is moving with respect to the axes. However, because the body has symmetry about the reference axes, the moments and products of inertia of the body remain constant as the body moves relative to the reference axes. Therefore the equations of motion for the body may be written with the assurance that the moments and products of inertia of the body do not change with time. The products of inertia of the body are zero, since the reference axes are also the principal axes.

The Euler angles were defined in Chapter 8. The Euler angular velocities are defined in Fig. 9–49 by the right-hand rule. The angular velocity of the reference coordinate system may be written as

$$\boldsymbol{\omega} = \dot{\theta}\bar{\boldsymbol{i}} + (\dot{\psi} \sin \theta)\bar{\boldsymbol{j}} + (\dot{\psi} \cos \theta)\bar{\boldsymbol{k}} \tag{9.59}$$

It is important to note that the angular velocity of the body, $\dot{\phi}$, about the axis of spin is not included in the expression. Recall that in writing the equation of motion of a body, $\boldsymbol{\omega}$ is the angular velocity of the moving reference system and is equal to the angular velocity of the body only when the system is fixed to the body.

The moment of momentum of the body about each axis may be written as

$$\begin{aligned} H_x &= I_x\omega_x = I_x\dot{\theta} \\ H_y &= I_y\omega_y = I_y\dot{\psi}\sin\theta \\ H_z &= I_z\omega_z = I_z(\dot{\phi} + \dot{\psi}\cos\theta) \end{aligned} \qquad \textbf{(9.60)}$$

Here it is noted that the total moment of momentum must be written, so that the total angular velocity of the body about the axis of spin, the z axis, must be $(\dot{\phi} + \dot{\psi}\cos\theta)$. Therefore the moment of momentum may be written as

$$\boldsymbol{H} = I_1\dot{\theta}\bar{\boldsymbol{i}} + I_1\dot{\psi}\sin\theta\bar{\boldsymbol{j}} + I(\dot{\phi} + \dot{\psi}\cos\theta)\bar{\boldsymbol{k}} \qquad \textbf{(9.61)}$$

where $I_1 = I_{xx} = I_{yy}$ and $I = I_{zz}$. Subsequently, the time derivative of the moment of momentum is taken and set equal to the moment on the body. Upon separating into the three components, we get

$$\begin{aligned} M_x &= I_1\ddot{\theta} + I(\dot{\phi} + \dot{\psi}\cos\theta)\dot{\psi}\sin\theta - I_1\dot{\psi}^2\sin\theta\cos\theta \\ M_y &= I_1\frac{d}{dt}(\dot{\psi}\sin\theta) + I_1\dot{\theta}\dot{\psi}\cos\theta - I\dot{\theta}(\dot{\phi} + \dot{\psi}\cos\theta) \\ M_z &= I\frac{d}{dt}(\dot{\phi} + \dot{\psi}\cos\theta) \end{aligned} \qquad \textbf{(9.62)}$$

The general solutions to these equations are discussed in almost every text in advanced dynamics. Since the details of the solutions are very involved, they will not be discussed here. We shall, however, show that this form agrees with that discussed earlier in this section.

Consider the case of the symmetrical top that is released in the horizontal plane, as shown in Fig. 9–50. Since it is known that the precession

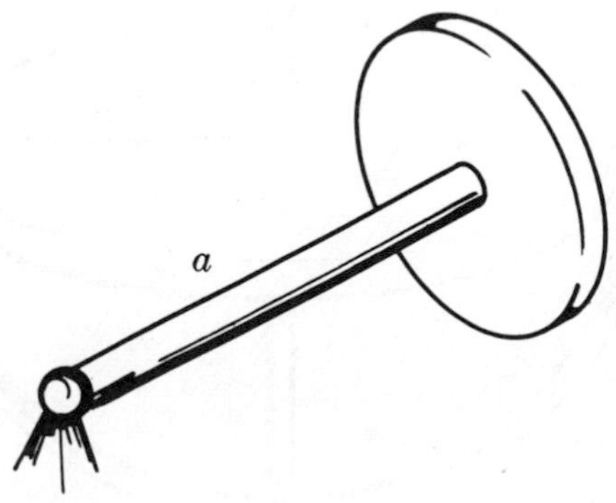

Figure 9-50

will take place about the vertical axis, it is assumed that the angle θ is equal to $\pi/2$ and remains at that value as the body moves. The moment of the gravitational force on the body is equal to Wa. Then the first of Eqs. 9.62 becomes

$$Wa = I\dot{\phi}\dot{\psi} \tag{9.63}$$

and this then agrees with the result obtained previously. (See Eq. 9–58).

PROBLEMS

9-80. A simple toy top consists of a solid cone 20 in. long and 5 in. in diameter at the base. The weight of the top is 6 lb. If the angular velocity of precession is 0.06 radian/sec, what is the angular velocity of spin of the body if the top precesses in a horizontal plane?

9-81. It is desired to try to stabilize a small ship with a gyroscope. The naval architect specifies that the gyroscope can weigh no more than 2000 lb and cannot be any larger than 5 ft in diameter. The motor driving the gyroscope will not operate above 3000 rpm. If the maximum moment required from the stabilizing gyroscope is 12,000 ft-lb, what must be the angular velocity of precession that is imparted to the gyroscopic system?

9-82. A problem with top priority in the fabrication of a gyroscopic system mounted on gimbals is how to make the frictional forces in the bearings as small as possible. In the gimbal mounting shown in Fig. P.9-82, each of the bearings is found by experiment to have a relatively constant frictional moment of approximately 0.002 ft-lb. What will be the angular velocity of precession of the spin of the gyroscope under the action of this torque if the spin of the gyro is 10,000 rpm and the weight of the gyro is 4 lb?

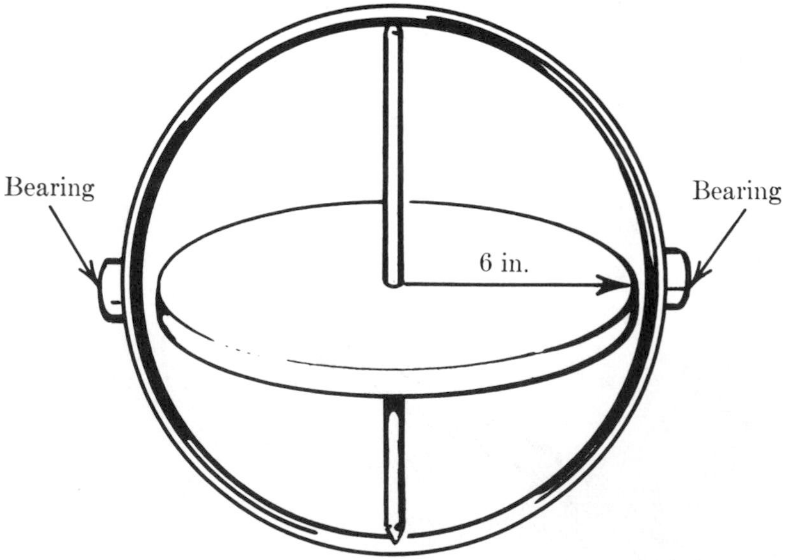

Figure Prob. 9-82

9-83. The propeller of an airplane acts as a gyroscope and exerts an undesired moment on the airplane as the airplane is moving in a circular path (either in a turn or pulling out of a dive). Determine the magnitude of the gyroscopic moment exerted by the propeller on the airplane if the prop is spinning with an angular velocity of 8000 rpm and the airplane is moving on a circular curve with a radius of curvature of 2000 ft with a speed of 300 mph. The propeller of the airplane has a radius of 6 ft, and each of its four blades weighs 20 lb. In the calculations for the moment of inertia, the blades may be assumed to be long, thin bars.

9-84. A turbine is mounted in a ship and shown schematically as a cylinder in Fig. P.9-84. In rough seas, the ship will pitch about the x' axis. If the turbine weighs 3220 lb, is shaped in cylindrical form, with a diameter of 10 ft, and operates with an angular velocity of 20,000 rpm, what will be the maximum gyroscopic moment exerted by the turbine on the ship if the angle of pitch of the ship is $\theta = 0.08 \sin 1.2t$?

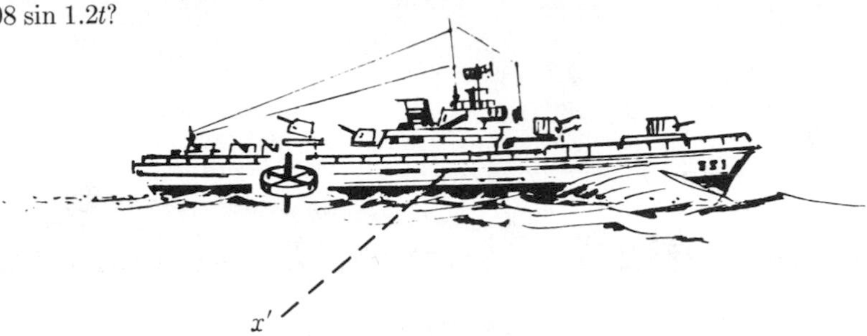

Figure Prob. 9-84

Appendix I. Moments of Inertia of Solids

The moments of inertia given below are the moments of inertia with respect to the centroidal axes. To determine the moments or products of inertia with respect to any other set of axes, the parallel axis theorem or the rotation theorem may be employed.

1. *The slender rod:*

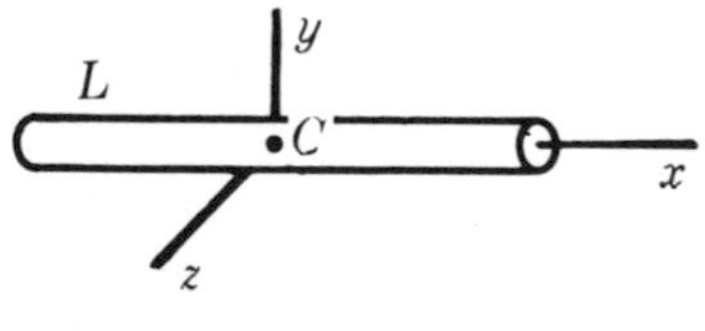

$$I_{xx} = 0$$
$$I_{yy} = I_{zz} = mL^2/12$$

2. *The cube:*

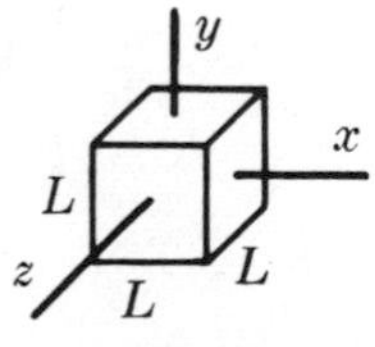

$$I_{xx} = I_{yy} = I_{zz} = mL^2/6$$

3. *The rectangular prism:*

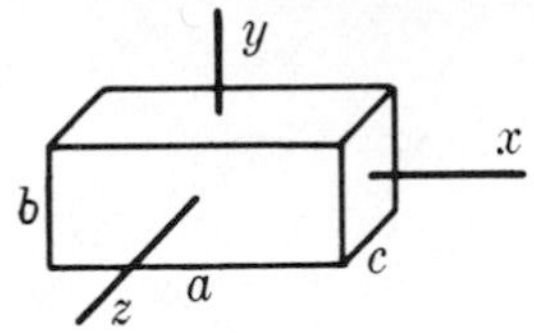

$$I_{xx} = m(b^2 + c^2)/12$$
$$I_{yy} = m(a^2 + c^2)/12$$
$$I_{zz} = m(a^2 + b^2)/12$$

4. *The thin, rectangular plate:*

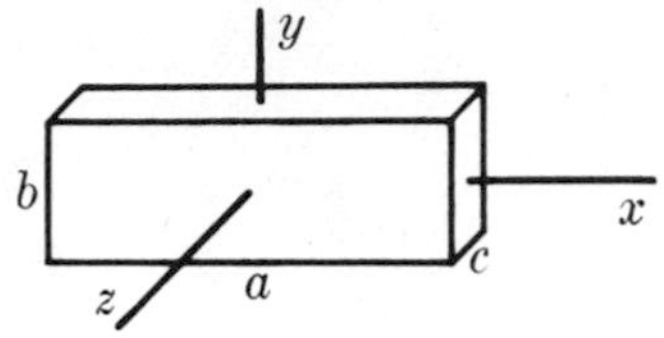

$$I_{xx} = mb^2/12$$
$$I_{yy} = ma^2/12$$
$$I_{zz} = m(a^2 + b^2)/12$$

5. *The cylinder:*

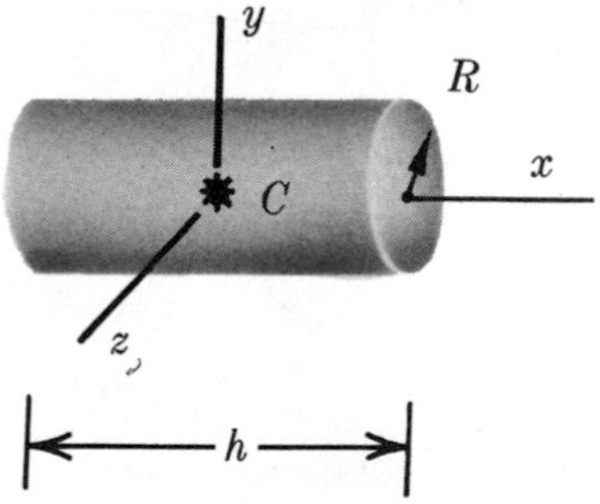

$$I_{xx} = mR^2/2$$
$$I_{yy} = I_{zz} = m(3R^2 + h^2)/12$$

6. *The thin disk:*

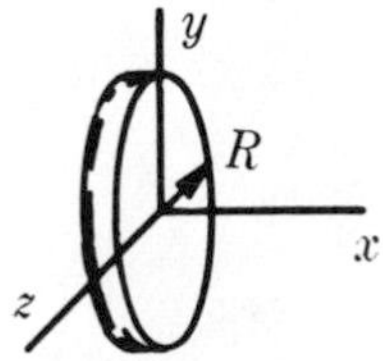

$$I_{xx} = mR^2/2$$
$$I_{yy} = I_{zz} = mR^2/4$$

7. *The sphere:*

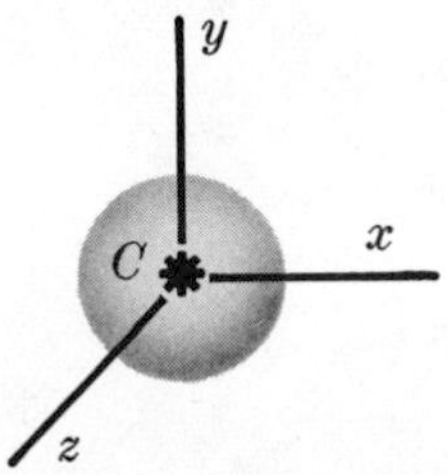

$$I_{xx} = I_{yy} = I_{zz} = 2mR^2/5$$

8. *The cone:*

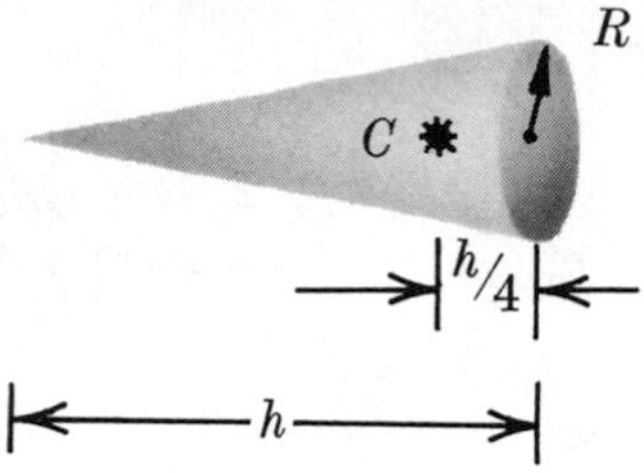

$$I_{xx} = 3mR^2/10$$
$$I_{yy} = I_{zz} = 3m(4R^2 + h^2)/80$$

Appendix II. Elements of Matrix Algebra

A collection of elements is said to form an *array*. An array with m rows and n columns is denoted by

$$[A] = \begin{bmatrix} a_{11} & a_{12} & a_{13} & \cdots & a_{1n} \\ a_{21} & a_{22} & & & \\ a_{31} & & & & \\ \cdot & & & & \\ \cdot & & & & \\ \cdot & & & & \\ a_{m1} & \cdots & \cdots & \cdots & a_{mn} \end{bmatrix} \tag{II.1}$$

The matrix A is said to be a *matrix* of order $m \times n$.

A *row matrix* has only one row (m is equal to 1):

$$[A] = [a_{11} \quad a_{12} \quad a_{13} \quad \cdots \quad a_{1n}] \tag{II.2}$$

A *column matrix* is a matrix with only one column (n is equal to 1):

$$[A] = \begin{bmatrix} a_{11} \\ a_{21} \\ a_{31} \\ \cdot \\ \cdot \\ \cdot \\ a_{m1} \end{bmatrix} \tag{II.3}$$

A *square matrix* has as many rows as it has columns (n is equal to m):

$$[A] = \begin{bmatrix} a_{11} & a_{12} & a_{13} \\ a_{21} & a_{22} & a_{23} \\ a_{31} & a_{32} & a_{33} \end{bmatrix} \tag{II.4}$$

Equality of matrices. Two matrices are equal if the corresponding elements of the matrices are equal. It must be that the two matrices are of the same order:

$$[A] = [B] \qquad \text{if } a_{ij} = b_{ij} \tag{II.5}$$

Multiplication of a matrix by a scalar. Each element of the matrix is multiplied by the scalar. If

$$[A] = \begin{bmatrix} a_{11} & a_{12} \\ a_{21} & a_{22} \end{bmatrix}$$

Then

$$k[A] = \begin{bmatrix} ka_{11} & ka_{12} \\ ka_{21} & ka_{22} \end{bmatrix} \tag{II.6}$$

Addition and subtraction of matrices. The corresponding elements of each matrix are added and subtracted:

$$[A] \pm [B] = [C] \tag{II.7}$$

where $C_{ij} = a_{ij} \pm b_{ij}$

Multiplication of matrices. The multiplication of two matrices $[A]$ and $[B]$ may be accomplished only if $[A]$ has the same number of columns as $[B]$ has rows:

$$[A][B] = [C]$$

where

$$C_{ij} = \sum_{k=1}^{p} a_{ik}b_{kj} \tag{II.8}$$

where p is equal to the number of rows in B.

Let

$$[A] = \begin{bmatrix} a & b \\ c & d \end{bmatrix} \quad \text{and} \quad [B] = \begin{bmatrix} f & g & h \\ k & l & m \end{bmatrix} \tag{II.9}$$

Then

$$[C] = [A][B] = \begin{bmatrix} a & b \\ c & d \end{bmatrix}\begin{bmatrix} f & g & h \\ k & l & m \end{bmatrix}$$

$$= \begin{bmatrix} (af + bk) & (ag + bl) & (ah + bm) \\ (cf + dk) & (cg + dl) & (ch + dm) \end{bmatrix} \tag{II.10}$$

Note that the matrix $[C]$ has the same number of rows as $[A]$ and the same number of columns as $[B]$. Also note that the matrix multiplication

$[B][A]$ is undefined because $[B]$ does not have the same number of columns as $[A]$ has rows.

A *unit matrix* (or identity matrix) is defined as

$$[I] = \begin{bmatrix} 1 & 0 & 0 & 0 \\ 0 & 1 & 0 & 0 \\ 0 & 0 & 1 & 0 \\ 0 & 0 & 0 & 1 \end{bmatrix} \tag{II.11}$$

The unit matrix has nonzero elements on the diagonal only, and all these elements are equal to 1. The unit matrix has the property that

$$[I][A] = [A][I] = [A] \tag{II.12}$$

The unit matrix plays a role in the matrix algebra similar to that played by the number 1 in the real number system.

The *transpose* of a matrix is a matrix with the rows and columns interchanged. If

$$[A] = \begin{bmatrix} 1 & 2 & 3 \\ 4 & 5 & 6 \end{bmatrix} \quad \text{then} \quad [A]^T = \begin{bmatrix} 1 & 4 \\ 2 & 5 \\ 3 & 6 \end{bmatrix} \tag{II.13}$$

The *inverse* of a matrix is a matrix having the property that the inverse times the matrix itself is equal to the unit matrix. It should be noted at the outset that only square matrices may have inverses, and the inverse of a square matrix will be itself a square matrix. The inverse of $[A]$ is given as $[A]^{-1}$:

$$[A][A]^{-1} = [A]^{-1}[A] = [I] \tag{II.14}$$

The following procedure is used to determine the inverse of a matrix:

$$[A]^{-1} = \frac{\text{adjoint of } [A]}{\text{determinant of } [A]} \tag{II.15}$$

The *adjoint* is the transpose of the matrix formed by the cofactors of A. As an example, determine the inverse of A, where

$$[A] = \begin{bmatrix} 1 & 2 & -1 \\ 3 & 0 & -2 \\ 2 & 1 & -3 \end{bmatrix} \tag{II.16}$$

The matrix of cofactors is

$$[A]_c = \begin{bmatrix} 2 & 5 & 3 \\ 5 & -1 & 3 \\ -4 & -1 & -6 \end{bmatrix} \tag{II.17}$$

The cofactor of the element in the first row and the second column, for instance, is the determinant of the array formed by striking the first row and the second column. The minus sign is associated with this number as in the case of the evaluation of the determinant of A. The plus-minus rule is used throughout the evaluation of the cofactors. The transpose of the matrix of cofactors is

$$[A]_c^T = \begin{bmatrix} 2 & 5 & -4 \\ 5 & -1 & -1 \\ 3 & 3 & -6 \end{bmatrix} \tag{II.18}$$

The determinant of the matrix $[A]$, when evaluated, is equal to 9. Thus, the inverse of the matrix is equal to

$$[A]^{-1} = \frac{1}{9}\begin{bmatrix} 2 & 5 & -4 \\ 5 & -1 & -1 \\ 3 & 3 & -6 \end{bmatrix} \tag{II.19}$$

Application of matrices. Two cases are presented below.

Representation of simultaneous linear algebraic equations. Consider the set of linear algebraic equations:

$$\begin{aligned} a_{11}x_1 + a_{12}x_2 + a_{13}x_3 &= b_1 \\ a_{21}x_1 + a_{22}x_2 + a_{23}x_3 &= b_2 \\ a_{31}x_1 + a_{32}x_2 + a_{33}x_3 &= b_3 \end{aligned} \tag{II.20}$$

This set of equations may be written in matrix form. Let

$$[A] = \begin{bmatrix} a_{11} & a_{12} & a_{13} \\ a_{21} & a_{22} & a_{23} \\ a_{31} & a_{32} & a_{33} \end{bmatrix}$$

$$\{x\} = \begin{bmatrix} x_1 \\ x_2 \\ x_3 \end{bmatrix} \qquad \{B\} = \begin{bmatrix} b_1 \\ b_2 \\ b_3 \end{bmatrix} \tag{II.21}$$

Then the set of equations written above may be expressed in matrix form:

$$[A]\{x\} = \{B\} \tag{II.22}$$

This may be easily verified by performing the matrix multiplication between $[A]$ and $\{x\}$. Here, as shown previously, three simultaneous equations can be expressed as one matrix equation. Similarly, much larger sets of simultaneous equations may be expressed as one matrix equation.

To determine the values of x_1, x_2, and x_3 that satisfy the set of equations given by Eq. II.20, premultiply both sides of the preceding matrix equation by the inverse of $[A]$. Thus,

$$[A]^{-1}[A]\{x\} = [A]^{-1}\{B\} \tag{II.23}$$

But the inverse of $[A] \times [A]$ is equal to the unit matrix, and the unit matrix times the matrix $\{x\}$ is equal to the matrix $\{x\}$, so that Eq. II.23 becomes

$$\{x\} = [A]^{-1}\{B\} \tag{II.24}$$

As an example, consider the following set of algebraic linear equations:

$$\begin{aligned} x + 2y - z &= 3 \\ 3x \qquad - 2z &= -2 \\ 2x + y - 3z &= -1 \end{aligned} \tag{II.25}$$

Find the values of x, y, and z that satisfy the equations.

The matrix $[A]$ is

$$[A] = \begin{bmatrix} 1 & 2 & -1 \\ 3 & 0 & -2 \\ 2 & 1 & -3 \end{bmatrix} \tag{II.26}$$

The inverse of $[A]$ (as determined in the example above) is

$$[A]^{-1} = \frac{1}{9}\begin{bmatrix} 2 & 5 & -4 \\ 5 & -1 & -1 \\ 3 & 3 & -6 \end{bmatrix} \tag{II.27}$$

The matrix $\{B\}$ is given as

$$\{B\} = \begin{bmatrix} 3 \\ -2 \\ -1 \end{bmatrix} \tag{II.28}$$

Then

$$[A]^{-1}\{B\} = \frac{1}{9}\begin{bmatrix} 2 & 5 & -4 \\ 5 & -1 & -1 \\ 3 & 3 & -6 \end{bmatrix}\begin{bmatrix} 3 \\ -2 \\ -1 \end{bmatrix} \tag{II.29}$$

Upon performing the matrix multiplication,

$$\{x\} = \begin{bmatrix} x \\ y \\ z \end{bmatrix} = [A]^{-1}\{B\} = \begin{bmatrix} 0 \\ 2 \\ 1 \end{bmatrix} \tag{II.30}$$

so that the values of x, y, and z that satisfy Eq. II.25 are

$$x = 0, \quad y = 2, \quad \text{and } z = 1 \tag{II.31}$$

Coordinate transformations. Given the coordinates of a point P in the x, y, z system as shown in the accompanying figure, what are the coordinates of this same point in the x_1, y_1, z_1 system?

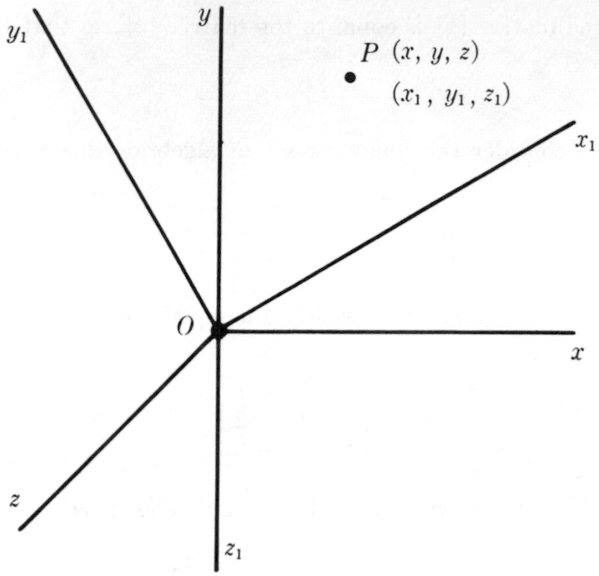

Appendix AII-1

From geometrical considerations, it can be shown that

$$\begin{aligned} x_1 &= l_{x_1x}x + l_{x_1y}y + l_{x_1z}z \\ y_1 &= l_{y_1x}x + l_{y_1y}y + l_{y_1z}z \\ z_1 &= l_{z_1x}x + l_{z_1y}y + l_{z_1z}z \end{aligned} \tag{II.32}$$

where l_{x_1x} is the cosine of the angle between the x_1 axis and the x axis, etc. Thus, it is seen that the transformation of coordinates of the point P from the x system to the x_1 system may be expressed in matrix form:

$$\{x_1\} = [T]\{x\} \tag{II.33}$$

where

$$\{x_1\} = \begin{bmatrix} x_1 \\ y_1 \\ z_1 \end{bmatrix} \qquad [T] = \begin{bmatrix} l_{x_1x} & l_{x_1y} & l_{x_1z} \\ l_{y_1x} & l_{y_1y} & l_{y_1z} \\ l_{z_1x} & l_{z_1y} & l_{z_1z} \end{bmatrix} \qquad \{x\} = \begin{bmatrix} x \\ y \\ z \end{bmatrix} \tag{II.34}$$

The matrix $[T]$ is called the *transformation matrix*. The transformation matrix will transform vector quantities such as angular velocity and moment of momentum from one system to another.

One useful property of the transformation matrix is that the inverse of $[T]$ is equal to the transpose of $[T]$:

$$[T]^{-1} = [T]^T \tag{II.35}$$

The evaluation of the inverse of $[T]$ becomes quite easy, since it is a simple task to take the transpose of a matrix.

REFERENCES FOR APPENDIX II

1. Pipes, L. A., *Applied Mathematics for Engineers and Physicists*, McGraw-Hill, 1958.
2. Frazer, Duncan, and Collar, *Elementary Matrices*, Cambridge University Press, 1938.
3. Goldstein, H., *Classical Mechanics*, Addison-Wesley, 1957.
4. Pipes, L. A., *Matrix Methods for Engineers*, Prentice-Hall, Inc., 1963.

Index

N

O

P

R

S

T

U

V

W